Short Courses

Teacher's Edition

WALK-THROUGH

Student Edition

CONTENTS IN BRIEF

HOLT, RINEHART AND WINSTON

A Harcourt Education Company

Orlando • **Austin** • New York • San Diego • Toronto • London

A program that gets EVERYONE pointed in the right direction.

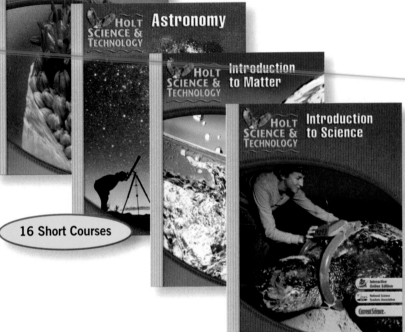

16 Short Courses

Every student, every class, every teacher is unique. Holt is here to help pave the way to success for each and every one.

MEETS THE INDIVIDUAL NEEDS OF YOUR STUDENTS

- Inclusion strategies and different learning styles are addressed to support all learners.
- Activities are labeled by ability level.
- Directed Reading worksheets and Chapter Tests are available that address different ability levels.
- English Language Learner support includes **ELL Strategies for Science**, a **Multilingual Glossary for Science**, and **Spanish Resources**.

FOSTERS READING FOR UNDERSTANDING

- The *Student Edition* is accessible with a clean, easy-to-follow design and highlighted vocabulary words that are defined in the margin at point of reference.
- Reading strategies are built into both the *Student Edition* and the *Teacher's Edition.*
- **Reading Comprehension Guide** and **Guided Reading Audio CDs** help students better understand the content.
- **Interactive Textbook** makes science content accessible to struggling readers and ELL students.
- **Live Ink**—exclusive to Holt—is a scientifically-researched tool that improves reading comprehension and raises test scores.
- **Student Edition on CD-ROM** provides students with the entire textbook on a CD-ROM so that they have less to carry home.

ASSESSMENT OPTIONS YOU CAN USE

- **Comprehensive Section** and **Chapter Reviews** and **Standardized Test Preparation** allow students to practice their test-taking skills.

- Customize your assessment with the **One-Stop Planner CD-ROM with Test Generator and State-Specific Resources.**

- **Science Tutor CD-ROM** serves as a personal tutor to help students practice what they learn.

- **Brain Food Video Quizzes** (on DVD and VHS) are game show-style quizzes that assess students' progress and help them prepare for tests.

BUILDS SCIENCE SKILLS THROUGH ACTIVITIES

- The laboratory program includes labs in each chapter, labs in the **LabBook** at the end of the *Student Edition,* six different lab books, and **Video Labs.**

- All labs are teacher-tested and rated by difficulty in the *Teacher's Edition,* so you can be sure that labs will be appropriate for your students.

- All of the program labs are provided on the **Holt Lab Generator CD-ROM.**

- **Virtual Investigations CD-ROM** provides a simulated lab experience in a safe environment with no clean up.

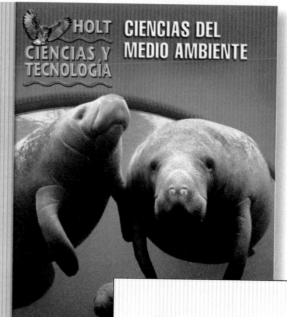

HOLT CIENCIAS Y TECNOLOGÍA

CIENCIAS DEL MEDIO AMBIENTE

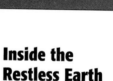

EcoLabs

HOLT SCIENCE & TECHNOLOGY

HOLT SCIENCE & TECHNOLOGY

Resource Disc
Chapters 1–11

HOLT RINEHART AND WINSTON

One-Stop Planner®
with Test Generator and State-Specific Resources
CD-ROM for Macintosh® and Windows®

HOLT SCIENCE & TECHNOLOGY

Chapter Resource Files for Short Course

F

Inside the Restless Earth

Skills Worksheets
Directed Reading A
Directed Reading B
Vocabulary and Section Summary
Section Reviews
Chapter Review
Reinforcement
Critical Thinking

Assessments
Section Quizzes
Chapter Test A
Chapter Test B
Chapter Test C
Performance-Based Assessment
Standardized Test Preparation

Labs and Activities
Datasheet for Chapter Lab
Datasheet for Quick Lab
Datasheet for LabBook
Vocabulary Activity
SciLinks® Activity

Answer Keys
Teacher Notes for Performance-Based Assessment
Lab Notes and Answers
Answer Key for Skills Worksheets, Assessments, and Activities

Teaching Transparency List
- L82 The Flow of Blood Through the Heart
- L83 The Flow of Blood Through the Body
- L84 The Role of Blood in Respiration
- P24 Exhaling, Pressure, and Fluid Flow
- Chapter Starter Transparencies
- Bellringer Transparencies
- Concept Mapping Transparencies

Programa de audio guiado en CD
Guided Reading Audio CD Program

HOLT CIENCIAS Y TECNOLOGÍA

LAS INTERACCIÓNES DE LA MATERIA

Direct Spanish read of the student text

L

Life Science

P INTRODUCTION TO SCIENCE

In addition to the short courses listed below, **Short Course P Introduction to Science** provides students with a sound foundation for their study of science including topics such as careers in science, scientific methods, models, and measurement.

A MICROORGANISMS, FUNGI, AND PLANTS

B ANIMALS

CHAPTER 1

It's Alive!! Or, Is It?
- Characteristics of living things
- Homeostasis
- Heredity and DNA
- Producers, consumers, and decomposers
- Biomolecules

Animals and Behavior
- Characteristics of animals
- Classification of animals
- Animal behavior
- Hibernation and estivation
- The biological clock
- Animal communication
- Living in groups

CHAPTER 2

Bacteria and Viruses
- Binary fission
- Characteristics of bacteria
- Nitrogen-fixing bacteria
- Antibiotics
- Pathogenic bacteria
- Characteristics of viruses
- Lytic cycle

Invertebrates
- General characteristics of invertebrates
- Types of symmetry
- Characteristics of sponges, cnidarians, arthropods, and echinoderms
- Flatworms versus roundworms
- Types of circulatory systems

CHAPTER 3

Protists and Fungi
- Characteristics of protists
- Types of algae
- Types of protozoa
- Protist reproduction
- Characteristics of fungi and lichens

Fishes, Amphibians, and Reptiles
- Characteristics of vertebrates
- Structure and kinds of fishes
- Development of lungs
- Structure and kinds of amphibians and reptiles
- Function of the amniotic egg

CHAPTER 4

Introduction to Plants
- Characteristics of plants and seeds
- Reproduction and classification
- Angiosperms versus gymnosperms
- Monocots versus dicots
- Structure and functions of roots, stems, leaves, and flowers

Birds and Mammals
- Structure and kinds of birds
- Types of feathers
- Adaptations for flight
- Structure and kinds of mammals
- Function of the placenta

CHAPTER 5

Plant Processes
- Pollination and fertilization
- Dormancy
- Photosynthesis
- Plant tropisms
- Seasonal responses of plants

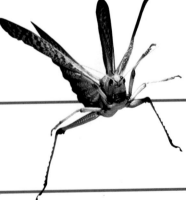

CHAPTER 6

CHAPTER 7

PROGRAM SCOPE AND SEQUENCE

Selecting the right books for your course is easy. Just review the topics presented in each book to determine the best match to your district curriculum.

C CELLS, HEREDITY, & CLASSIFICATION	**D** HUMAN BODY SYSTEMS & HEALTH	**E** ENVIRONMENTAL SCIENCE
Cells: The Basic Units of Life • Cells, tissues, and organs • Cell theory • Surface-to-volume ratio • Prokaryotic versus eukaryotic cells • Cell organelles	**Body Organization and Structure** • Homeostasis • Types of tissue • Organ systems • Structure and function of the skeletal system, muscular system, and integumentary system	**Interactions of Living Things** • Biotic versus abiotic parts of the environment • Producers, consumers, and decomposers • Food chains and food webs • Factors limiting population growth • Predator-prey relationships • Symbiosis and coevolution
The Cell in Action • Diffusion and osmosis • Passive versus active transport • Endocytosis versus exocytosis • Photosynthesis • Cellular respiration and fermentation • Cell cycle	**Circulation and Respiration** • Structure and function of the cardiovascular system, lymphatic system, and respiratory system • Respiratory disorders	**Cycles in Nature** • Water cycle • Carbon cycle • Nitrogen cycle • Ecological succession
Heredity • Dominant versus recessive traits • Genes and alleles • Genotype, phenotype, the Punnett square and probability • Meiosis • Determination of sex	**The Digestive and Urinary Systems** • Structure and function of the digestive system • Structure and function of the urinary system	**The Earth's Ecosystems** • Kinds of land and water biomes • Marine ecosystems • Freshwater ecosystems
Genes and Gene Technology • Structure of DNA • Protein synthesis • Mutations • Heredity disorders and genetic counseling	**Communication and Control** • Structure and function of the nervous system and endocrine system • The senses • Structure and function of the eye and ear	**Environmental Problems and Solutions** • Types of pollutants • Types of resources • Conservation practices • Species protection
The Evolution of Living Things • Adaptations and species • Evidence for evolution • Darwin's work and natural selection • Formation of new species	**Reproduction and Development** • Asexual versus sexual reproduction • Internal versus external fertilization • Structure and function of the human male and female reproductive systems • Fertilization, placental development, and embryo growth • Stages of human life	**Energy Resources** • Types of resources • Energy resources and pollution • Alternative energy resources
The History of Life on Earth • Geologic time scale and extinctions • Plate tectonics • Human evolution	**Body Defenses and Disease** • Types of diseases • Vaccines and immunity • Structure and function of the immune system • Autoimmune diseases, cancer, and AIDS	
Classification • Levels of classification • Cladistic diagrams • Dichotomous keys • Characteristics of the six kingdoms	**Staying Healthy** • Nutrition and reading food labels • Alcohol and drug effects on the body • Hygiene, exercise, and first aid	

Earth Science

F INSIDE THE RESTLESS EARTH	**G** EARTH'S CHANGING SURFACE
CHAPTER 1	
Minerals of the Earth's Crust • Mineral composition and structure • Types of minerals • Mineral identification • Mineral formation and mining	**Maps as Models of the Earth** • Structure of a map • Cardinal directions • Latitude, longitude, and the equator • Magnetic declination and true north • Types of projections • Aerial photographs • Remote sensing • Topographic maps
CHAPTER 2	
Rocks: Mineral Mixtures • Rock cycle and types of rocks • Rock classification • Characteristics of igneous, sedimentary, and metamorphic rocks	**Weathering and Soil Formation** • Types of weathering • Factors affecting the rate of weathering • Composition of soil • Soil conservation and erosion prevention
CHAPTER 3	
The Rock and Fossil Record • Uniformitarianism versus catastrophism • Superposition • The geologic column and unconformities • Absolute dating and radiometric dating • Characteristics and types of fossils • Geologic time scale	**Agents of Erosion and Deposition** • Shoreline erosion and deposition • Wind erosion and deposition • Erosion and deposition by ice • Gravity's effect on erosion and deposition
CHAPTER 4	
Plate Tectonics • Structure of the Earth • Continental drifts and sea floor spreading • Plate tectonics theory • Types of boundaries • Types of crust deformities	
CHAPTER 5	
Earthquakes • Seismology • Features of earthquakes • P and S waves • Gap hypothesis • Earthquake safety	
CHAPTER 6	
Volcanoes • Types of volcanoes and eruptions • Types of lava and pyroclastic material • Craters versus calderas • Sites and conditions for volcano formation • Predicting eruptions	

WATER ON EARTH

 WEATHER AND CLIMATE

 ASTRONOMY

The Flow of Fresh Water
- Water cycle
- River systems
- Stream erosion
- Life cycle of rivers
- Deposition
- Aquifers, springs, and wells
- Ground water
- Water treatment and pollution

The Atmosphere
- Structure of the atmosphere
- Air pressure
- Radiation, convection, and conduction
- Greenhouse effect and global warming
- Characteristics of winds
- Types of winds
- Air pollution

Studying Space
- Astronomy
- Keeping time
- Types of telescope
- Radioastronomy
- Mapping the stars
- Scales of the universe

Exploring the Oceans
- Properties and characteristics of the oceans
- Features of the ocean floor
- Ocean ecology
- Ocean resources and pollution

Understanding Weather
- Water cycle
- Humidity
- Types of clouds
- Types of precipitation
- Air masses and fronts
- Storms, tornadoes, and hurricanes
- Weather forecasting
- Weather maps

Stars, Galaxies, and the Universe
- Composition of stars
- Classification of stars
- Star brightness, distance, and motions
- H-R diagram
- Life cycle of stars
- Types of galaxies
- Theories on the formation of the universe

The Movement of Ocean Water
- Types of currents
- Characteristics of waves
- Types of ocean waves
- Tides

Climate
- Weather versus climate
- Seasons and latitude
- Prevailing winds
- Earth's biomes
- Earth's climate zones
- Ice ages
- Global warming
- Greenhouse effect

Formation of the Solar System
- Birth of the solar system
- Structure of the sun
- Fusion
- Earth's structure and atmosphere
- Planetary motion
- Newton's Law of Universal Gravitation

A Family of Planets
- Properties and characteristics of the planets
- Properties and characteristics of moons
- Comets, asteroids, and meteoroids

Exploring Space
- Rocketry and artificial satellites
- Types of Earth orbit
- Space probes and space exploration

Physical Science

	K INTRODUCTION TO MATTER	**L** INTERACTIONS OF MATTER
CHAPTER 1	**The Properties of Matter** • Definition of matter • Mass and weight • Physical and chemical properties • Physical and chemical change • Density	**Chemical Bonding** • Types of chemical bonds • Valence electrons • Ions versus molecules • Crystal lattice
CHAPTER 2	**States of Matter** • States of matter and their properties • Boyle's and Charles's laws • Changes of state	**Chemical Reactions** • Writing chemical formulas and equations • Law of conservation of mass • Types of reactions • Endothermic versus exothermic reactions • Law of conservation of energy • Activation energy • Catalysts and inhibitors
CHAPTER 3	**Elements, Compounds, and Mixtures** • Elements and compounds • Metals, nonmetals, and metalloids (semiconductors) • Properties of mixtures • Properties of solutions, suspensions, and colloids	**Chemical Compounds** • Ionic versus covalent compounds • Acids, bases, and salts • pH • Organic compounds • Biomolecules
CHAPTER 4	**Introduction to Atoms** • Atomic theory • Atomic model and structure • Isotopes • Atomic mass and mass number	**Atomic Energy** • Properties of radioactive substances • Types of decay • Half-life • Fission, fusion, and chain reactions
CHAPTER 5	**The Periodic Table** • Structure of the periodic table • Periodic law • Properties of alkali metals, alkaline-earth metals, halogens, and noble gases	
CHAPTER 6		

M FORCES, MOTION, AND ENERGY

 N ELECTRICITY AND MAGNETISM

O SOUND AND LIGHT

Matter in Motion
- Speed, velocity, and acceleration
- Measuring force
- Friction
- Mass versus weight

Forces in Motion
- Terminal velocity and free fall
- Projectile motion
- Inertia
- Momentum

Forces in Fluids
- Properties in fluids
- Atmospheric pressure
- Density
- Pascal's principle
- Buoyant force
- Archimedes' principle
- Bernoulli's principle

Work and Machines
- Measuring work
- Measuring power
- Types of machines
- Mechanical advantage
- Mechanical efficiency

Energy and Energy Resources
- Forms of energy
- Energy conversions
- Law of conservation of energy
- Energy resources

Heat and Heat Technology
- Heat versus temperature
- Thermal expansion
- Absolute zero
- Conduction, convection, radiation
- Conductors versus insulators
- Specific heat capacity
- Changes of state
- Heat engines
- Thermal pollution

Introduction to Electricity
- Law of electric charges
- Conduction versus induction
- Static electricity
- Potential difference
- Cells, batteries, and photocells
- Thermocouples
- Voltage, current, and resistance
- Electric power
- Types of circuits

Electromagnetism
- Properties of magnets
- Magnetic force
- Electromagnetism
- Solenoids and electric motors
- Electromagnetic induction
- Generators and transformers

Electronic Technology
- Properties of semiconductors
- Integrated circuits
- Diodes and transistors
- Analog versus digital signals
- Microprocessors
- Features of computers

The Energy of Waves
- Properties of waves
- Types of waves
- Reflection and refraction
- Diffraction and interference
- Standing waves and resonance

The Nature of Sound
- Properties of sound waves
- Structure of the human ear
- Pitch and the Doppler effect
- Infrasonic versus ultrasonic sound
- Sound reflection and echolocation
- Sound barrier
- Interference, resonance, diffraction, and standing waves
- Sound quality of instruments

The Nature of Light
- Electromagnetic waves
- Electromagnetic spectrum
- Law of reflection
- Absorption and scattering
- Reflection and refraction
- Diffraction and interference

Light and Our World
- Luminosity
- Types of lighting
- Types of mirrors and lenses
- Focal point
- Structure of the human eye
- Lasers and holograms

Program resources make teaching and learning easier.

CHAPTER RESOURCES

A *Chapter Resources book* accompanies each of the 16 *Short Courses*. Here you'll find everything you need to make sure your students are getting the most out of learning science—all in one book.

Skills Worksheets
- Directed Reading A: Basic
- Directed Reading B: Special Needs
- Vocabulary and Chapter Summary
- Section Review
- Chapter Review
- Reinforcement
- Critical Thinking

Labs & Activities
- Datasheets for Chapter Labs
- Datasheets for Quick Labs
- Datasheets for LabBook Labs
- Vocabulary Activity
- SciLinks® Activity

Assessments
- Section Quizzes
- Chapter Test A: General
- Chapter Test B: Advanced
- Chapter Test C: Special Needs
- Performance-Based Assessment
- Standardized Test Preparation

Teacher Resources
- Lab Notes and Answers
- Teacher Notes for Performance-Based Assessment
- Answer Keys
- Lesson Plans
- Full-color Teaching Transparencies, plus section Bellringers, Concept Mapping, and Chapter Starter Transparencies.

ENGLISH-LANGUAGE LEARNER RESOURCES

- **Multilingual Glossary** provides simple definitions of key science terms in multiple languages.

Spanish materials are available for each *Short Course:*

- *Student Edition*
- **Spanish Resources** booklet contains worksheets and assessments translated into Spanish with an English **Answer Key.**
- **Guided Reading Audio CD Program**

ONLINE RESOURCES

- *Enhanced Online Editions* engage students and assist teachers with a host of interactive features that are available anytime and anywhere you can connect to the Internet.
- **Live Ink®** Reading Help—exclusive to Holt—is a scientifically-researched tool to improve students' reading comprehension and is proven to raise students' test scores.
- **SciLinks**—a Web service developed and maintained by the National Science Teachers Association—links you and your students to up-to-date online resources directly related to chapter topics.
- **go.hrw.com** links you and your students to online chapter activities and resources.
- **Current Science** articles relate to students' lives.

T10

ADDITIONAL LAB AND SKILLS RESOURCES

- *Calculator-Based Labs* incorporates scientific instruments, offering students insight into modern scientific investigation.
- *EcoLabs & Field Activities* develops awareness of the natural world.
- *Holt Science Skills Workshop: Reading in the Content Area* contains exercises that target key reading skills.
- *Inquiry Labs* taps students' natural curiosity and creativity with a focus on the process of discovery.
- *Labs You Can Eat* safely incorporates edible items into the classroom.
- *Long-Term Projects & Research Ideas* extends and enriches lessons.
- *Math Skills for Science* provides additional explanations, examples, and math problems so students can develop their skills.
- *Science Skills Worksheets* helps your students hone important learning skills.
- *Whiz-Bang Demonstrations* gets your students' attention at the beginning of a lesson.

ADDITIONAL RESOURCES

- *Assessment Checklists & Rubrics* gives you guidelines for evaluating students' progress.
- *Holt Anthology of Science Fiction* sparks your students' imaginations with thought-provoking stories.
- *Holt Science Posters* visually reinforces scientific concepts and themes with seven colorful posters including **The Periodic Table of the Elements.**

- *Professional Reference for Teachers* contains professional articles that discuss a variety of topics, such as classroom management.
- *Program Introduction Resource File* explains the program and its features and provides several additional references, including lab safety, scoring rubrics, and more.
- *Science Fair Guide* gives teachers, students, and parents tips for planning and assisting in a science fair.
- *Science Puzzlers, Twisters & Teasers* activities challenge students to think about science concepts in different ways.

TECHNOLOGY RESOURCES

- *Guided Reading Audio CD Program*, available in English and Spanish, provides students with a direct read of each section.
- *HRW Earth Science Videotape* takes your students on a geology "field trip" with full-motion video.
- *Interactive Explorations CD-ROM Program* develops students' inquiry and decision-making skills as they investigate science phenomena in a virtual lab setting.
- *Holt Lab Generator CD-ROM* features all the labs from the *Holt Science & Technology* program and lab bank. Labs can be edited to fit classroom needs.
- *Virtual Investigations CD-ROM* makes it easy for students to practice science skills without the expense. Students perform lab activities in a safe, simulated environment.

- *One-Stop Planner CD-ROM®* organizes everything you need on one disc, including printable worksheets, customizable lesson plans, a powerful test generator, **PowerPoint® Resources, Lab Materials QuickList Software, Holt Calendar Planner, Interactive Teacher's Edition,** and more.
- *Science Tutor CD-ROMs* help students practice what they learn and provides immediate feedback.
- *Lab Videos* make it easier to integrate more experiments into your lessons without the preparation time and costs. Available on DVD and VHS.
- *Brain Food Video Quizzes* are game-show style quizzes that assess students' progress. Available on DVD and VHS.
- *Visual Concepts CD-ROMs* include graphics, animations, and movie clips that demonstrate key chapter concepts.

Science and Math Worksheets

The **Holt Science & Technology** program helps you meet the needs of a wide variety of students, regardless of their skill level. The following pages provide examples of the worksheets available to improve your students' science and math skills whether they already have a strong science and math background or are weak in these areas. Samples of assessment checklists and rubrics are also provided.

In addition to the skills worksheets represented here, **Holt Science & Technology** provides a variety of worksheets that are correlated directly with each chapter of the program. Representations of these worksheets are found at the beginning of each chapter in this *Teacher Edition*.

Many worksheets are also available on the Holt Web site. The address is **go.hrw.com**.

Science Skills Worksheets: Thinking Skills

BEING FLEXIBLE

USING YOUR SENSES

THINKING OBJECTIVELY
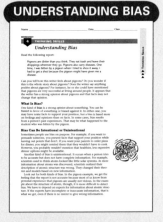

UNDERSTANDING BIAS

USING LOGIC

BOOSTING YOUR MEMORY
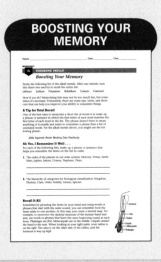

IMPROVING YOUR STUDY HABITS

READING A SCIENCE TEXTBOOK
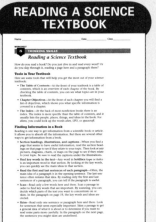

Science Skills Worksheets: Experimenting Skills

SAFETY RULES!
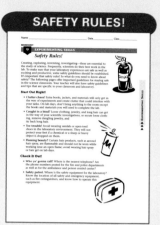

DOING A LAB WRITE-UP
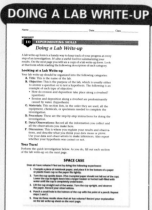

UNDERSTANDING VARIABLES
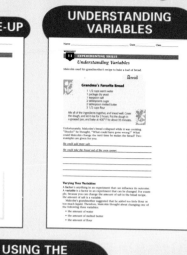

WORKING WITH HYPOTHESES
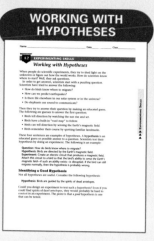

DESIGNING AN EXPERIMENT
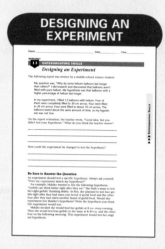

USING THE INTERNATIONAL SYSTEM OF UNITS (SI)

MEASURING
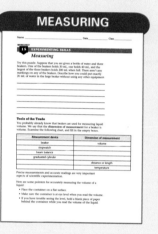

Science Skills Worksheets: Researching Skills

CHOOSING YOUR TOPIC
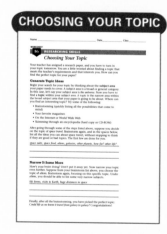

ORGANIZING YOUR RESEARCH
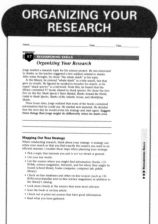

FINDING USEFUL SOURCES
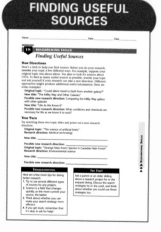

RESEARCHING ON THE WEB
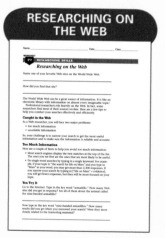

Science Skills Worksheets: Researching Skills (continued)

IDENTIFYING BIAS

TAKING NOTES

Science Skills Worksheets: Communicating Skills

SCIENCE WRITING

SCIENCE DRAWING

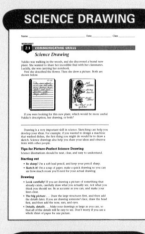

USING MODELS TO COMMUNICATE

INTRODUCTION TO GRAPHS

GRASPING GRAPHING

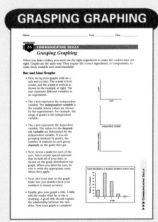

INTERPRETING YOUR DATA

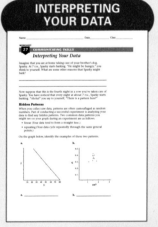

RECOGNIZING BIAS IN GRAPHS

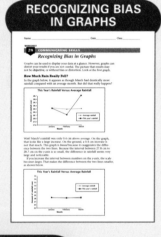

MAKING DATA MEANINGFUL

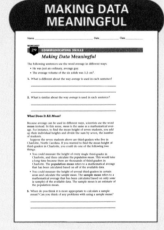

HINTS FOR ORAL PRESENTATIONS

Math Skills for Science

ADDITION AND SUBTRACTION

MULTIPLICATION

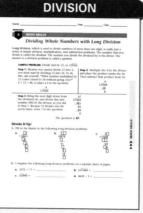

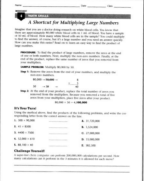

DIVISION

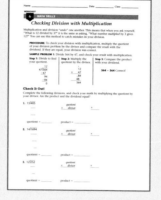

AVERAGES

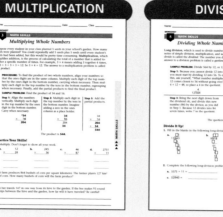

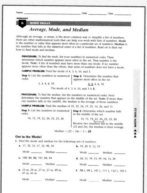

POSITIVE AND NEGATIVE NUMBERS

FRACTIONS

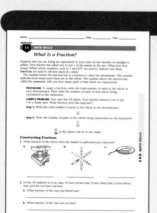

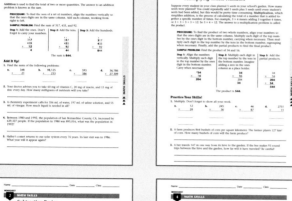

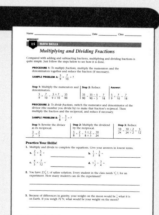

Math Skills for Science (continued)

RATIOS AND PROPORTIONS

DECIMALS

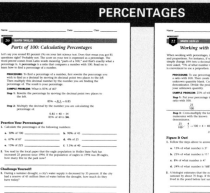

PERCENTAGES

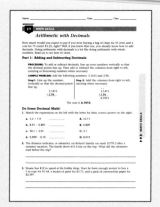

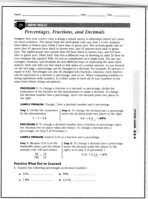

POWERS OF 10

SCIENTIFIC NOTATION

SI MEASUREMENT AND CONVERSION

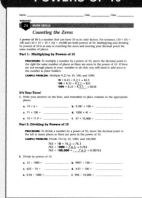

HOLT SCIENCE & TECHNOLOGY

Cells, Heredity, and Classification

HOLT, RINEHART AND WINSTON

A Harcourt Education Company

Orlando • **Austin** • New York • San Diego • Toronto • London

Acknowledgments

Contributing Authors

Linda Ruth Berg, Ph.D.
Adjunct Professor of Natural Sciences
St. Petersburg College
St. Petersburg, Florida

Barbara Christopher
Science Writer and Editor
Austin, Texas

Mark F. Taylor, Ph.D.
Associate Professor of Biology
Biology Department
Baylor University
Waco, Texas

Inclusion and Special Needs Consultant

Ellen McPeek Glisan
Special Needs Consultant
San Antonio, Texas

Safety Reviewer

Jack Gerlovich, Ph.D.
Associate Professor
School of Education
Drake University
Des Moines, Iowa

Academic Reviewers

Glenn Adelson, Ph.D.
Instructor
Department of Organismic and Evolutionary Biology
Harvard University
Cambridge, Massachusetts

Joe W. Crim, Ph.D.
Professor and Head of Cellular Biology
Department of Cellular Biology
University of Georgia
Athens, Georgia

Jim Denbow, Ph.D.
Associate Professor of Archaeology
Department of Anthropology and Archaeology
University of Texas at Austin
Austin, Texas

David Haig, Ph.D.
Professor of Biology
Department of Organismic and Evolutionary Biology
Harvard University
Cambridge, Massachusetts

Laurie Santos, Ph.D.
Assistant Professor
Department of Psychology
Yale University
New Haven, Connecticut

Patrick K. Schoff, Ph.D.
Research Associate
Natural Resources Research Institute
University of Minnesota—Duluth
Duluth, Minnesota

Richard P. Vari, Ph.D.
Research Scientist and Curator
Division of Fishes
National Museum of Natural History
Washington, D.C.

Teacher Reviewers

Diedre S. Adams
Physical Science Instructor
West Vigo Middle School
West Terre Haute, Indiana

Sarah Carver
Science Teacher
Jackson Creek Middle School
Bloomington, Indiana

Hilary Cochran
Science Teacher
Indian Crest Junior High School
Souderton, Pennsylvania

Karen Dietrich, S.S.J., Ph.D.
Principal and Biology Instructor
Mount Saint Joseph Academy
Flourtown, Pennsylvania

Debra S. Kogelman, MAed.
Science Teacher
University of Chicago Laboratory Schools
Chicago, Illinois

Elizabeth Rustad
Science Teacher
Higley School District
Gilbert, Arizona

Helen P. Schiller
Instructional Coach
Sevier Middle School
Greenville, South Carolina

Stephanie Snowden
Science Teacher
Canyon Vista Middle School
Austin, Texas

Angie Williams
Teacher
Riversprings Middle School
Crawfordville, Florida

Lab Development

Diana Scheidle Bartos
Research Associate
School of Mines
Golden, Colorado

Carl Benson
General Science Teacher
Plains High School
Plains, Montana

Charlotte Blassingame
Technology Coordinator
White Station
    Middle School
Memphis, Tennessee

Marsha Carver
*Science Teacher and
    Department Chair*
McLean County
    High School
Calhoun, Kentucky

Kenneth E. Creese
Science Teacher
White Mountain Junior
    High School
Rock Springs, Wyoming

Linda A. Culp
*Science Teacher and
    Department Chair*
Thorndale High School
Thorndale, Texas

James Deaver
*Science Teacher and
    Department Chair*
West Point High School
West Point, Nebraska

Frank McKinney, Ph.D.
Professor of Geology
Appalachian State
    University
Boone, North Carolina

Alyson M. Mike
*Science Teacher and
    Department Chair*
East Valley Middle School
East Helena, Montana

C. Ford Morishita
Biology Teacher
Clackamas High School
Milwaukie, Oregon

Patricia D. Morrell, Ph.D.
Associate Professor
School of Education
University of Portland
Portland, Oregon

Hilary C. Olson, Ph.D.
Research Associate
Institute for Geophysics
The University of Texas
    at Austin
Austin, Texas

James B. Pulley
*Science Editor and Former
    Science Teacher*
North Kansas City, Missouri

Denice Lee Sandefur
Science Chairperson
Nucla High School
Nucla, Colorado

Patti Soderberg
Science Writer
The BioQUEST Curriculum
    Consortium
Biology Department
Beloit College
Beloit, Wisconsin

Phillip Vavala
*Science Teacher and
    Department Chair*
Salesianum School
Wilmington, Delaware

Albert C. Wartski, M.A.T.
Biology Teacher
Chapel Hill High School
Chapel Hill, North Carolina

Lynn Marie Wartski
*Science Writer and Former
    Science Teacher*
Hillsborough, North
    Carolina

Ivora D. Washington
*Science Teacher and
    Department Chair*
Hyattsville Middle School
Washington, D.C.

Lab Testing

Georgiann Delgadillo
Science Teacher
East Valley Continuous
    Curriculum School
Spokane, Washington

Susan Gorman
Science Teacher
North Ridge Middle School
North Richland Hills, Texas

Karma Houston-Hughes
Science Mentor
Kyrene Middle School
Tempe, Arizona

Kerry A. Johnson
Science Teacher
Isbell Middle School
Santa Paula, California

M. R. Penny Kisiah
*Science Teacher and
    Department Chair*
Fairview Middle School
Tallahassee, Florida

Kathy LaRoe
Science Teacher
East Valley Middle School
East Helena, Montana

Maurine O. Marchani
*Science Teacher and
    Department Chair*
Raymond Park Middle
    School
Indianapolis, Indiana

Terry J. Rakes
Science Teacher
Elmwood Junior High
    School
Rogers, Arkansas

Debra A. Sampson
Science Teacher
Booker T. Washington
    Middle School
Elgin, Texas

Feature Development

Hatim Belyamani
John A. Benner
David Bradford
Jennifer Childers
Mickey Coakley
Susan Feldkamp
Jane Gardner
Erik Hahn
Christopher Hess
Deena Kalai
Charlotte W. Luongo, MSc
Michael May
Persis Mehta, Ph.D.
Eileen Nehme, MPH
Catherine Podeszwa
Dennis Rathnaw
Daniel B. Sharp
April Smith West
John M. Stokes
Molly F. Wetterschneider

Answer Checking

Hatim Belyamani
Austin, Texas

Cells, Heredity, and Classification

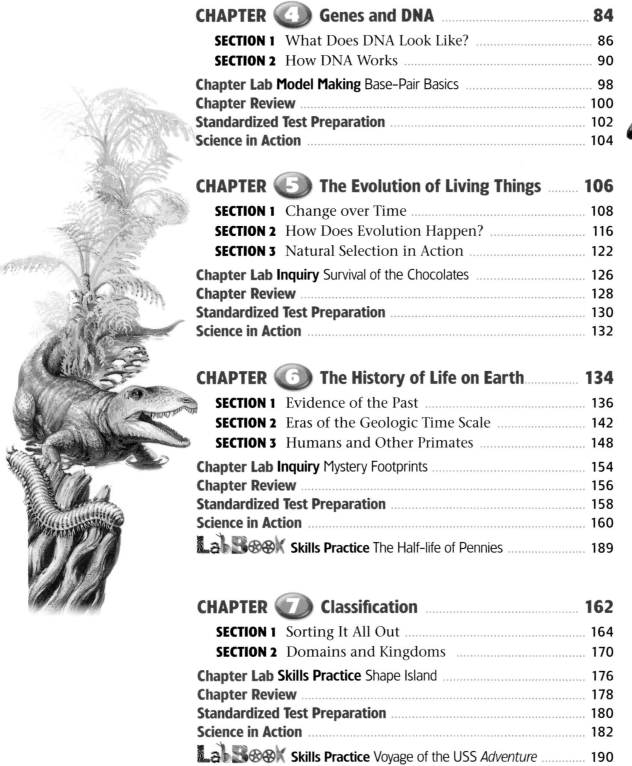

Labs and Activities

How to Use Your Textbook

Your Roadmap for Success with Holt Science and Technology

What You Will Learn

At the beginning of every section you will find the section's objectives and vocabulary terms. The objectives tell you what you'll need to know after you finish reading the section.

Vocabulary terms are listed for each section. Learn the definitions of these terms because you will most likely be tested on them. Each term is highlighted in the text and is defined at point of use and in the margin. You can also use the glossary to locate definitions quickly.

STUDY TIP Reread the objectives and the definitions to the terms when studying for a test to be sure you know the material.

Get Organized

A Reading Strategy at the beginning of every section provides tips to help you organize and remember the information covered in the section. Keep a science notebook so that you are ready to take notes when your teacher reviews the material in class. Keep your assignments in this notebook so that you can review them when studying for the chapter test.

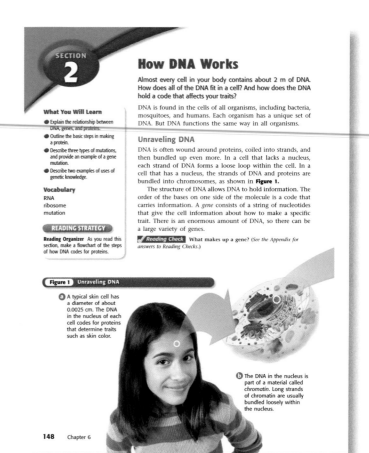

SECTION 2

How DNA Works

Almost every cell in your body contains about 2 m of DNA. How does all of the DNA fit in a cell? And how does the DNA hold a code that affects your traits?

DNA is found in the cells of all organisms, including bacteria, mosquitoes, and humans. Each organism has a unique set of DNA. But DNA functions the same way in all organisms.

Unraveling DNA

DNA is often wound around proteins, coiled into strands, and then bundled up even more. In a cell that lacks a nucleus, each strand of DNA forms a loose loop within the cell. In a cell that has a nucleus, the strands of DNA and proteins are bundled into chromosomes, as shown in **Figure 1.**

The structure of DNA allows DNA to hold information. The order of the bases on one side of the molecule is a code that carries information. A *gene* consists of a string of nucleotides that give the cell information about how to make a specific trait. There is an enormous amount of DNA, so there can be a large variety of genes.

Reading Check What makes up a gene? (*See the Appendix for answers to Reading Checks.*)

What You Will Learn

- Explain the relationship between DNA, genes, and proteins.
- Outline the basic steps in making a protein.
- Describe three types of mutations, and provide an example of a gene mutation.
- Describe two examples of uses of genetic knowledge.

Vocabulary
RNA
ribosome
mutation

READING STRATEGY

Reading Organizer As you read this section, make a flowchart of the steps of how DNA codes for proteins.

Figure 1 Unraveling DNA

ⓐ A typical skin cell has a diameter of about 0.0025 cm. The DNA in the nucleus of each cell codes for proteins that determine traits such as skin color.

ⓑ The DNA in the nucleus is part of a material called *chromatin.* Long strands of chromatin are usually bundled loosely within the nucleus.

148 Chapter 6

↗ Be Resourceful—Use the Web

SciLinks boxes in your textbook take you to resources that you can use for science projects, reports, and research papers. Go to **scilinks.org** and type in the **SciLinks code** to find information on a topic.

Visit go.hrw.com
Check out the **Current Science®** magazine articles and other materials that go with your textbook at **go.hrw.com.** Click on the textbook icon and the table of contents to see all of the resources for each chapter.

An Example of a Substitution

A mutation, such as a substitution, can be harmful because it may cause a gene to produce the wrong protein. Consider the DNA sequence GAA. When copied as mRNA, this sequence gives the instructions to place the amino acid glutamic acid into the growing protein. If a mistake happens and the original DNA sequence is changed to GTA, the sequence will code for the amino acid valine instead.

This simple change in an amino acid can cause the disease *sickle cell disease*. Sickle cell disease affects red blood cells. When valine is substituted for glutamic acid in a blood protein, as shown in **Figure 4**, the red blood cells are changed into a sickle shape.

The sickle cells are not as good at carrying oxygen as normal red blood cells are. Sickle cells are also likely to get stuck in blood vessels and cause painful and dangerous clots.

Reading Check What causes sickle cell disease?

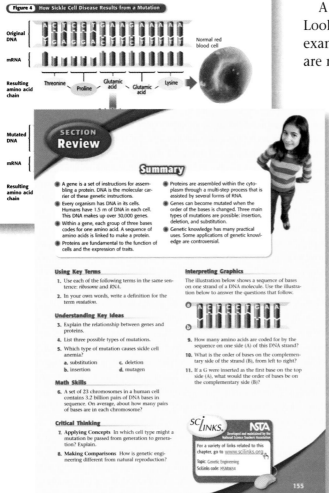

Figure 4 How Sickle Cell Disease Results from a Mutation

155

SCHOOL to HOME

An Error in the Message

The sentence below is the result of an error similar to a DNA mutation. The original sentence was made up of three-letter words, but an error was made in this copy. Explain the idea of mutations to your parent or guardian. Then, work together to find the mutation, and write the sentence correctly.

THE IGB ADC ATA TET HEB IGR EDR AT.

ACTIVITY

Use the Illustrations and Photos

Art shows complex ideas and processes. Learn to analyze the art so that you better understand the material you read in the text.

Tables and graphs display important information in an organized way to help you see relationships.

A picture is worth a thousand words. Look at the photographs to see relevant examples of science concepts that you are reading about.

Answer the Section Reviews

Section Reviews test your knowledge of the main points of the section. Critical Thinking items challenge you to think about the material in greater depth and to find connections that you infer from the text.

STUDY TIP When you can't answer a question, reread the section. The answer is usually there.

Do Your Homework

Your teacher may assign worksheets to help you understand and remember the material in the chapter.

STUDY TIP Don't try to answer the questions without reading the text and reviewing your class notes. A little preparation up front will make your homework assignments a lot easier. Answering the items in the Chapter Review will help prepare you for the chapter test.

Visit Holt Online Learning

If your teacher gives you a special password to log onto the **Holt Online Learning** site, you'll find your complete textbook on the Web. In addition, you'll find some great learning tools and practice quizzes. You'll be able to see how well you know the material from your textbook.

SAFETY FIRST!

Exploring, inventing, and investigating are essential to the study of science. However, these activities can also be dangerous. To make sure that your experiments and explorations are safe, you must be aware of a variety of safety guidelines. You have probably heard of the saying, "It is better to be safe than sorry." This is particularly true in a science classroom where experiments and explorations are being performed. Being uninformed and careless can result in serious injuries. Don't take chances with your own safety or with anyone else's.

The following pages describe important guidelines for staying safe in the science classroom. Your teacher may also have safety guidelines and tips that are specific to your classroom and laboratory. Take the time to be safe.

Safety Rules!

Start Out Right

Always get your teacher's permission before attempting any laboratory exploration. Read the procedures carefully, and pay particular attention to safety information and caution statements. If you are unsure about what a safety symbol means, look it up or ask your teacher. You cannot be too careful when it comes to safety. If an accident does occur, inform your teacher immediately regardless of how minor you think the accident is.

Safety Symbols

All of the experiments and investigations in this book and their related worksheets include important safety symbols to alert you to particular safety concerns. Become familiar with these symbols so that when you see them, you will know what they mean and what to do. It is important that you read this entire safety section to learn about specific dangers in the laboratory.

If you are instructed to note the odor of a substance, wave the fumes toward your nose with your hand. Never put your nose close to the source.

Eye protection	Clothing protection	Hand safety

Heating safety	Electric safety	Chemical safety

Animal safety	Sharp object	Plant safety

x

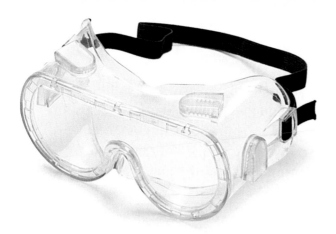

Eye Safety

Wear safety goggles when working around chemicals, acids, bases, or any type of flame or heating device. Wear safety goggles any time there is even the slightest chance that harm could come to your eyes. If any substance gets into your eyes, notify your teacher immediately and flush your eyes with running water for at least 15 minutes. Treat any unknown chemical as if it were a dangerous chemical. Never look directly into the sun. Doing so could cause permanent blindness.

Avoid wearing contact lenses in a laboratory situation. Even if you are wearing safety goggles, chemicals can get between the contact lenses and your eyes. If your doctor requires that you wear contact lenses instead of glasses, wear eye-cup safety goggles in the lab.

Safety Equipment

Know the locations of the nearest fire alarms and any other safety equipment, such as fire blankets and eyewash fountains, as identified by your teacher, and know the procedures for using the equipment.

Neatness

Keep your work area free of all unnecessary books and papers. Tie back long hair, and secure loose sleeves or other loose articles of clothing, such as ties and bows. Remove dangling jewelry. Don't wear open-toed shoes or sandals in the laboratory. Never eat, drink, or apply cosmetics in a laboratory setting. Food, drink, and cosmetics can easily become contaminated with dangerous materials.

Certain hair products (such as aerosol hair spray) are flammable and should not be worn while working near an open flame. Avoid wearing hair spray or hair gel on lab days.

Sharp/Pointed Objects

Use knives and other sharp instruments with extreme care. Never cut objects while holding them in your hands. Place objects on a suitable work surface for cutting.

Be extra careful when using any glassware. When adding a heavy object to a graduated cylinder, tilt the cylinder so the object slides slowly to the bottom.

Chemicals

Wear safety goggles when handling any potentially dangerous chemicals, acids, or bases. If a chemical is unknown, handle it as you would a dangerous chemical. Wear an apron and protective gloves when you work with acids or bases or whenever you are told to do so. If a spill gets on your skin or clothing, rinse it off immediately with water for at least 5 minutes while calling to your teacher.

Never mix chemicals unless your teacher tells you to do so. Never taste, touch, or smell chemicals unless you are specifically directed to do so. Before working with a flammable liquid or gas, check for the presence of any source of flame, spark, or heat.

Heat

Wear safety goggles when using a heating device or a flame. Whenever possible, use an electric hot plate as a heat source instead of using an open flame. When heating materials in a test tube, always angle the test tube away from yourself and others. To avoid burns, wear heat-resistant gloves whenever instructed to do so.

Electricity

Be careful with electrical cords. When using a microscope with a lamp, do not place the cord where it could trip someone. Do not let cords hang over a table edge in a way that could cause equipment to fall if the cord is accidentally pulled. Do not use equipment with damaged cords. Be sure that your hands are dry and that the electrical equipment is in the "off" position before plugging it in. Turn off and unplug electrical equipment when you are finished.

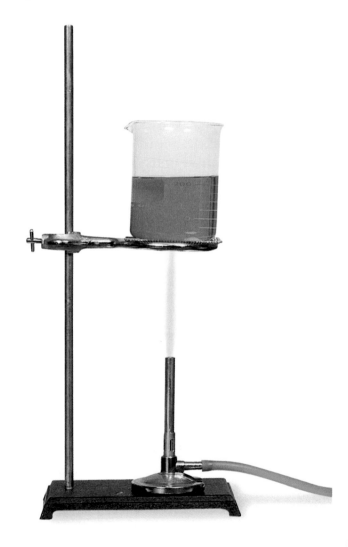

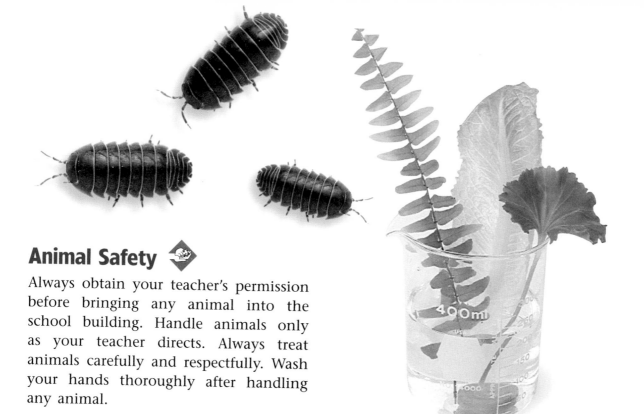

Animal Safety

Always obtain your teacher's permission before bringing any animal into the school building. Handle animals only as your teacher directs. Always treat animals carefully and respectfully. Wash your hands thoroughly after handling any animal.

Plant Safety

Do not eat any part of a plant or plant seed used in the laboratory. Wash your hands thoroughly after handling any part of a plant. When in nature, do not pick any wild plants unless your teacher instructs you to do so.

Glassware

Examine all glassware before use. Be sure that glassware is clean and free of chips and cracks. Report damaged glassware to your teacher. Glass containers used for heating should be made of heat-resistant glass.

Cells: The Basic Units of Life
Chapter Planning Guide

Compression guide:
To shorten instruction because of time limitations, omit the Chapter Lab.

OBJECTIVES	LABS, DEMONSTRATIONS, AND ACTIVITIES	TECHNOLOGY RESOURCES
PACING • 135 min pp. 2–11 **Chapter Opener**	SE **Start-up Activity**, p. 3 ◆ GENERAL	OSP **Parent Letter** ■ CD **Student Edition on CD-ROM** CD **Guided Reading Audio CD** ■ TR **Chapter Starter Transparency*** VID **Brain Food Video Quiz**
Section 1 The Diversity of Cells • State the parts of the cell theory. • Explain why cells are so small. • Describe the parts of a cell. • Describe how bacteria are different from archaea. • Explain the difference between prokaryotic cells and eukaryotic cells.	TE **Activity** Modeling Cell Discovery, p. 4 ◆ GENERAL SE **Connection to Physics** Microscopes, p. 5 GENERAL SE **Quick Lab** Bacteria in Your Lunch?, p. 8 ◆ GENERAL CRF **Datasheet for Quick Lab*** TE **Group Activity** Archaea, p. 8 ADVANCED SE **Connection to Social Studies** Where Do They Live?, p. 9 GENERAL SE **Model-Making Lab** Elephant-Sized Amoebas?, p. 24 ◆ GENERAL CRF **Datasheet for Chapter Lab*** SE **Skills Practice Lab** Cells Alive!, p. 184 ◆ GENERAL CRF **Datasheet for LabBook***	OSP **Lesson Plans** (also in print) TR **Bellringer Transparency*** TR **L6 Math Focus: Surface Area–to–Volume Ratio*** TR **L114 A Typical Eukaryotic Cell*** VID **Lab Videos for Life Science** TE **Internet Activity**, p. 10 GENERAL CD **Science Tutor**
PACING • 45 min pp. 12–19 **Section 2 Eukaryotic Cells** • Identify the different parts of a eukaryotic cell. • Explain the function of each part of a eukaryotic cell.	TE **Demonstration** Cell Walls and Cell Membranes, p. 13 BASIC TE **Activity** Cellular Sieve, p. 13 ◆ BASIC TE **Group Activity** Drawing Cells, p. 14 BASIC TE **Activity** Cell Models, p. 15 GENERAL TE **Activity** Vacuole Model, p. 18 ◆ BASIC LB **Whiz-Bang Demonstrations** Grand Strand* ◆ GENERAL LB **Labs You Can Eat** The Incredible Edible Cell* ◆ ADVANCED LB **Long-Term Projects & Research Ideas** Ewe Again, Dolly?* ◆ ADVANCED	OSP **Lesson Plans** (also in print) TR **Bellringer Transparency*** TR **L115 A Plant Cell and an Animal Cell** TR **LINK TO PHYSICAL SCIENCE P61 Structural Formulas*** TR **L116 Organelles and Their Functions*** CRF **SciLinks Activity*** GENERAL CD **Science Tutor**
PACING • 45 min pp. 20–23 **Section 3 The Organization of Living Things** • List three advantages of being multicellular. • Describe the four levels of organization in living things. • Explain the relationship between the structure and function of a part of an organism.	TE **Activity** Concept Mapping, p. 20 ◆ GENERAL TE **Activity** Explain It to a Friend, p. 23 BASIC SE **Science in Action** Math, Social Studies, and Language Arts Activities, pp. 30–31 GENERAL	OSP **Lesson Plans** (also in print) TR **Bellringer Transparency*** TR **L8 Levels of Organization in the Cardiovascular System*** CD **Science Tutor**

PACING • 90 min

CHAPTER REVIEW, ASSESSMENT, AND STANDARDIZED TEST PREPARATION

CRF **Vocabulary Activity*** GENERAL
SE **Chapter Review**, pp. 26–27 GENERAL
CRF **Chapter Review*** ■ GENERAL
CRF **Chapter Tests A*** ■ GENERAL, **B*** ADVANCED, **C*** SPECIAL NEEDS
SE **Standardized Test Preparation**, pp. 28–29 GENERAL
CRF **Standardized Test Preparation*** GENERAL
CRF **Performance-Based Assessment*** GENERAL
OSP **Test Generator, Test Item Listing**

Online and Technology Resources

Visit go.hrw.com for access to Holt Online Learning, or enter the keyword **HL7 Home** for a variety of free online resources.

 **One-Stop Planner® CD-ROM**

This CD-ROM package includes:
• Lab Materials QuickList Software
• Holt Calendar Planner
• Customizable Lesson Plans
• Printable Worksheets
• ExamView® Test Generator
• Interactive Teacher's Edition
• Holt PuzzlePro®
• Holt PowerPoint® Resources

SKILLS DEVELOPMENT RESOURCES	SECTION REVIEW AND ASSESSMENT	CORRELATIONS
SE Pre-Reading Activity, p. 2 GENERAL **OSP** Science Puzzlers, Twisters & Teasers GENERAL		National Science Education Standards UCP 1; HNS 3; LS 1b, 5b
CRF Directed Reading A* ■ BASIC, B* SPECIAL NEEDS **IT** Interactive Textbook* Struggling Readers **CRF** Vocabulary and Section Summary* ■ GENERAL **SE** Reading Strategy Reading Organizer, p. 4 GENERAL **TE** Inclusion Strategies, p. 5 **TE** Support for English Language Learners, p. 5 **SE** Math Focus Surface Area-to-Volume Ratio, p. 6 GENERAL **TE** Reading Strategy Prediction Guide, p. 6 GENERAL **TE** Reading Strategy Prediction Guide, p. 7 GENERAL **TE** Research Be a Good Host, p. 9 GENERAL **MS** Math Skills for Science What Is a Ratio?* GENERAL **MS** Math Skills for Science Finding Perimeter and Area* GENERAL **MS** Math Skills for Science Finding Volume* GENERAL	**SE** Reading Checks, pp. 5, 6, 7, 9, 10 GENERAL **TE** Reteaching, p. 10 BASIC **TE** Quiz, p. 10 GENERAL **TE** Alternative Assessment, p. 10 GENERAL **SE** Section Review,* p. 11 ■ GENERAL **CRF** Section Quiz* ■ GENERAL	UCP 4, 5; SAI 1, 2; ST 2; SPSP 5; LS 1a, 1b, 1c, 2c, 3b, 5a; *Chapter Lab:* UCP 1, 2, 3; SAI 2; LS 1b, 1c, 3a, 3b; *LabBook:* UCP 1, 2, 5; SAI 1; ST 2; SPSP 5; HNS 1, 3; LS 1a, 1b, 1c, 1d, 2c, 3a, 5a
CRF Directed Reading A* ■ BASIC, B* SPECIAL NEEDS **IT** Interactive Textbook* Struggling Readers **CRF** Vocabulary and Section Summary* ■ GENERAL **SE** Reading Strategy Reading Organizer, p. 12 GENERAL **SE** Connection to Language Arts The Great Barrier, p. 13 GENERAL **TE** Support for English Language Learners, p. 13 **TE** Inclusion Strategies, p. 14 **TE** Reading Strategy Prediction Guide, p. 16 GENERAL **CRF** Reinforcement Worksheet Building a Eukaryotic Cell* BASIC	**SE** Reading Checks, pp. 13, 14, 16, 18 GENERAL **TE** Homework, p. 15 GENERAL **TE** Homework, p. 17 GENERAL **TE** Reteaching, p. 18 BASIC **TE** Quiz, p. 18 GENERAL **TE** Alternative Assessment, p. 18 GENERAL **SE** Section Review,* p. 19 ■ GENERAL **CRF** Section Quiz* ■ GENERAL	UCP 1, 4, 5; LS 1b, 1c, 3a, 5a, 5b
CRF Directed Reading A* ■ BASIC, B* SPECIAL NEEDS **IT** Interactive Textbook* Struggling Readers **CRF** Vocabulary and Section Summary* ■ GENERAL **SE** Reading Strategy Paired Summarizing, p. 20 GENERAL **TE** Support for English Language Learners, p. 21 **SE** Math Practice A Pet Protist, p. 21 GENERAL **CRF** Critical Thinking Cellular Construction* ADVANCED	**SE** Reading Checks, pp. 20, 21, 22 GENERAL **TE** Homework, p. 21 GENERAL **TE** Reteaching, p. 22 BASIC **TE** Quiz, p. 22 GENERAL **TE** Alternative Assessment, p. 22 GENERAL **SE** Section Review,* p. 23 ■ GENERAL **CRF** Section Quiz* ■ GENERAL	UCP 1, 2, 5; LS 1a, 1b, 1d

SC LINKS
NSTA
www.scilinks.org
Maintained by the **National Science Teachers Association.** See Chapter Enrichment pages that follow for a complete list of topics.

Current Science®
Check out *Current Science* articles and activities by visiting the HRW Web site at **go.hrw.com.** Just type in the keyword **HL5CS03T.**

Classroom Videos
• **Lab Videos** demonstrate the chapter lab.
• **Brain Food Video Quizzes** help students review the chapter material.

Classroom CD-ROMs
• **Guided Reading Audio CD** (Also in Spanish)
• **Interactive Explorations**
• **Virtual Investigations**
• **Visual Concepts**
• **Science Tutor**

Holt Lab Generator CD-ROM
Search for any lab by topic, standard, difficulty level, or time. Edit any lab to fit your needs, or create your own labs. Use the Lab Materials QuickList software to customize your lab materials list.

1 Chapter Resources

Visual Resources

Cells: The Basic Units of Life · CHAPTER STARTER

What If . . . ?

Imagine this scene from a horror film. A young man sits down to dinner to find that his mother has made asparagus again. The young man eats the dreaded asparagus stalks. Later, he finds out that instead of being digested, one of the stalks has taken up residence inside his body and is very much alive! Too horrifying to think about? What if the asparagus began to do wonderful things for the young man, such as giving him more energy than he ever dreamed possible? Lynn Margulis, a scientist, thinks that something similar may have happened to certain one-celled organisms that lived more than a billion years ago, giving rise to the kinds of cells that we are made of today.

According to Margulis's theory, about 1.2 billion years ago, some larger cells began eating smaller cells for dinner. Like the white blood cell on this page, these larger cells trapped the smaller cells with extensions of their cell body. But some of these smaller cells resisted being digested. In fact, they began to do very well in their new homes. The larger cells also benefited from their new guests. The smaller cells released large amounts of energy from food taken in by the larger cells. Other kinds of small cells used the energy in sunlight to make enough food to feed themselves and the larger cell. The energy-producing structures of most cells, including yours, are thought to have descended from these smaller cells. In this chapter, you will learn more about cells and their structures.

BELLRINGER TRANSPARENCIES

Cells: The Basic Units of Life · BELLRINGER TRANSPARENCY

Section: The Diversity of Cells
Why do you think cells weren't discovered until 1665? What invention do you think made their discovery possible? Do you think people can ever see cells with the naked eye? Explain your answer.

Write your responses in your **science journal.**

Section: Eukaryotic Cells
List three differences between *prokaryotic* and *eukaryotic* cells. Draw two diagrams illustrating the differences.

Write your responses in your **science journal.**

TEACHING TRANSPARENCIES

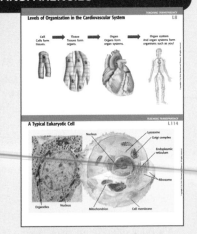

Math Focus: Surface Area–to–Volume Ratio

Levels of Organization in the Cardiovascular System — L8

A Typical Eukaryotic Cell — L114

TEACHING TRANSPARENCIES

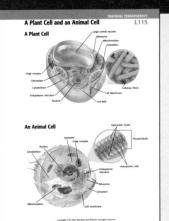

A Plant Cell and an Animal Cell — L115

A Plant Cell

An Animal Cell

Organelles and Their Functions — L116

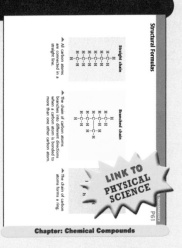

Structural Formulas — P61

LINK TO PHYSICAL SCIENCE

Chapter: Chemical Compounds

CONCEPT MAPPING TRANSPARENCY

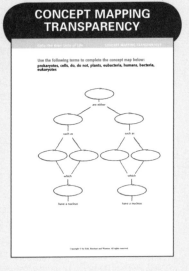

Cells: The Basic Units of Life · CONCEPT MAPPING TRANSPARENCY

Use the following terms to complete the concept map below:
prokaryotes, cells, do, do not, plants, eubacteria, humans, bacteria, eukaryotes

Planning Resources

LESSON PLANS

Lesson Plan SAMPLE

Section: Waves

Pacing
Regular Schedule: with lab(s):2 days without lab(s):If days
Block Schedule: with lab(s):1 1/2 days without lab(s):f day

Objectives
1. Relate the seven properties of life to a living organism.
2. Describe seven themes that can help you to organize what you learn about biology.
3. Identify the tiny structures that make up all living organisms.
4. Differentiate between reproduction and heredity and between metabolism and homeostasis.

National Science Education Standards Covered
LSInter6:Cells have particular structures that underlie their functions.
LSMat1: Most cell functions involve chemical reactions.
LSBeh1: Cells store and use information to guide their functions.
UCP1:Cell functions are regulated.
SI1: Cells differentiate and form complete multicellular organisms.
PS1: Species evolve over time.
ESS1: The great diversity of organisms is the result of more than 3.5 billion years of evolution.
ESS2: Natural selection and its evolutionary consequences provide a scientific explanation for the fossil record of ancient life forms as well as for the striking molecular similarities observed among the diverse species of living organisms.
ST1: The millions of different species of plants, animals, and microorganisms that live on earth today are related by descent from common ancestors.
ST2: The energy for life primarily comes from the sun.
SPSP1: The complexity and organization of organisms accommodates the need for obtaining, transforming, transporting, releasing, and eliminating the matter and energy used to sustain the organism.
SPSP6: An essential aspect of this standard involves recognition that an organism lives in an environment where different levels of organization of living systems—cells, organs, communities—and between living systems and the physical environment, chemical elements are recombined in different ways.
HNS1: Organisms have behavioral responses to internal changes and to external stimuli.

PARENT LETTER

SAMPLE

Dear Parent,

Your son's or daughter's science class will soon begin exploring the chapter entitled "The World of Physical Science." In this chapter, students will learn about how the scientific method applies to the study of physical science and the role of physical science in the world. By the end of the chapter, students should demonstrate a clear understanding of the chapter's main ideas and be able to discuss the following topics:

1. physical science is the study of energy and matter (Section 1)
2. the role of physical science in the world around them (Section 1)
3. careers that rely on physical science (Section 1)
4. the steps used in the scientific method (Section 2)
5. examples of technology (Section 2)
6. how the scientific method is used to answer questions and solve problems (Section 2)
7. how our knowledge of science changes over time (Section 2)
8. how models represent real objects or systems (Section 3)
9. examples of different ways models are used in science (Section 3)
10. the importance of the International System of Units (Section 4)
11. the appropriate units to use for particular measurements (Section 4)
12. how area and density are derived quantities (Section 4)

Questions to Ask Along the Way

You can help your son or daughter learn about these topics by asking interesting questions such as the following:

• What are some surprising careers that use physical science?
• What is a characteristic of a good hypothesis?
• Where is a good idea to use a model?
• Why do Americans measure things in terms of inches and yards and meters ?

ALSO IN SPANISH

TEST ITEM LISTING

TEST ITEM LISTING
The World of Science SAMPLE

MULTIPLE CHOICE

1. A limitation of models is that
   a. they are large enough to see.
   b. they do not act exactly like the things that they model.
   c. they are smaller than the things that they model.
   d. they model unfamiliar things.
   Answer: B Difficulty: 1 Section: 3 Objective: 2

2. The length 10 m is equal to
   a. 100 cm. c. 10,000 mm.
   b. 1,000 cm. d. Both (b) and (c)
   Answer: B Difficulty: 1 Section: 3 Objective: 2

3. To be valid, a hypothesis must be
   a. testable. c. made into a law.
   b. supported by evidence. d. Both (a) and (b)
   Answer: B Difficulty: 1 Section: 3 Objective: 2

4. The statement "Sheila has a state on her shirt" is an example of a(n)
   a. law. c. observation.
   b. hypothesis. d. prediction.
   Answer: B Difficulty: 1 Section: 3 Objective: 2

5. A hypothesis is often developed out of
   a. observations. c. laws.
   b. experiments. d. Both (a) and (c)
   Answer: B Difficulty: 1 Section: 3 Objective: 2

6. How many milliliters are in 3.5 kL?
   a. 3,500 mL. c. 3,500, 000 mL.
   b. 0.0039 mL. d. 3,500 mL
   Answer: B Difficulty: 1 Section: 3 Objective: 2

7. A map of bottle is an example of a
   a. law. c. model.
   b. experiment. d. unit
   Answer: B Difficulty: 1 Section: 3 Objective: 2

8. A lab has the safety icons shown below. These icons mean that you should wear
   a. safety goggles. c. safety goggles and a lab apron.
   b. only a lab apron. d. safety goggles, a lab apron, and gloves.
   Answer: B Difficulty: 1 Section: 3 Objective: 2

9. The law of conservation of mass says the the of mass before a chemical change is
   a. more than the total mass after the change. c. less than the total mass after the change.
   b. less than the total mass after the change. d. not the same as the total mass after the change.
   Answer: B Difficulty: 1 Section: 3 Objective: 2

10. In which of the following would you find a geochemist at work?
    a. studying the chemistry of the rocks c. studying fishes
    b. studying forestry d. studying the atmosphere
    Answer: B Difficulty: 1 Section: 3 Objective: 2

One-Stop Planner® CD-ROM

This CD-ROM includes all of the resources shown here and the following time-saving tools:

• **Lab Materials QuickList Software**
• **Customizable lesson plans**
• **Holt Calendar Planner**
• **The powerful ExamView® Test Generator**

For a preview of available worksheets covering math and science skills, see pages T12–T19. All of these resources are also on the One-Stop Planner®.

Meeting Individual Needs

DIRECTED READING A
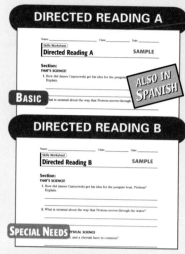
BASIC / **ALSO IN SPANISH**

DIRECTED READING B
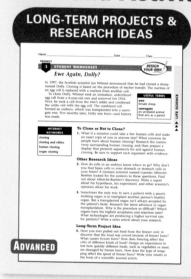
SPECIAL NEEDS

VOCABULARY ACTIVITY
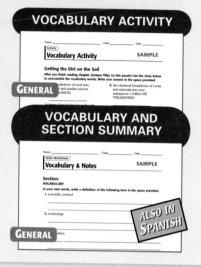
GENERAL

VOCABULARY AND SECTION SUMMARY
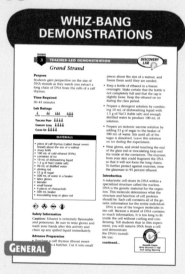
GENERAL / **ALSO IN SPANISH**

REINFORCEMENT
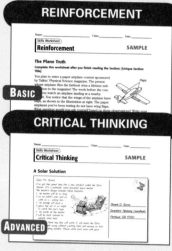
BASIC

CRITICAL THINKING
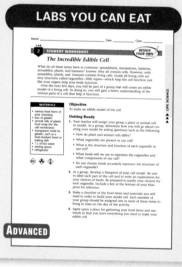
ADVANCED

SCILINKS ACTIVITY

GENERAL

SCIENCE PUZZLERS, TWISTERS & TEASERS

GENERAL

Labs and Activities

LONG-TERM PROJECTS & RESEARCH IDEAS
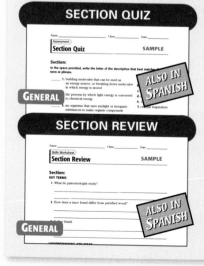
ADVANCED

WHIZ-BANG DEMONSTRATIONS
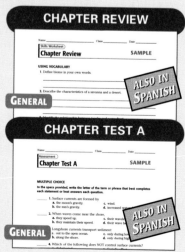
GENERAL

LABS YOU CAN EAT
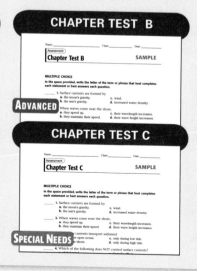
ADVANCED

DATASHEETS FOR QUICK LABS
DATASHEETS FOR CHAPTER LABS
DATASHEETS FOR LABBOOK
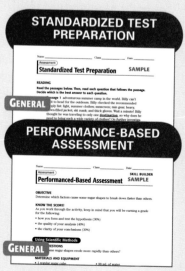

Review and Assessments

SECTION QUIZ
GENERAL / **ALSO IN SPANISH**

SECTION REVIEW
GENERAL / **ALSO IN SPANISH**

CHAPTER REVIEW
GENERAL / **ALSO IN SPANISH**

CHAPTER TEST A
GENERAL / **ALSO IN SPANISH**

CHAPTER TEST B
ADVANCED

CHAPTER TEST C
SPECIAL NEEDS

STANDARDIZED TEST PREPARATION
GENERAL

PERFORMANCE-BASED ASSESSMENT
GENERAL

This Chapter Enrichment provides relevant and interesting information to expand and enhance your presentation of the chapter material.

Section 1

The Diversity of Cells

Microtomy

- The development of high-magnification microscopes required that the preparation of specimens for viewing also become more sophisticated. Microtomy once referred only to specimen cutting, because a microtome is the instrument used to slice tissue sections. Today, microtomy refers collectively to the art of preparing specimens by any number of techniques.

- When microscopic organisms are viewed as whole- mounts, they are preserved, stained, dried (alcohol removes the water), and made transparent with clove or cedar oil. Then, the organism is mounted in a drop of resin on a glass slide and covered with a piece of glass only 0.005 mm thick.

Physiology and the Cell Theory

- The development of the cell theory aided research in other fields. In the mid-1800s, French physiologist Claude Bernard proposed that plants and animals are composed of sets of control mechanisms that work to maintain the internal conditions necessary for life. He recognized that a mammal can sustain a constant body temperature regardless of the outside temperature. Today, we recognize the ability of organisms to regulate their physiological processes to maintain specific conditions as *homeostasis*. But at the time, no one knew what the "organized sets of control mechanisms" were. The discovery of cells and the way their many components function to sustain life in an organism gave credence to Bernard's position.

Is That a Fact!

- The Earth is 4.5 billion years old, and the oldest cell-like fossils are about 3.5 billion years old!

- Aeolid nudibranchs are mollusks that eat hydroids, small polyps that have protective stinging cells. The nudibranch's digestive system carefully sorts out the hydroid's stinging cells and sends them to the protective tentacles on the nudibranch's own back.

Section 2

Eukaryotic Cells

"Protein" Therapy

- Decades of investigation into cell biology have produced what scientists call *gene therapy,* which refers to the use of genetic material to cure disease. It might be more appropriate to call this rapidly expanding field of science *protein therapy.*

- The gene can be thought of as a recipe for the proteins essential to life. For example, people with Duchenne muscular dystrophy lack dystrophin, an essential muscle protein that maintains the structure of muscle cells. Researchers have been able to remove the harmful genetic components of a virus and replace them with the gene for dystrophin. Their plan is to inject the dystrophin gene (the gene that codes for the dystrophin protein) directly into the muscles of Duchenne muscular dystrophy patients. If the process is successful, the dystrophin gene in the virus will compensate for patients' faulty dystrophin gene.

Tiny Scientists?

- Microbiologists study the characteristics of bacteria and other microorganisms to understand how they interact with other organisms. Virologists investigate viruses, which are active only inside a living host cell. Mycologists study fungi, which include molds and yeasts. Environmental microbiologists inspect the water in rivers and lakes. Microbiologists in agriculture study organisms that affect soil quality and crops.

Is That a Fact!

◆ The oldest unquestionably eukaryotic fossil is about 2.1 billion years old.

Section 3

The Organization of Living Things

In a Heartbeat

● The heart will function properly only if the cells that form its connective tissue and muscle perform their jobs in coordination. Scientists can use an enzyme to dissolve an embryonic heart into its individual cells. When placed in a dish, these cells, called *myocytes,* will continue to beat, although they are out of sync with each other. After a couple of days, sheets of interconnected cells form, and the myocytes beat in unison. Why do these changes happen? Openings develop between cells that touch, and their cytoplasms connect, which allows the cells to communicate directly with each other.

Organs: Delicate Workhorses

● The most frequently transplanted organ is the kidney, followed by the liver, the heart, and the lung. Most transplants must be done within a few hours after the organ is removed from a donor because organs are too delicate to survive current long-term storage procedures.

● Cryobiologists, scientists who study how life systems tolerate low temperatures, are studying the possibility of storing organs and organ systems at subfreezing temperatures. They are investigating the fluids that keep insects and some frogs alive in subfreezing temperatures. Cryobiologists hope that knowledge gained from such studies can be applied to human organs.

Development

● In a multicellular organism, almost every cell has the same set of genes. (Some specialized cells delete or duplicate sections of their DNA.) Yet, different cell types are structurally distinct and perform widely different functions. Part of the reason is that each cell expresses some genes but not others. Sometimes, genes can be expressed in tissues where they should not be. For example, some types of tumors contain hair and teeth!

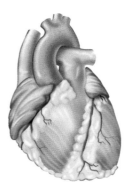

Is That a Fact!

◆ The oldest fossils of multicellular organisms are fossils of tiny algae approximately 1.2 billion years old.

◆ In 1931, a doctor removed a patient's parathyroid glands in error. These glands control the amount of calcium in the blood, which in turn regulates the heart. As a last-ditch effort to save the patient, a cow's parathyroid glands were ground up and injected into the patient. The patient recuperated and lived another 30 years with similar treatments.

SCILINKS.

NSTA
Developed and maintained by the National Science Teachers Association

SciLinks is maintained by the National Science Teachers Association to provide you and your students with interesting, up-to-date links that will enrich your classroom presentation of the chapter.

Visit www.scilinks.org and enter the SciLinks code for more information about the topic listed.

Topic: Prokaryotic Cells
SciLinks code: HSM1225

Topic: Eukaryotic Cells
SciLinks code: HSM0541

Topic: Cell Structures
SciLinks code: HSM0240

Topic: Archaebacteria
SciLinks code: HSM0091

Topic: Organization of Life
SciLinks code: HSM1080

Topic: Body Systems
SciLinks code: HSM0184

Overview

This chapter will help students understand the great diversity of cells. The chapter will take students from the time when cells were unknown through the discovery of cells to the understanding of the tremendous diversity of cells. Students will learn about cell structures and will also learn how cells, tissues, and organs form organisms.

Assessing Prior Knowledge

Students should be familiar with the following topic:

• characteristics of a living thing

Identifying Misconceptions

Students may not understand that all cells and organisms have the same basic structures. Also, students may not have a sense of scale. When asked to draw a molecule, most students will draw something that resembles a cell. Instruction should emphasize the relationship between molecules and cells. For example, many students believe that proteins and molecules are bigger than cells.

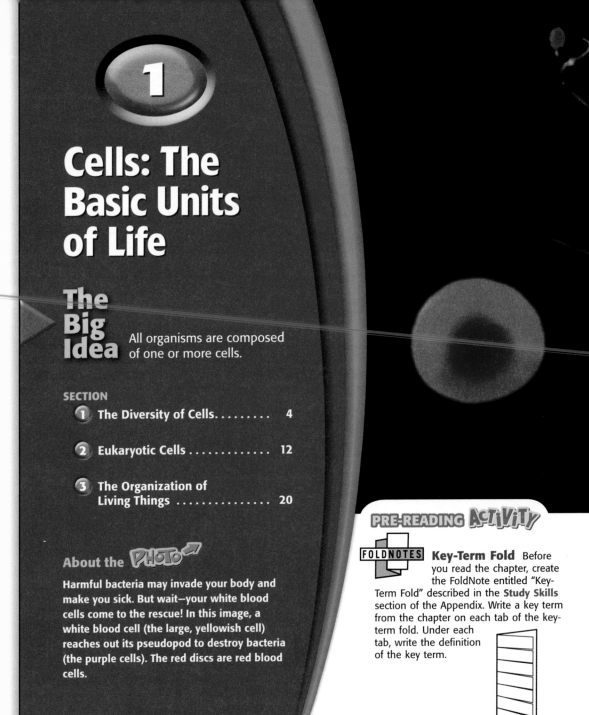

1

Cells: The Basic Units of Life

The Big Idea

All organisms are composed of one or more cells.

About the PHOTO

Harmful bacteria may invade your body and make you sick. But wait—your white blood cells come to the rescue! In this image, a white blood cell (the large, yellowish cell) reaches out its pseudopod to destroy bacteria (the purple cells). The red discs are red blood cells.

PRE-READING ACTIVITY

FOLDNOTES **Key-Term Fold** Before you read the chapter, create the FoldNote entitled "Key-Term Fold" described in the **Study Skills** section of the Appendix. Write a key term from the chapter on each tab of the key-term fold. Under each tab, write the definition of the key term.

Standards Correlations

National Science Education Standards

The following codes indicate the National Science Education Standards that correlate to this chapter. The full text of the standards is at the front of the book.

Chapter Opener
UCP 1; HNS 3; LS 1b, 5b

Section 1 The Diversity of Cells
UCP 4, 5; SAI 1, 2; ST 2; SPSP 5; LS 1a, 1b, 1c, 2c, 3b, 5a;
LabBook: UCP 1, 2, 5; SAI 1; ST 2; SPSP 5; HNS 1, 3; LS 1a, 1b, 1c, 1d, 2c, 3a, 5a

Section 2 Eukaryotic Cells
UCP 1, 4, 5; LS 1b, 1c, 3a, 5a, 5b

Section 3 The Organization of Living Things
UCP 1, 2, 5; LS 1a, 1b, 1d

Chapter Lab
UCP 1, 2, 3; SAI 2; LS 1b, 1c, 3a, 3b

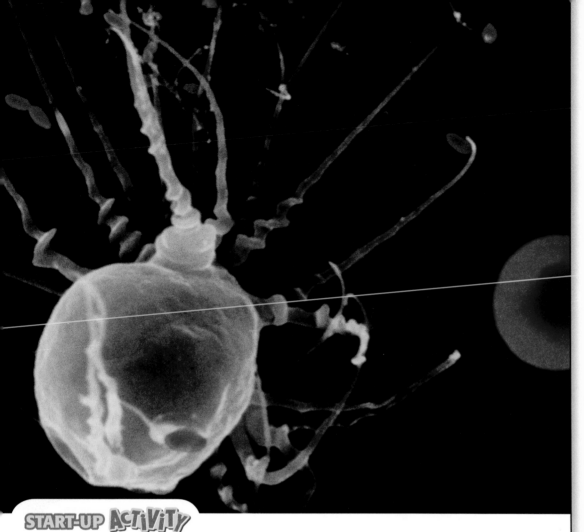

START-UP ACTIVITY
MATERIALS

FOR EACH STUDENT
- coverslip, plastic
- elodea, small leaf
- forceps
- microscope
- microscope slide, plastic
- water

Safety Caution: Remind students to review all safety cautions and icons before beginning this activity.

Answers

1. Students should be able to describe accurately the cells that they see. Students should observe that all of the cells share similar structures but that not all of the cells are exactly the same.

2. Accept all reasonable responses. Students may note that plant cells differ from human body cells but that plant and animal cells share many of the same structures.

START-UP ACTIVITY

What Are Plants Made Of?

All living things, including plants, are made of cells. What do plant cells look like? Do this activity to find out.

Procedure

1. Tear off a **small leaf** from near the tip of an **Elodea sprig.**

2. Using **forceps,** place the whole leaf in a **drop of water** on a **microscope slide.**

3. Place a **coverslip** on top of the water drop by putting one edge of the coverslip on the slide near the water drop. Next, lower the coverslip slowly so that the coverslip does not trap air bubbles.

4. Place the slide on your **microscope.**

5. Using the lowest-powered lens first, find the plant cells. When you can see the cells under the lower-powered lens, switch to a higher-powered lens.

6. Draw a picture of what you see.

Analysis

1. Describe the shape of the *Elodea* cells. Are all of the cells in the *Elodea* the same?

2. Do you think human cells look like *Elodea* cells? How do you think they are different? How might they be similar?

Chapter Review
UCP 1; SAI 1; HNS 1; LS 1a, 1b, 1c, 1d, 3a, 3b

Science in Action
SAI 2; ST 2; SPSP 5; HNS 1; LS 3a, 3c

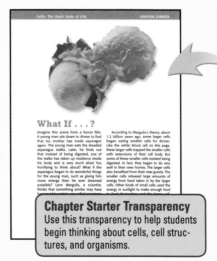

What If . . . ?

Imagine this scene from a horror film. A young man sits down to dinner to find that his mother has made asparagus again. The young man eats the dreaded asparagus stalks. Later, he finds out that instead of being digested, one of the stalks has taken up residence inside his body and is very much alive! Too horrifying to think about? What if the asparagus began to do wonderful things for the young man, such as giving him more energy than he ever dreamed possible? Lynn Margulis, a scientist, thinks that something similar may have

According to Margulis's theory, about 1.2 billion years ago, some larger cells began eating smaller cells for dinner. Like the white blood cell on this page, these larger cells trapped the smaller cells with extensions of their cell body. But some of these smaller cells resisted being digested. In fact, they began to do very well in their new homes. The larger cells also benefited from their new guests. The smaller cells released large amounts of energy from food taken in by the larger cells. Other kinds of small cells used the energy in sunlight to make enough food

Chapter Starter Transparency
Use this transparency to help students begin thinking about cells, cell structures, and organisms.

CHAPTER RESOURCES

Technology

 Transparencies
- Chapter Starter Transparency

READING SKILLS

 Student Edition on CD-ROM

Guided Reading Audio CD
- English or Spanish

 Classroom Videos
- Brain Food Video Quiz

Workbooks

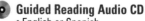 **Science Puzzlers, Twisters & Teasers**
- Cells: The Basic Units of Life GENERAL

Focus

Overview

This section introduces students to cells, their discovery, and their diversity. Students will learn about the parts of a cell and the reason that cells are so small. Finally, students will learn about eubacterial, archaebacterial, and eukaryotic cells.

 Bellringer

Write the following questions on the board:

Why weren't cells discovered until 1665? What invention made their discovery possible?

(Cells weren't discovered until 1665 because almost all cells are too small to be seen with the naked eye. The microscope is the invention that made their discovery possible.)

Motivate

ACTIVITY ——————— GENERAL

Modeling Cell Discovery Before students begin this section, have them model Robert Hooke's discovery. Organize the class into small groups. Provide each group with a microscope and a prepared slide of cork cells. Have students describe and sketch their observations. **LS** Visual

What You Will Learn

- State the parts of the cell theory.
- Explain why cells are so small.
- Describe the parts of a cell.
- Describe how bacteria are different from archaea.
- Explain the difference between prokaryotic cells and eukaryotic cells.

Vocabulary

cell	nucleus
cell membrane	prokaryote
organelle	eukaryote

READING STRATEGY

Reading Organizer As you read this section, create an outline of the section. Use the headings from the section in your outline.

The Diversity of Cells

Most cells are so small they can't be seen by the naked eye. So how did scientists find cells? By accident, that's how! The first person to see cells wasn't even looking for them.

All living things are made of tiny structures called cells. A **cell** is the smallest unit that can perform all the processes necessary for life. Because of their size, cells weren't discovered until microscopes were invented in the mid-1600s.

Cells and the Cell Theory

Robert Hooke was the first person to describe cells. In 1665, he built a microscope to look at tiny objects. One day, he looked at a thin slice of cork. Cork is found in the bark of cork trees. The cork looked like it was made of little boxes. Hooke named these boxes *cells*, which means "little rooms" in Latin. Hooke's cells were really the outer layers of dead cork cells. Hooke's microscope and his drawing of the cork cells are shown in **Figure 1.**

Hooke also looked at thin slices of living plants. He saw that they too were made of cells. Some cells were even filled with "juice." The "juicy" cells were living cells.

Hooke also looked at feathers, fish scales, and the eyes of houseflies. But he spent most of his time looking at plants and fungi. The cells of plants and fungi have cell walls. This makes them easy to see. Animal cells do not have cell walls. This absence of cell walls makes it harder to see the outline of animal cells. Because Hooke couldn't see their cells, he thought that animals weren't made of cells.

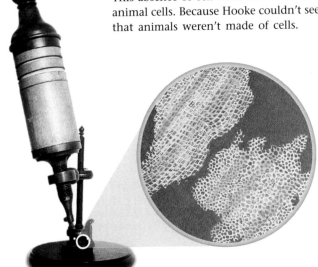

Figure 1 *Hooke discovered cells using this microscope. Hooke's drawing of cork cells is shown to the right of his microscope.*

CHAPTER RESOURCES

Chapter Resource File

- **Lesson Plan**
- **Directed Reading A** BASIC
- **Directed Reading B** SPECIAL NEEDS

Technology

- **Transparencies**
  - Bellringer

Workbooks

- **Interactive Textbook** Struggling Readers

 Cultural Awareness GENERAL

Yeast Yeast is a fungus. Yeast used in baking is related to wild fungi living in the air around us. Strains of native yeasts vary regionally. For example, sourdough from San Francisco has its characteristic taste because bakers there use a yeast that is common in the air around that city. Not all breads require yeast. Many cultures have flat breads, such as tortillas from Mexico.

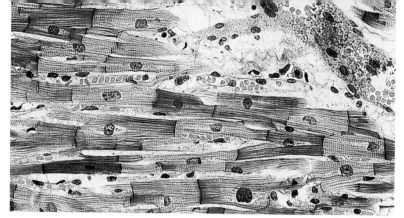

Figure 2 *This photomicrograph shows cardiac muscle tissue. Cardiac muscle tissue is made up of many cardiac cells.*

Cells Working Together

A **tissue** is a group of cells that work together to perform a specific job. The material around and between the cells is also part of the tissue. The cardiac muscle tissue, shown in **Figure 2,** is made of many cardiac muscle cells. Cardiac muscle tissue is just one type of tissue in a heart.

Animals have four basic types of tissues: nerve tissue, muscle tissue, connective tissue, and protective tissue. In contrast, plants have three types of tissues: transport tissue, protective tissue, and ground tissue. Transport tissue moves water and nutrients through a plant. Protective tissue covers the plant. It helps the plant retain water and protects the plant against damage. Photosynthesis takes place in ground tissue.

Tissues Working Together

A structure that is made up of two or more tissues working together to perform a specific function is called an **organ.** For example, your heart is an organ. It is made mostly of cardiac muscle tissue. But your heart also has nerve tissue and tissues of the blood vessels that all work together to make your heart the powerful pump that it is.

Another organ is your stomach. It also has several kinds of tissue. In the stomach, muscle tissue makes food move in and through the stomach. Special tissues make chemicals that help digest your food. Connective tissue holds the stomach together, and nervous tissue carries messages back and forth between the stomach and the brain. Other organs include the intestines, brain, and lungs.

Plants also have different kinds of tissues that work together as organs. A leaf is a plant organ that contains tissue that traps light energy to make food. Other examples of plant organs are stems and roots.

Reading Check What is an organ?

tissue a group of similar cells that perform a common function

organ a collection of tissues that carry out a specialized function of the body

A Pet Protist

Imagine that you have a tiny box-shaped protist for a pet. To care for your pet protist properly, you have to figure out how much to feed it. The dimensions of your protist are roughly 25 μm × 20 μm × 2 μm. If seven food particles per second can enter through each square micrometer of surface area, how many particles can your protist eat in 1 min?

Teach

Discussion — GENERAL

Muscles Ask students to list ways that they use their muscles. Responses will probably include walking, riding a bike, swimming, and throwing or kicking a ball. Lead students to understand that muscles are also involved in swallowing food (tongue and esophagus), digestion (stomach and intestines), and blinking eyes (eyelids). Also, help students understand that sometimes muscles act voluntarily (jumping, writing), and sometimes they act involuntarily (heart beating). **LS** Auditory/Logical

Homework — GENERAL

Writing **Respiration Variations** Not all living things have the same kinds of tissues and organs. Yet all living things must perform similar life processes. Have students compare the structures a fish uses to breathe with those that a human uses. Students' reports should also answer the question "What parts of the human and fish respiratory systems are similar?" (Even though a fish has gills and a human has lungs, both have cells that exchange and transport oxygen and carbon dioxide.) **LS** Logical

Answer to Math Practice

The surface area of the protist is [(25 μm × 20 μm) + (25 μm × 2 μm) + (20 μm × 2 μm)] × 2 = 1,180 μm², so it can eat 1,180 μm² × 7 particles per second = 8,260 particles of food every second, or 60 s/min × 8,260 particles/s = 495,600 particles of food per minute.

Answer to Reading Check

An organ is a structure of two or more tissues working together to perform a specific function in the body.

SUPPORT FOR

English Language Learners

Pros and Cons Higher order thinking skills in a second language can be extremely difficult. For practice, ask students if they can think of any disadvantages to being a multicellular organism. Call on students to ensure participation. Suggest aspects to consider, if necessary. (What about growth period? Greater complexity? Specialized cells?) Remind students that the section heads can give them starting points in their thinking. **LS** Verbal

MISCONCEPTION ALERT

Dead Cells Students may think that hair is alive: advertisements for shampoo create the impression that hair is living tissue. Hair—and fingernails, too—are dead. Hair and fingernails grow out of specialized skin cells. They grow continuously, but both are composed of dead cells and a protein called *keratin*. If hair and fingernails were alive and contained nerve cells as the deep skin layers do, haircuts and manicures would be painful.

Levels of Organization Write the following headings on the board:

Cell, Tissue, Organ, Organ system, Organism

Have students write these headings on their paper and list at least two examples under each heading. **English Language Learners**
LS Verbal/Logical

Quiz — GENERAL

1. What is the relationship between your digestive system, stomach, and intestines? (The digestive system is an organ system. The stomach and intestines are organs that are parts of the digestive system.)

2. What is the main difference between a unicellular organism and a multicellular organism in the way life processes are carried out? (Sample answer: A unicellular organism must perform all life functions by itself. A multicellular organism may have specialized cells that work together to carry out each function.)

Alternative Assessment — GENERAL

Concept Mapping Have students choose an organ system and identify its component organs. Then, have students make a concept map describing the function of the organs and their relationship to one another. LS Logical/Visual

---

organ system a group of organs that work together to perform body functions

organism a living thing; anything that can carry out life processes independently

structure the arrangement of parts in an organism

function the special, normal, or proper activity of an organ or part

---

Organs Working Together

A group of organs working together to perform a particular function is called an **organ system.** Each organ system has a specific job to do in the body.

For example, the digestive system is made up of several organs, including the stomach and intestines. The digestive system's job is to break down food into small particles. Other parts of the body then use these small particles as fuel. In turn, the digestive system depends on the respiratory and cardiovascular systems for oxygen. The cardiovascular system, shown in **Figure 3,** includes organs and tissues such as the heart and blood vessels. Plants also have organ systems. They include leaf systems, root systems, and stem systems.

✓ **Reading Check** List the levels of organization in living things.

Organisms

Anything that can perform life processes by itself is an **organism.** An organism made of a single cell is called a *unicellular organism.* Prokaryotes, most protists, and some kinds of fungi are unicellular. Although some of these organisms live in colonies, they are still unicellular. They are unicellular organisms living together, and all of the cells in the colony are the same. Each cell must carry out all life processes in order for that cell to survive. In contrast, even the simplest multicellular organism has specialized cells that depend on each other for the organism to survive.

 Figure 3 Levels of Organization in the Cardiovascular System

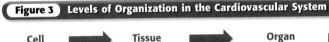
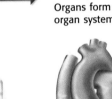
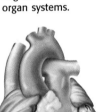
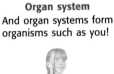
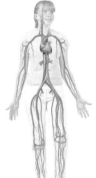

Cell
Cells form tissues.

Tissue
Tissues form organs.

Organ
Organs form organ systems.

Organ system
And organ systems form organisms such as you!

Is That a Fact!

An elephant's trunk is constructed of 135 kg (300 lb) of hair, skin, connective tissue, nerves, and muscles. The muscle tissue is composed of 150,000 tiny subunits of muscle, each of which is coordinated with the others to enable an elephant to greet its friends, breathe, grab, and drink.

Answer to Reading Check
cell, tissue, organ, organ system

Structure and Function

In organisms, structure and function are related. **Structure** is the arrangement of parts in an organism. It includes the shape of a part and the material of which the part is made. **Function** is the job the part does. For example, the structure of the lungs is a large, spongy sac. In the lungs, there are millions of tiny air sacs called *alveoli*. Blood vessels wrap around the alveoli, as shown in **Figure 4.** Oxygen from air in the alveoli enters the blood. Blood then brings oxygen to body tissues. Also, in the alveoli, carbon dioxide leaves the blood and is exhaled.

The structures of alveoli and blood vessels enable them to perform a function. Together, they bring oxygen to the body and get rid of its carbon dioxide.

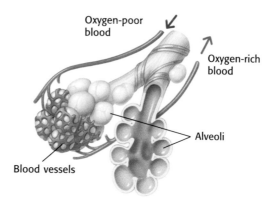

Figure 4 The Structure and Function of Alveoli

Oxygen-poor blood

Oxygen-rich blood

Alveoli

Blood vessels

SECTION Review

Summary

- Advantages of being multicellular are larger size, longer life, and cell specialization.
- Four levels of organization are cell, tissue, organ, and organ system.
- A *tissue* is a group of cells working together. An *organ* is two or more tissues working together. An *organ system* is two or more organs working together.
- In organisms, a part's structure and function are related.

Using Key Terms

1. Use each of the following terms in a separate sentence: *tissue, organ,* and *function.*

Understanding Key Ideas

2. What are the four levels of organization in living things?
   a. cell, multicellular, organ, organ system
   b. single cell, multicellular, tissue, organ
   c. larger size, longer life, specialized cells, organs
   d. cell, tissue, organ, organ system

Math Skills

3. One multicellular organism is a cube. Each of its sides is 3 cm long. Each of its cells is 1 cm³. How many cells does it have? If each side doubles in length, how many cells will it then have?

Critical Thinking

4. **Applying Concepts** Explain the relationship between structure and function. Use alveoli as an example. Be sure to include more than one level of organization.

5. **Making Inferences** Why can multicellular organisms be more complex than unicellular organisms? Use the three advantages of being multicellular to help explain your answer.

SCiLINKS®

NSTA

Developed and maintained by the National Science Teachers Association

For a variety of links related to this chapter, go to www.scilinks.org

Topic: Organization of Life
SciLinks code: HSM1080

Answers to Section Review

1. Sample answer: The body has several different kinds of tissue. I think that the most important organ in the body is the brain. Sometimes a part of the body with a certain structure performs more than one function.

2. d

3. 3 cm × 3 cm × 3 cm = 27 cm³
   27 cm³ ÷ 1 cm³ = 27 cells;
   If each side doubles in length, the organism will have 216 cells (6 × 6 × 6 = 216).

4. Sample answer: Alveoli are tiny sacs whose function is to contain and exchange gases such as oxygen and carbon dioxide. The structure of alveoli, as tiny sacs surrounded by tiny blood vessels, includes the cells that make up the tissue of the alveoli and the tissue that joins the alveoli to the bronchioles, which are part of the lung. The lungs are made of several kinds of tissue, such as the bronchi, bronchioles, and alveoli.

5. Sample answer: The main reason that multicellular organisms can be more complex than unicellular organisms is that multicellular organisms have cell specialization. Specialization allows some cells to do only digestion while others do respiration or circulation. Therefore, the organism is more efficient. Being multicellular also means that an organism may grow larger than a unicellular organism. Size is an advantage because, in general, the larger the organism is, the fewer predators it faces. Finally, being unicellular means that when your one cell dies, you are dead. In a multicellular organism, the death of one cell does not mean the death of the organism.

Teacher's Note: In fact, only multicellular organisms can have an efficient vascular system, which is the key to efficient delivery of materials to cells and removal of wastes from cells. Most students will probably not know this, but some advanced or interested students may grasp this idea.

Elephant-Sized Amoebas?

Teacher's Notes

Time Required
Two 45-minute class periods

Lab Ratings

EASY ————————→ HARD

Teacher Prep 🧪🧪
Student Set-Up 🧪🧪
Concept Level 🧪🧪🧪
Clean Up 🧪

Safety Caution
Remind students to review all safety cautions and icons before beginning this lab activity.

Preparation Notes
Some students may find it difficult to work with a nonspecific unit of measurement. If so, the cube models easily convert to centimeters. You may want to add some small items, such as peas, beans, popcorn, or peppercorns, to the sand to represent organelles floating in the cytoplasm. Some students may need to review what a ratio is and how ratios are used.

Model-Making Lab

Elephant-Sized Amoebas?

An amoeba is a single-celled organism. Like most cells, amoebas are microscopic. Why can't amoebas grow as large as elephants? If an amoeba grew to the size of a quarter, the amoeba would starve to death. To understand how this can be true, build a model of a cell and see for yourself.

OBJECTIVES

Explore why a single-celled organism cannot grow to the size of an elephant.

Create a model of a cell to illustrate the concept of surface area–to-volume ratio.

MATERIALS

- calculator (optional)
- cubic cell patterns
- heavy paper or poster board
- sand, fine
- scale or balance
- scissors
- tape, transparent

SAFETY

Procedure

① Use heavy paper or poster board to make four cube-shaped cell models from the patterns supplied by your teacher. Cut out each cell model, fold the sides to make a cube, and tape the tabs on the sides. The smallest cell model has sides that are each one unit long. The next larger cell has sides of two units. The next cell has sides of three units, and the largest cell has sides of four units. These paper models represent the cell membrane, the part of a cell's exterior through which food and wastes pass.

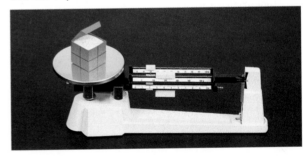

Holt Lab Generator CD-ROM

Search for any lab by topic, standard, difficulty level, or time. Edit any lab to fit your needs, or create your own labs. Use the Lab Materials QuickList software to customize your lab materials list.

Terry Rakes
Elmwood Junior
High School
Rogers, Arkansas

CHAPTER RESOURCES

Chapter Resource File

- 📑 • **Datasheet for Chapter Lab**
  • **Lab Notes and Answers**

Technology

- 📀 **Classroom Videos**
  • Lab Video

- 📹 **LabBook**

• Cells Alive!

CHAPTER RESOURCES

Workbooks

- 📘 **Whiz-Bang Demonstrations**
  • Grand Strand **GENERAL**

- 📘 **Labs You Can Eat**
  • The Incredible Edible Cell **ADVANCED**

- 📘 **Long-Term Projects & Research Ideas**
  • Ewe Again, Dolly? **ADVANCED**

Data Table for Measurements

Length of side	Area of one side $(A = S \times S)$	Total surface area of cube cell $(TA = S \times S \times 6)$	Volume of cube cell $(V = S \times S \times S)$	Mass of filled cube cell
1 unit	1 unit^2	6 unit^2	1 unit^3	
2 unit				
3 unit				
4 unit				

DO NOT WRITE IN BOOK

Key to Formula Symbols

S = the length of one side

A = area

6 = number of sides

V = volume

TA = total area

2. Copy the data table shown above. Use each formula to calculate the data about your cell models. Record your calculations in the table. Calculations for the smallest cell have been done for you.

3. Carefully fill each model with fine sand until the sand is level with the top edge of the model. Find the mass of the filled models by using a scale or a balance. What does the sand in your model represent?

4. Record the mass of each filled cell model in your Data Table for Measurements. (Always remember to use the appropriate mass unit.)

Analyze the Results

1. **Constructing Tables** Make a data table like the one shown at right.

2. **Organizing Data** Use the data from your Data Table for Measurements to find the ratios for each of your cell models. For each of the cell models, fill in the Data Table for Ratios.

Draw Conclusions

3. **Interpreting Information** As a cell grows larger, does the ratio of total surface area to volume increase, decrease, or stay the same?

4. **Interpreting Information** As a cell grows larger, does the total surface area-to-mass ratio increase, decrease, or stay the same?

5. **Drawing Conclusions** Which is better able to supply food to all the cytoplasm of the cell: the cell membrane of a small cell or the cell membrane of a large cell? Explain your answer.

6. **Evaluating Data** In the experiment, which is better able to feed all of the cytoplasm of the cell: the cell membrane of a cell that has high mass or the cell membrane of a cell that has low mass? You may explain your answer in a verbal presentation to the class, or you may choose to write a report and illustrate it with drawings of your models.

Data Table for Ratios

Length of side	Ratio of total surface area to volume	Ratio of total surface area to mass
1 unit		
2 unit		
3 unit		
4 unit		

DO NOT WRITE IN BOOK

Cell Model Template

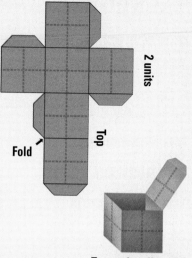

2 units

Top

Fold

Two-unit cell model

Using the template above, prepare four patterns for students to use to make their cubes. Make one cube 1 unit wide, one cube 2 units wide, one cube 3 units wide, and one cube 4 units wide. The unit can be the size of your choosing.

Procedure

3. The sand represents cytoplasm.

4. Masses may vary.

Analyze the Results

2. See the tables below.

Draw Conclusions

3. decreases

4. decreases

5. the cell membrane of a small cell; a small cell has a higher surface area-to-volume ratio than a large cell has, so more nutrients per cubic unit of volume can enter a small cell.

6. the cell membrane of a cell that has a low mass

Data Table for Measurements

Length of side S	Area of one side (square units)	Total surface area of cube cell (square units)	Volume of cube cell (cubic units)	Mass of cube cell (sample answer, in grams)
1	1	6	1	4.5
2	4	24	8	30
3	9	54	27	105
4	16	96	64	230

Data Table for Ratios

Length of side S	Total surface area-to-volume ratio	Total surface area-to-mass ratio (sample answer)
1	6:1	6:4.5 = 1.33:1
2	24:8 = 3:1	24:30 = 0.80:1
3	54:27 = 2:1	54:105 = 0.51:1
4	96:64 = 1.5:1	96:230 = 0.42:1

Chapter Review

Assignment Guide

Section	Questions
1	1, 4, 10–13, 23
2	3, 6, 9, 16–19, 22, 24–26
3	2, 5, 7–8, 14–15, 20–21

ANSWERS

Using Key Terms

1. cell
2. function
3. organelles
4. eukaryote
5. tissue
6. cell wall

Understanding Key Ideas

7. c
8. d
9. a
10. b
11. b
12. c

USING KEY TERMS

Complete each of the following sentences by choosing the correct term from the word bank.

cell	organ
cell membrane	prokaryote
organelles	eukaryote
cell wall	tissue
structure	function

1 A(n) ___ is the most basic unit of all living things.

2 The job that an organ does is the ___ of that organ.

3 Ribosomes and mitochondria are types of ___.

4 A(n) ___ is an organism whose cells have a nucleus.

5 A group of cells working together to perform a specific function is a(n) ___.

6 Only plant cells have a(n) ___.

UNDERSTANDING KEY IDEAS

Multiple Choice

7 Which of the following best describes an organ?

a. a group of cells that work together to perform a specific job

b. a group of tissues that belong to different systems

c. a group of tissues that work together to perform a specific job

d. a body structure, such as muscles or lungs

8 The benefits of being multicellular include

a. small size, long life, and cell specialization.

b. generalized cells, longer life, and ability to prey on small animals.

c. larger size, more enemies, and specialized cells.

d. longer life, larger size, and specialized cells.

9 In eukaryotic cells, which organelle contains the DNA?

a. nucleus   c. smooth ER

b. Golgi complex   d. vacuole

10 Which of the following statements is part of the cell theory?

a. All cells suddenly appear by themselves.

b. All cells come from other cells.

c. All organisms are multicellular.

d. All cells have identical parts.

11 The surface area–to-volume ratio of a cell limits

a. the number of organelles that the cell has.

b. the size of the cell.

c. where the cell lives.

d. the types of nutrients that a cell needs.

12 Two types of organisms whose cells do not have a nucleus are

a. prokaryotes and eukaryotes.

b. plants and animals.

c. bacteria and archaea.

d. single-celled and multicellular organisms.

---

13. Cells must be small in order to have a large enough surface area–to-volume ratio to get sufficient nutrients to survive and to get rid of wastes.

14. Cells are the smallest unit of all living things. Cells combine to make tissues. Different tissues combine to make organs, which have specialized jobs in the body. Organs work together in organ systems, which perform body functions.

Short Answer

⓭ Explain why most cells are small.

⓮ Describe the four levels of organization in living things.

⓯ What is the difference between the structure of an organ and the function of the organ?

⓰ Name two functions of a cell membrane.

⓱ What are the structure and function of the cytoskeleton in a cell?

CRITICAL THINKING

⓲ **Concept Mapping** Use the following terms to create a concept map: *cells, organisms, Golgi complex, organ systems, organs, nucleus, organelle,* and *tissues.*

⓳ **Making Comparisons** Compare and contrast the functions of the endoplasmic reticulum and the Golgi complex.

⓴ **Identifying Relationships** Explain how the structure and function of an organism's parts are related. Give an example.

㉑ **Evaluating Hypotheses** One of your classmates states a hypothesis that all organisms must have organ systems. Is your classmate's hypothesis valid? Explain your answer.

㉒ **Predicting Consequences** What would happen if all of the ribosomes in your cells disappeared?

㉓ **Expressing Opinions** Scientists think that millions of years ago the surface of the Earth was very hot and that the atmosphere contained a lot of methane. In your opinion, which type of organism, a bacterium or an archaeon, is the older form of life? Explain your reasoning.

INTERPRETING GRAPHICS

Use the diagram below to answer the questions that follow.

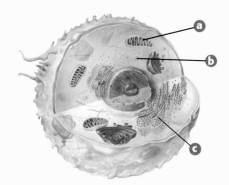

㉔ What is the name of the structure identified by the letter *a*?

㉕ Which letter identifies the structure that digests food particles and foreign invaders?

㉖ Which letter identifies the structure that makes proteins, lipids, and other materials and that contains tubes and passageways that enable substances to move to different places in the cell?

Critical Thinking

18. An answer to this exercise can be found at the end of this book.

19. Sample answer: The endoplasmic reticulum (ER) is a series of folded membranes within a cell where many proteins, lipids, and other materials are made in the cell. The smooth ER also helps break down toxic materials. The ER is the part of the internal delivery system in a cell. The Golgi complex modifies, packages, and distributes proteins to other parts of the cell. It takes materials from the ER and encloses them in a small bubble of membrane. Then, it delivers them to where they are needed in other parts of the cell as well as outside the cell.

20. Sample answer: The structure of a part is its shape and the material it is made of. The function of a part is what that shape and material enable that part to do in the body; for example, alveoli are tiny sacs in the lungs that hold gases. Alveoli are made of a membrane that enables oxygen and carbon dioxide to pass into and out of the blood.

21. Sample answer: not valid; Some organisms are unicellular and have no tissues, organ, or organ systems.

22. Ribosomes make proteins, which all cells and all organisms need to survive. If your ribosomes disappeared, you would die.

23. Sample answer: Archaebacteria are older because there are many types of methane-making archaebacteria and because many types of archaebacteria live in very hot places.

Interpreting Graphics

24. mitochondrion
25. b
26. c

Standardized Test Preparation

Teacher's Note

To provide practice under more realistic testing conditions, give students 20 minutes to answer all of the questions in this Standardized Test Preparation.

MISCONCEPTION ///ALERT\\\

Answers to the standardized test preparation can help you identify student misconceptions and misunderstandings.

READING

Passage 1

1. D

2. G

3. B

TEST DOCTOR

Question 1: Students may select incorrect answer B if they misread the part of the passage about snottites eventually becoming rock. Snottites themselves are a mixture of bacteria, sticky fluids, and minerals.

Question 2: Students may select incorrect answer I if, again, they misread the part of the passage about snottites eventually hardening into rock structures. Snottites do not create other structures in caves. The best answer is that snottite bacteria do not need sunlight because snottites live deep underground and are acidophiles that do not depend on sunlight for food.

READING

Read each of the passages below. Then, answer the questions that follow each passage.

Passage 1 Exploring caves can be dangerous but can also lead to interesting discoveries. For example, deep in the darkness of Cueva de Villa Luz, a cave in Mexico, are slippery formations called *snottites*. They were named snottites because they look just like a two-year-old's runny nose. If you use an electron microscope to look at them, you see that snottites contain prokaryotes; thick, sticky fluids; and small amounts of minerals produced by the prokaryotes. As tiny as they are, these prokaryotes can build up snottite structures that may eventually turn into rock. Formations in other caves look like hardened snottites. The prokaryotes in snottites are acidophiles. Acidophiles live in environments that are highly acidic. Snottite prokaryotes produce sulfuric acid and live in an environment that is similar to the inside of a car battery.

1. Which statement best describes snottites?

  A Snottites are prokaryotes that live in car batteries.

  B Snottites are rock formations found in caves.

  C Snottites were named for a cave in Mexico.

  D Snottites are made of prokaryotes, sticky fluids, and minerals.

2. Based on this passage, which conclusion about snottites is most likely to be correct?

  F Snottites are found in caves everywhere.

  G Snottite prokaryotes do not need sunlight.

  H You could grow snottites in a greenhouse.

  I Snottites create prokaryotes in caves.

3. What is the main idea of this passage?

  A Acidophiles are unusual organisms.

  B Snottites are strange formations.

  C Exploring caves is dangerous.

  D Snottites are slippery prokaryotes.

Passage 2 The world's smallest mammal may be a bat about the size of a jelly bean. The scientific name for this tiny animal, which was unknown until 1974, is *Craseonycteris thonglong-yai*. It is so small that it is sometimes called the *bumblebee bat*. Another name for this animal is the *hog-nosed bat*. Hog-nosed bats were given their name because one of their distinctive features is a piglike muzzle. Hog-nosed bats differ from other bats in another way: they do not have a tail. But, like other bats, hog-nosed bats do eat insects that they catch in mid-air. Scientists think that the bats eat small insects that live on the leaves at the tops of trees. Hog-nosed bats live deep in limestone caves and have been found in only one country, Thailand.

1. According to the passage, which statement about hog-nosed bats is most accurate?

  A They are the world's smallest animal.

  B They are about the size of a bumblebee.

  C They eat leaves at the tops of trees.

  D They live in hives near caves in Thailand.

2. Which of the following statements describes distinctive features of hog-nosed bats?

  F The bats are very small and eat leaves.

  G The bats live in caves and have a tail.

  H The bats live in Thailand and are birds.

  I The bats have a piglike muzzle and no tail.

3. From the information in this passage, which conclusion is most likely to be correct?

  A Hog-nosed bats are similar to other bats.

  B Hog-nosed bats are probably rare.

  C Hog-nosed bats can sting like a bumblebee.

  D Hog-nosed bats probably eat fruit.

Passage 2

1. B

2. I

3. B

TEST DOCTOR

Question 1: Students may select incorrect answer A if they misread "world's smallest mammal" as being "world's smallest animal."

Question 3: Students may select incorrect answer A if they overlook information in the passage that describes how hog-nosed bats are both similar to and different from other bats.

The diagrams below show two kinds of cells. Use these cell diagrams to answer the questions that follow.

Cell 1

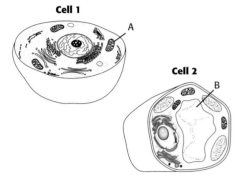

Cell 2

1. What is the name of the organelle labeled *A* in Cell 1?
   - **A** endoplasmic reticulum
   - **B** mitochondrion
   - **C** vacuole
   - **D** nucleus

2. What type of cell is Cell 1?
   - **F** a bacterial cell
   - **G** a plant cell
   - **H** an animal cell
   - **I** a prokaryotic cell

3. What is the name and function of the organelle labeled *B* in Cell 2?
   - **A** The organelle is a vacuole, and it stores water and other materials.
   - **B** The organelle is the nucleus, and it contains the DNA.
   - **C** The organelle is the cell wall, and it gives shape to the cell.
   - **D** The organelle is a ribosome, where proteins are put together.

4. What type of cell is Cell 2? How do you know?
   - **F** prokaryotic; because it does not have a nucleus
   - **G** eukaryotic; because it does not have a nucleus
   - **H** prokaryotic; because it has a nucleus
   - **I** eukaryotic; because it has a nucleus

Read each question below, and choose the best answer.

1. What is the surface area–to-volume ratio of the rectangular solid shown in the diagram below?

   6 cm

   3 cm   2 cm

   - **A** 0.5:1
   - **B** 2:1
   - **C** 36:1
   - **D** 72:1

2. Look at the diagram of the cell below. Three molecules of food per cubic unit of volume per minute are required for the cell to survive. One molecule of food can enter through each square unit of surface area per minute. What will happen to this cell?

   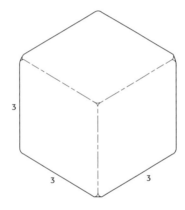

   3

   3   3

   - **F** The cell is too small, and it will starve.
   - **G** The cell is too large, and it will starve.
   - **H** The cell is at a size that will allow it to survive.
   - **I** There is not enough information to determine the answer.

Standardized Test Preparation

1. B
2. H
3. A
4. I

TEST DOCTOR

Question 2: The cell is not a bacterium or a prokaryotic cell because it has a nucleus, and it is not a plant cell because it has no cell wall.

Question 4: The cell has a nucleus, and only eukaryotic cells have a nucleus. Answer I is the only answer that has that combination of facts.

1. B
2. G

TEST DOCTOR

Question 2: When students calculate the cell's surface area–to-volume ratio, they will find that it is 2.00:1. Therefore, only 2.00 food molecules can enter per minute. Because the cell needs 3 molecules of food per minute, the cell is too large, and it will starve. It may help students to understand how the surface area–to-volume ratio affects survival by showing students a variety of three-dimensional models.

CHAPTER RESOURCES

Chapter Resource File

- **Standardized Test Preparation** GENERAL

State Resources

For specific resources for your state, visit **go.hrw.com** and type in the keyword **HSMSTR**.

Weird Science

Background

Within the last 20 years, biologists' ideas of which environments would be suitable for life have increased dramatically. Discoveries of organisms that live under extreme conditions of temperature and pressure have led to the use of the word *extremophile* for these life-forms.

Scientific Discoveries

Background

It is important to note that stem cells are very different from other cells. All stem cells—embryonic or adult—have three unique characteristics. First, stem cells are unspecialized. So, a stem cell in its original form cannot perform the function of a muscle cell or a blood cell. But these unspecialized cells can give rise to specialized cells that can perform such functions. Second, stem cells can divide and renew for long periods of time. Scientists have shown that as long as a stem cell remains unspecialized, it can continue to divide for an extended period of time. Third, stem cells can evolve into specialized cells through the process of differentiation.

Science in Action

Scientific Discoveries

Discovery of the Stem Cell

What do Parkinson's disease, diabetes, aplastic anemia, and Alzheimer's disease have in common? All of these diseases are diseases for which stem cells may provide treatment or a cure. Stem cells are unspecialized cells from which all other kinds of cells can grow. And research on stem cells has been going on almost since microscopes were invented. But scientists have been able to culture, or grow, stem cells in laboratories for only about the last 20 years. Research during these 20 years has shown scientists that stem cells can be useful in treating—and possibly curing—a variety of diseases.

Language Arts ACTIVITY

WRITING SKILL Imagine that you are a doctor who treats diseases such as Parkinson's disease. Design and create a pamphlet or brochure that you could use to explain what stem cells are. Include in your pamphlet a description of how stem cells might be used to treat one of your patients who has Parkinson's disease. Be sure to include information about Parkinson's disease.

Weird Science

Extremophiles

Are there organisms on Earth that can give scientists clues about possible life elsewhere? Yes, there are! These organisms are called *extremophiles,* and they live where the environment is extreme. For example, some extremophiles live in the hot volcanic thermal vents deep in the ocean. Other extremophiles live in the extreme cold of Antarctica. But these organisms do not live only in extreme environments. Research shows that extremophiles may be abundant in plankton in the ocean. And not all extremophiles are archaea; some extremophiles are bacteria.

Social Studies ACTIVITY

Choose one of the four types of extremophiles. Do some research about the organism you have chosen and make a poster showing what you learned about it, including where it can be found, under what conditions it lives, how it survives, and how it is used.

Answer to Social Studies Activity

Students' posters should reflect the research they have done. For example, a student who chooses methanogens may show that these extremophiles live in a wide variety of places and in a large number of geographical locations. The poster may also include an explanation of how these organisms get nutrients and how the metabolism of methanogens is different from human metabolism. Students should also show any commercial, industrial, or medical uses of whichever organism they have chosen.

Answer to Language Arts Activity

Students' pamphlets or brochures should present a basic explanation of what stem cells are, where they come from, why they are useful, and how they may be used specifically to treat Parkinson's disease. So, the student will also have to include a little information about Parkinson's disease.

People in Science

Caroline Schooley

Microscopist Imagine that your assignment is the following: Go outside. Look at 1 ft² of the ground for 30 min. Make notes about what you observe. Be prepared to describe what you see. If you look at the ground with just your naked eyes, you may quickly run out of things to see. But what would happen if you used a microscope to look? How much more would you be able to see? And how much more would you have to talk about? Caroline Schooley could tell you.

Caroline Schooley joined a science club in middle school. That's when her interest in looking at things through a microscope began. Since then, Schooley has spent many years studying life through a microscope. She is a microscopist. A *microscopist* is someone who uses a microscope to look at small things. Microscopists use their tools to explore the world of small things that cannot be seen by the naked eye. And with today's powerful electron microscopes, microscopists can study things we could never see before, things as small as atoms.

Math ACTIVITY

An average bacterium is about 0.000002 m long. A pencil point is about 0.001 m wide. Approximately how many bacteria would fit on a pencil point?

go.hrw.com
To learn more about these Science in Action topics, visit **go.hrw.com** and type in the keyword **HL5CELF**.

Current Science
Check out Current Science® articles related to this chapter by visiting go.hrw.com. Just type in the keyword **HL5CS03**.

People in Science

Background

Caroline Schooley wants students to think about microscopes and microscopy. The field is changing. One of the newest uses of microscopy is in nanotechnology. *Nanotechnology* is the science of manipulating materials on an atomic or molecular level to build microscopic devices. To do so, scientists will develop tiny machines (called *assemblers*) that can manipulate atoms and molecules as directed. Tiny nanomachines (called *replicators*) will be then programmed to build more assemblers. Nanotechnology can be thought of as molecular manufacturing.

Answer to Math Activity

0.001 m (size of pencil point) ÷ 0.000002 m (size of bacteria) = 500

So, approximately 500 bacteria could fit on a pencil point.

The Cell in Action
Chapter Planning Guide

Compression guide:
To shorten instruction because of time limitations, omit the Chapter Lab.

OBJECTIVES	LABS, DEMONSTRATIONS, AND ACTIVITIES	TECHNOLOGY RESOURCES
PACING • 135 min pp. 32–37 **Chapter Opener**	SE **Start-up Activity**, p. 33 ◆ `GENERAL`	OSP **Parent Letter** ■ CD **Student Edition on CD-ROM** CD **Guided Reading Audio CD** ■ TR **Chapter Starter Transparency*** VID **Brain Food Video Quiz**
Section 1 Exchange with the Environment • Explain the process of diffusion. • Describe how osmosis occurs. • Compare passive transport with active transport. • Explain how large particles get into and out of cells.	TE **Demonstration** Membrane Model, p. 34 ◆ `GENERAL` SE **Quick Lab** Bead Diffusion, p. 35 ◆ `GENERAL` CRF **Datasheet for Quick Lab*** SE **Inquiry Lab** The Perfect Taters Mystery, p. 46 ◆ `GENERAL` CRF **Datasheet for Chapter Lab*** LB **Inquiry Labs** Fish Farms in Space* ◆ `GENERAL` LB **Whiz-Bang Demonstrations** It's in the Bag!* ◆ `BASIC`	OSP **Lesson Plans** (also in print) TR **Bellringer Transparency*** TR **L9 Passive and Active Transport*** TR **L10 Endocytosis; Exocytosis*** CRF **SciLinks Activity*** `GENERAL` VID **Lab Videos for Life Science** CD **Interactive Explorations CD-ROM** The Nose Knows `GENERAL` CD **Science Tutor**
PACING • 45 min pp. 38–41 **Section 2 Cell Energy** • Describe photosynthesis and cellular respiration. • Compare cellular respiration with fermentation.	TE **Demonstration** Leaves and Light, p. 38 `GENERAL` SE **Connection to Chemistry**, Earth's Early Atmosphere p. 39 `GENERAL` TE **Group Activity** Recycling Carbon, p. 39 `GENERAL` TE **Group Activity** Photosynthesis and Cellular Respiration, p. 40 `GENERAL` SE **Skills Practice Lab** Stayin' Alive!, p. 185 `GENERAL` CRF **Datasheet for LabBook***	OSP **Lesson Plans** (also in print) TR **Bellringer Transparency*** TR **L11 The Connection Between Photosynthesis and Respiration*** TR *LINK TO PHYSICAL SCIENCE* P44 Solar Heating Systems* CD **Science Tutor**
PACING • 45 min pp. 42–45 **Section 3 The Cell Cycle** • Explain how cells produce more cells. • Describe the process of mitosis. • Explain how cell division differs in animals and plants.	TE **Activity** Making Models, p. 42 `GENERAL` SE **Connection to Language Arts** Picking Apart Vocabulary, p. 43 `GENERAL` TE **Connection Activity** Math, p. 43 `ADVANCED` LB **Labs You Can Eat** The Mystery of the Runny Gelatin* ◆ `GENERAL` LB **Whiz-Bang Demonstrations** Stop Picking on My Enzyme* ◆ `BASIC` LB **Long-Term Projects & Research Ideas** Taming the Wild Yeast* ◆ `ADVANCED` SE **Science in Action** Math, Social Studies, and Language Arts Activities, pp. 52–53 `GENERAL`	OSP **Lesson Plans** (also in print) TR **Bellringer Transparency*** TR **L12 The Cell Cycle*** TE **Internet Activity**, p. 44 `GENERAL` CD **Science Tutor**

PACING • 90 min

CHAPTER REVIEW, ASSESSMENT, AND STANDARDIZED TEST PREPARATION

CRF **Vocabulary Activity*** `GENERAL`
SE **Chapter Review**, pp. 48–49 `GENERAL`
CRF **Chapter Review*** ■ `GENERAL`
CRF **Chapter Tests A*** ■ `GENERAL`, **B*** `ADVANCED`, **C*** `SPECIAL NEEDS`
SE **Standardized Test Preparation**, pp. 50–51 `GENERAL`
CRF **Standardized Test Preparation*** `GENERAL`
CRF **Performance-Based Assessment*** `GENERAL`
OSP **Test Generator, Test Item Listing**

Online and Technology Resources

 Holt Online Learning

Visit **go.hrw.com** for access to Holt Online Learning, or enter the keyword **HL7 Home** for a variety of free online resources.

 One-Stop Planner® CD-ROM

This CD-ROM package includes:
• Lab Materials QuickList Software
• Holt Calendar Planner
• Customizable Lesson Plans
• Printable Worksheets
• ExamView® Test Generator
• Interactive Teacher's Edition
• Holt PuzzlePro®
• Holt PowerPoint® Resources

START-UP ACTIVITY
MATERIALS
FOR EACH STUDENT
- cup, small plastic
- ruler
- stirring rod
- sugar solution
- test tube, large plastic
- test-tube rack
- test tube, small plastic
- yeast-and-water mixture

Safety Caution: Remind students to review all safety cautions and icons before beginning this lab activity. Students should wear safety goggles at all times and wash their hands when they are finished. Students should not taste the solutions.

Teacher's Notes: The yeast suspension is prepared by mixing one package of dry yeast in 250 mL of water. The sugar solution is prepared by dissolving 30 mL (2 tbsp) of sugar in 100 mL of water.

Answers

1. Answers may vary. Students should subtract the first measurement from the second measurement.

2. When the yeast cells released the energy in sugar, the CO_2 that the cells produced increased the volume of air in the smaller tube and pushed more yeast-and-sugar mixture into the larger tube, increasing the height of the liquid in the larger tube.

START-UP ACTIVITY

Cells in Action

Yeast are single-celled fungi that are an important ingredient in bread. Yeast cells break down sugar molecules to release energy. In the process, carbon dioxide gas is produced, which causes bread dough to rise.

Procedure

1. Add **4 mL of a sugar solution** to **10 mL of a yeast-and-water mixture.** Use a **stirring rod** to thoroughly mix the two liquids.

2. Pour the stirred mixture into a small test tube.

3. Place a slightly **larger test tube** over the **small test tube.** The top of the small test tube should touch the bottom of the larger test tube.

4. Hold the test tubes together, and quickly turn both test tubes over. Place the test tubes in a test-tube rack.

5. Use a **ruler** to measure the height of the fluid in the large test tube. Wait 20 min, and then measure the height of the liquid again.

Analysis

1. What is the difference between the first height measurement and the second height measurement?

2. What do you think caused the change in the fluid's height?

 Happy 140th Birthday!

What If . . . ?

How long would you like to live? What if you could live to 120 years old? or 150 and beyond? Since ancient times, people have searched in vain for a magical fountain or potion that could give them eternal youth. No one has yet found the secret of immortality, but scientists past the time when cells would normally stop dividing and die. Researchers hope that the enzyme can someday be used to understand and treat certain cancers and other incurable diseases. Although the so-called immortalizing enzyme won't help people live forever, it may

Chapter Starter Transparency
Use this transparency to help students begin thinking about the relationship between cells and their environment.

CHAPTER RESOURCES

Technology

 Transparencies — READING SKILLS
- Chapter Starter Transparency

Student Edition on CD-ROM

Guided Reading Audio CD
- English or Spanish

Classroom Videos
- Brain Food Video Quiz

Workbooks

 Science Puzzlers, Twisters & Teasers
- The Cell in Action GENERAL

SECTION
1

Focus

Overview

This section explains the processes of diffusion and osmosis. Students will compare the passive and active transport of particles into and out of cells.

🔊 Bellringer

Write the following on the board:

Which of the following best describes a living cell: a building block, a living organism, a complex factory, or all of the above? Explain your choice.

Motivate

Demonstration —— GENERAL

Membrane Model Blow soap bubbles for the class. Explain that soap bubbles have properties, such as flexibility, that are similar to biological membranes. Components of soap film and of cell membranes move around freely. Soap bubbles and membranes are self-sealing. If two bubbles or membranes collide, they fuse. If one is cut in half, two smaller but whole bubbles or membranes form.

English Language Learners

LS Visual

What You Will Learn

● Explain the process of diffusion.
● Describe how osmosis occurs.
● Compare passive transport with active transport.
● Explain how large particles get into and out of cells.

Vocabulary

diffusion
osmosis
passive transport
active transport
endocytosis
exocytosis

READING STRATEGY

Reading Organizer As you read this section, make a table comparing active transport and passive transport.

diffusion the movement of particles from regions of higher density to regions of lower density

Figure 1 The particles of the dye and the gelatin slowly mix by diffusion.

Exchange with the Environment

What would happen to a factory if its power were shut off or its supply of raw materials never arrived? What would happen if the factory couldn't get rid of its garbage?

Like a factory, an organism must be able to obtain energy and raw materials and get rid of wastes. An organism's cells perform all of these functions. These functions keep cells healthy so that they can divide. Cell division allows organisms to grow and repair injuries.

The exchange of materials between a cell and its environment takes place at the cell's membrane. To understand how materials move into and out of the cell, you need to know about diffusion.

What Is Diffusion?

What happens if you pour dye on top of a layer of gelatin? At first, it is easy to see where the dye ends and the gelatin begins. But over time, the line between the two layers will blur, as shown in **Figure 1.** Why? Everything, including the gelatin and the dye, is made up of tiny moving particles. Particles travel from where they are crowded to where they are less crowded. This movement from areas of high concentration (crowded) to areas of low concentration (less crowded) is called **diffusion** (di FYOO zhuhn). Dye particles diffuse from where they are crowded (near the top of the glass) to where they are less crowded (in the gelatin). Diffusion also happens within and between living cells. Cells do not need to use energy for diffusion.

CHAPTER RESOURCES

Chapter Resource File

📁 • Lesson Plan
• Directed Reading A **BASIC**, B **SPECIAL NEEDS**

Technology

💻 **Transparencies**
• Bellringer

Workbooks

📓 **Interactive Textbook** Struggling Readers

📓 **Science Skills**
• Doing a Lab Write-Up **BASIC**
• Taking Notes **BASIC**

📓 **Math Skills for Science**
• Multiplying Whole Numbers **BASIC**
• Dividing Whole Numbers with Long Division **BASIC**

CONNECTION to Math —— GENERAL

Gas Diffusion Have students solve the following problem in class or as part of their homework:

Gases diffuse about 10,000 times faster in air than in water. If a gas diffuses to fill a room completely in 6 min, how long would it take the gas to fill a similar volume of still water? (60,000 min) How many hours would that be? (1,000 h) How many days? (41.67 days) **LS** Logical

Figure 2 Osmosis

❶ The side that holds only pure water has the higher concentration of water particles.

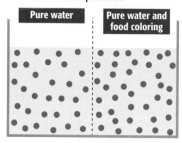

Pure water	Pure water and food coloring

❷ During osmosis, water particles move to where they are less concentrated.

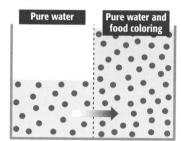

Pure water	Pure water and food coloring

Diffusion of Water

The cells of organisms are surrounded by and filled with fluids that are made mostly of water. The diffusion of water through cell membranes is so important to life processes that it has been given a special name—**osmosis** (ahs MOH sis).

Water is made up of particles, called *molecules*. Pure water has the highest concentration of water molecules. When you mix something, such as food coloring, sugar, or salt, with water, you lower the concentration of water molecules. **Figure 2** shows how water molecules move through a membrane that is semipermeable (SEM i PUHR mee uh buhl). *Semipermeable* means that only certain substances can pass through. The picture on the left in **Figure 2** shows liquids that have different concentrations of water. Over time, the water molecules move from the liquid with the high concentration of water molecules to the liquid with the lower concentration of water molecules.

The Cell and Osmosis

Osmosis is important to cell functions. For example, red blood cells are surrounded by plasma. Plasma is made up of water, salts, sugars, and other particles. The concentration of these particles is kept in balance by osmosis. If red blood cells were in pure water, water molecules would flood into the cells and cause them to burst. When red blood cells are put into a salty solution, the concentration of water molecules inside the cell is higher than the concentration of water outside. This difference makes water move out of the cells, and the cells shrivel up. Osmosis also occurs in plant cells. When a wilted plant is watered, osmosis makes the plant firm again.

✔ **Reading Check** Why would red blood cells burst if you placed them in pure water? (*See the Appendix for answers to Reading Checks.*)

osmosis the diffusion of water through a semipermeable membrane

Bead Diffusion

1. Put three groups of **colored beads** on the bottom of a **plastic bowl.** Each group should be made up of five beads of the same color.

2. Stretch some **clear plastic wrap** tightly over the top of the bowl. Gently shake the bowl for 10 seconds while watching the beads.

3. How is the scattering of the beads like the diffusion of particles? How is it different from the diffusion of particles?

English Language Learners

Diagrams When students create their own diagrams they can demonstrate conceptual understanding even at a beginning language level. Have students diagram the process of osmosis on a cellular level. They should label the important parts of the cell and use arrows to show movement of particles and other matter. Ask them to create a second diagram to explain visually how diffusion relates to this process as well. Evaluate the diagrams on the clarity of the visual explanations. **LS** Visual/Verbal

MATERIALS

FOR EACH GROUP
• colored beads, 3 groups
• plastic bowl
• plastic wrap, clear

Answers

3. Beads moved from areas of more-concentrated colors to areas of less-concentrated colors. Eventually, different-colored beads were mixed somewhat evenly. Mixing beads required the use of students' energy and occurred more quickly than diffusion normally occurs.

INCLUSION Strategies

• *Visually Impaired*
• *Attention Deficit Disorder*

Organize the class into teams of four or five. Ask each team to use clay to show the steps in endocytosis and exocytosis. Point out that the first step in exocytosis and the last step in endocytosis are basically the same because the two procedures are essentially the opposite of each other. English Language Learners
LS Kinesthetic

Answer to Reading Check

Red blood cells would burst in pure water because water particles move from outside, where particles were dense, to inside the cell, where particles were less dense. This movement of water would cause red blood cells to fill up and burst.

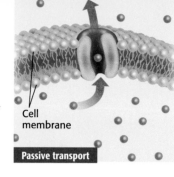
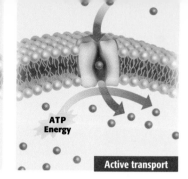

Passive transport

Active transport

ATP Energy

Cell membrane

Figure 3 *In passive transport, particles travel through proteins to areas of lower concentration. In active transport, cells use energy to move particles, usually to areas of higher concentration.*

passive transport the movement of substances across a cell membrane without the use of energy by the cell

active transport the movement of substances across the cell membrane that requires the cell to use energy

endocytosis the process by which a cell membrane surrounds a particle and encloses the particle in a vesicle to bring the particle into the cell

Moving Small Particles

Small particles, such as sugars, cross the cell membrane through passageways called *channels*. These channels are made up of proteins in the cell membrane. Particles travel through these channels by either passive or active transport. The movement of particles across a cell membrane without the use of energy by the cell is called **passive transport**, and is shown in **Figure 3**. During passive transport, particles move from an area of high concentration to an area of low concentration. Diffusion and osmosis are examples of passive transport.

A process of transporting particles that requires the cell to use energy is called **active transport**. Active transport usually involves the movement of particles from an area of low concentration to an area of high concentration.

Moving Large Particles

Small particles cross the cell membrane by diffusion, passive transport, and active transport. Large particles move into and out of the cell by processes called *endocytosis* and *exocytosis*.

Endocytosis

The active-transport process by which a cell surrounds a large particle, such as a large protein, and encloses the particle in a vesicle to bring the particle into the cell is called **endocytosis** (EN doh sie TOH sis). *Vesicles* are sacs formed from pieces of cell membrane. **Figure 4** shows endocytosis.

Figure 4 Endocytosis

① The cell comes into contact with a particle.

② The cell membrane begins to wrap around the particle.

③ Once the particle is completely surrounded, a vesicle pinches off.

This photo shows the end of *endocytosis,* which means "within the cell."

Figure 5   Exocytosis

 ❶ Large particles that must leave the cell are packaged in vesicles.

 ❷ The vesicle travels to the cell membrane and fuses with it.

 ❸ The cell releases the particle to the outside of the cell.

 *Exocytosis* means "outside the cell."

Exocytosis

When large particles, such as wastes, leave the cell, the cell uses an active-transport process called **exocytosis** (EK soh sie TOH sis). During exocytosis, a vesicle forms around a large particle within the cell. The vesicle carries the particle to the cell membrane. The vesicle fuses with the cell membrane and releases the particle to the outside of the cell. **Figure 5** shows exocytosis.

exocytosis the process in which a cell releases a particle by enclosing the particle in a vesicle that then moves to the cell surface and fuses with the cell membrane

✓ Reading Check What is exocytosis?

SECTION Review

Summary

- Diffusion is the movement of particles from an area of high concentration to an area of low concentration.
- Osmosis is the diffusion of water through a semipermeable membrane.
- Cells move small particles by diffusion, which is an example of passive transport, and by active transport.
- Large particles enter the cell by endocytosis, and exit the cell by exocytosis.

Using Key Terms

For each pair of terms, explain how the meanings of the terms differ.

1. *diffusion* and *osmosis*

2. *active transport* and *passive transport*

3. *endocytosis* and *exocytosis*

Understanding Key Ideas

4. The movement of particles from a less crowded area to a more crowded area requires
   - **a.** sunlight.
   - **c.** a membrane.
   - **b.** energy.
   - **d.** osmosis.

5. What structures allow small particles to cross cell membranes?

Math Skills

6. The area of particle 1 is 2.5 mm². The area of particle 2 is 0.5 mm². The area of particle 1 is how many times as big as the area of particle 2?

Critical Thinking

7. **Predicting Consequences** What would happen to a cell if its channel proteins were damaged and unable to transport particles? What would happen to the organism if many of its cells were damaged in this way? Explain your answer.

8. **Analyzing Ideas** Why does active transport require energy?

For a variety of links related to this chapter, go to www.scilinks.org

Topics: Diffusion; Osmosis
SciLinks code: HSM0406; HSM1090

CHAPTER RESOURCES

Chapter Resource File

- Section Quiz GENERAL
- Section Review GENERAL
- Vocabulary and Section Summary GENERAL
- Reinforcement Worksheet BASIC
- SciLinks Activity GENERAL
- Datasheet for Quick Lab

Technology

 Interactive Explorations CD-ROM
- The Nose Knows GENERAL

Overview
This section introduces energy and the cell. Students learn about solar energy and the process of photosynthesis. Finally, students learn about cellular respiration and fermentation.

Bellringer
Ask students to make a list of all the reasons why a cell might need energy. Remind students that there are many types of cells doing many different jobs.

Motivate

Demonstration — GENERAL

Leaves and Light Ask students what they think would happen if a plant could not get sunlight. A few days before teaching this section, cut out a square from black construction paper. Fold the square over a leaf of any common plant, such as a geranium. Affix the square with a paper clip. Be sure the leaf does not receive any sunlight. Leave the leaf covered for about one week. Remove the black square. The leaf will be paler than the other leaves. In the absence of sunlight, chlorophyll is depleted and not replenished. The leaf's green color will have faded.
LS Visual — English Language Learners

What You Will Learn
- Describe photosynthesis and cellular respiration.
- Compare cellular respiration with fermentation.

Vocabulary
photosynthesis
cellular respiration
fermentation

READING STRATEGY
Discussion Read this section silently. Write down questions that you have about this section. Discuss your questions in a small group.

photosynthesis the process by which plants, algae, and some bacteria use sunlight, carbon dioxide, and water to make food

---

Cell Energy

Why do you get hungry? Feeling hungry is your body's way of telling you that your cells need energy.

All cells need energy to live, grow, and reproduce. Plant cells get their energy from the sun. Many animal cells get the energy they need from food.

From Sun to Cell

Nearly all of the energy that fuels life comes from the sun. Plants capture energy from the sun and change it into food through a process called **photosynthesis.** The food that plants make supplies them with energy. This food also becomes a source of energy for the organisms that eat the plants.

Photosynthesis

Plant cells have molecules that absorb light energy. These molecules are called *pigments*. Chlorophyll (KLAWR uh FIL), the main pigment used in photosynthesis, gives plants their green color. Chlorophyll is found in chloroplasts.

Plants use the energy captured by chlorophyll to change carbon dioxide and water into food. The food is in the form of the simple sugar glucose. Glucose is a carbohydrate. When plants make glucose, they convert the sun's energy into a form of energy that can be stored. The energy in glucose is used by the plant's cells. Photosynthesis also produces oxygen. Photosynthesis is summarized in **Figure 1.**

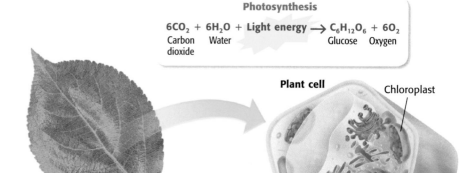

Photosynthesis
$$6CO_2 + 6H_2O + \text{Light energy} \rightarrow C_6H_{12}O_6 + 6O_2$$
Carbon dioxide — Water — Glucose — Oxygen

Plant cell — Chloroplast

Figure 1 *Photosynthesis takes place in chloroplasts. Chloroplasts are found inside plant cells.*

MISCONCEPTION ALERT

Not the Only Steps The processes of photosynthesis and respiration are complex chemical reactions that involve several steps shown by many chemical reactions. The much simpler equations shown for the processes of respiration and photosynthesis in this chapter are the *net* equations for those reactions.

CHAPTER RESOURCES

Chapter Resource File
- Lesson Plan
- Directed Reading A BASIC, B SPECIAL NEEDS

Technology

Transparencies
- Bellringer
- LINK TO PHYSICAL SCIENCE P44 Solar Heating Systems

Workbooks

Interactive Textbook Struggling Readers

Science Skills
- Using Logic BASIC

Getting Energy from Food

Animal cells have different ways of getting energy from food. One way, called **cellular respiration,** uses oxygen to break down food. Many cells can get energy without using oxygen through a process called **fermentation.** Cellular respiration will release more energy from a given food than fermentation will.

Cellular Respiration

The word *respiration* means "breathing," but cellular respiration is different from breathing. Breathing supplies the oxygen needed for cellular respiration. Breathing also removes carbon dioxide, which is a waste product of cellular respiration. But cellular respiration is a chemical process that occurs in cells.

Most complex organisms, such as plants and animals, obtain energy through cellular respiration. During cellular respiration, food (such as glucose) is broken down into CO_2 and H_2O, and energy is released. In animals, most of the energy released maintains body temperature. Some of the energy is used to form adenosine triphosphate (ATP). ATP supplies energy that fuels cell activities.

Most of the process of cellular respiration takes place in the cell membrane of prokaryotic cells. But in the cells of eukaryotes, cellular respiration takes place mostly in the mitochondria. The process of cellular respiration is summarized in **Figure 2.** Does the equation in the figure remind you of the equation for photosynthesis? **Figure 3** on the next page shows how photosynthesis and respiration are related.

✓ Reading Check What is the difference between cellular respiration and breathing? (*See the Appendix for answers to Reading Checks.*)

cellular respiration the process by which cells use oxygen to produce energy from food

fermentation the breakdown of food without the use of oxygen

Figure 2 *The mitochondria in the cells of this cow will use cellular respiration to release the energy stored in the grass.*

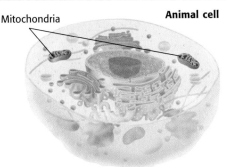

Cellular Respiration

$$C_6H_{12}O_6 + 6O_2 \rightarrow 6CO_2 + 6H_2O + \text{energy (ATP)}$$

Glucose   Oxygen   Carbon dioxide   Water

Mitochondria   **Animal cell**

Close

Reteaching — BASIC

Concept Mapping Have students draw a concept map of energy transfer using the following images:

> sunshine; tree, for firewood; sugar cane; yeast consuming sugar, making bread rise; person chopping firewood, for baking oven; person eating bread

Students should note on their maps which organisms use photosynthesis, which use respiration, and which use fermentation. **LS** Visual

Quiz — GENERAL

Ask students whether the following statements are true or false.

1. Plants and animals capture their energy from the sun. (false)

2. Cellular respiration describes how a cell breathes. (false)

3. Fermentation in animals produces ATP and lactic acid. (true)

Alternative Assessment — GENERAL

Lungs of the Earth Tell students that plants are sometimes called the "lungs of the Earth." Ask students to think about this and to prepare an illustrated presentation for the class. Students may want to research the role that rain forests play as Earth's "lungs" and explain the contributions rain forests make to the health of the planet. **LS** Verbal/Visual

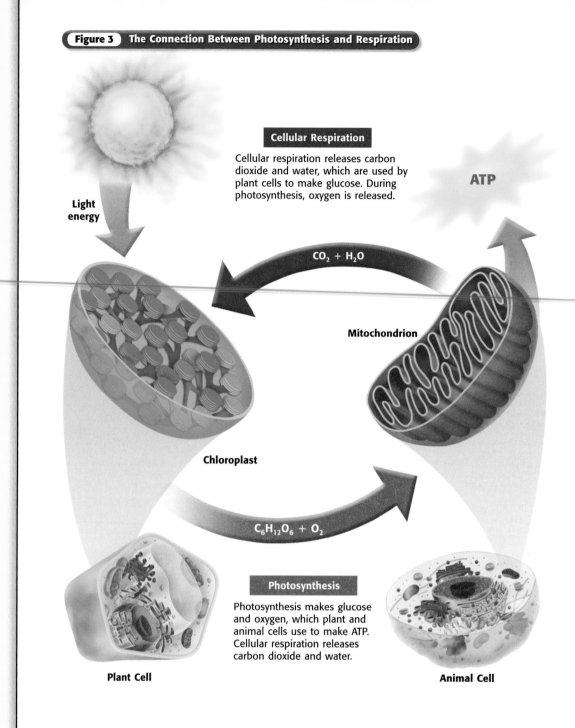

Figure 3 The Connection Between Photosynthesis and Respiration

Light energy

Cellular Respiration
Cellular respiration releases carbon dioxide and water, which are used by plant cells to make glucose. During photosynthesis, oxygen is released.

ATP

$CO_2 + H_2O$

Mitochondrion

Chloroplast

$C_6H_{12}O_6 + O_2$

Photosynthesis
Photosynthesis makes glucose and oxygen, which plant and animal cells use to make ATP. Cellular respiration releases carbon dioxide and water.

Plant Cell

Animal Cell

Group Activity — GENERAL

Photosynthesis and Cellular Respiration
Have students work in pairs and refer to the diagram on this page. Have each pair compare and contrast photosynthesis and respiration. Ask students to answer the following questions: "What happens to the ATP? Where does the ATP go? How is ATP used by the cell? How is the cell's use of CO_2 and H_2O similar to people's recycling of paper and glass bottles?" **LS** Interpersonal/Logical

Homework — ADVANCED

Comparing Cell Processes Newer kinds of solar cells simulate photosynthesis more closely than older solar cells do. Just as plant cells use energy from the sun to change water and carbon dioxide into energy-rich sugars, these new solar cells use the sun's energy to convert water into energy-rich hydrogen gas, which can be used as fuel. The byproduct of this process is oxygen. Have students research these newer solar cells and make a poster showing how they work. **LS** Visual

Connection Between Photosynthesis and Respiration

As shown in **Figure 3,** photosynthesis transforms energy from the sun into glucose. During photosynthesis, cells use CO_2 to make glucose, and the cells release O_2. During cellular respiration, cells use O_2 to break down glucose and release energy and CO_2. Each process makes the materials that are needed for the other process to occur elsewhere.

Fermentation

Have you ever felt a burning sensation in your leg muscles while you were running? When muscle cells can't get the oxygen needed for cellular respiration, they use the process of fermentation to get energy. One kind of fermentation happens in your muscles and produces lactic acid. The buildup of lactic acid contributes to muscle fatigue and causes a burning sensation. This kind of fermentation also happens in the muscle cells of other animals and in some fungi and bacteria. Another type of fermentation occurs in some types of bacteria and in yeast as described in **Figure 4.**

✓ Reading Check What are two kinds of fermentation?

Figure 4 *Yeast forms carbon dioxide during fermentation. The bubbles of CO_2 gas cause the dough to rise and leave small holes in bread after it is baked.*

Summary

- Most of the energy that fuels life processes comes from the sun.
- The sun's energy is converted into food by the process of photosynthesis.
- Cellular respiration breaks down glucose into water, carbon dioxide, and energy.
- Fermentation is a way that cells get energy from their food without using oxygen.

SECTION Review

Using Key Terms

1. In your own words, write a definition for the term *fermentation*.

Understanding Key Ideas

2. O_2 is released during
   a. cellular respiration.
   b. photosynthesis.
   c. breathing.
   d. fermentation.

3. How are photosynthesis and cellular respiration related?

4. How are respiration and fermentation similar? How are they different?

Math Skills

5. Cells of plant A make 120 molecules of glucose an hour. Cells of plant B make half as much glucose as plant A does. How much glucose does plant B make every minute?

Critical Thinking

6. **Analyzing Relationships** Why are plants important to the survival of all other organisms?

7. **Applying Concepts** You have been given the job of restoring life to a barren island. What types of organisms would you put on the island? If you want to have animals on the island, what other organisms must you bring? Explain your answer.

Developed and maintained by the National Science Teachers Association

For a variety of links related to this chapter, go to www.scilinks.org

Topic: Cell Energy; Photosynthesis
SciLinks code: HSM0237; HSM1140

Answers to Section Review

1. Sample answer: Fermentation is the process by which some organisms get energy from food without using oxygen.

2. b

3. Photosynthesis uses the waste materials of cellular respiration, CO_2 and H_2O, to generate glucose. Cellular respiration uses the waste material of photosynthesis, O_2, to break down glucose.

4. Cellular respiration and fermentation both release the energy stored in food. Fermentation does not use oxygen, and cellular respiration does use oxygen.

5. The cells of plant B make an average of 1 glucose molecule per minute.

6. Sample answer: Plants turn energy from the sun into chemical energy. Animals that eat the plants use the stored energy. Plants also produce O_2.

7. Sample answer: Animals such as birds, insects, and mammals would be good on the island. Plants must be on the island in order to provide a source of food for the animals.

Answer to Reading Check

One kind of fermentation produces CO_2, and the other kind produces lactic acid.

CHAPTER RESOURCES

Chapter Resource File

- Section Quiz **GENERAL**
- Section Review **GENERAL**
- Vocabulary and Section Summary **GENERAL**
- Reinforcement Worksheet **BASIC**

Technology

🗄 **Transparencies**
- L11 The Connection Between Photosynthesis and Respiration

Overview

This section introduces the life cycle of a cell. Students will learn how cells reproduce and how mitosis is important. Finally, students will learn how cell division differs between plants and animals.

Bellringer

On the board, write the following:

> Biology is the only science in which multiplication means the same thing as division.

Have students write an explanation of this sentence. (When cells divide, they are multiplying. Some students may point out that multiplying a number by a fraction is the same as division.)

Motivate

ACTIVITY ——————— GENERAL

Making Models Have pairs of students use string for the cell membrane and pieces of pipe cleaners for chromosomes to demonstrate the basic steps of mitosis, as described in this section. **LS** Visual/Interpersonal

---

SECTION

3

The Cell Cycle

In the time that it takes you to read this sentence, your body will have made millions of new cells! Making new cells allows you to grow and replace cells that have died.

The environment in your stomach is so acidic that the cells lining your stomach must be replaced every few days. Other cells are replaced less often, but your body is constantly making new cells.

The Life of a Cell

As you grow, you pass through different stages in life. Your cells also pass through different stages in their life cycle. The life cycle of a cell is called the **cell cycle.**

The cell cycle begins when the cell is formed and ends when the cell divides and forms new cells. Before a cell divides, it must make a copy of its deoxyribonucleic acid (DNA). DNA is the hereditary material that controls all cell activities, including the making of new cells. The DNA of a cell is organized into structures called **chromosomes.** Copying chromosomes ensures that each new cell will be an exact copy of its parent cell. How does a cell make more cells? It depends on whether the cell is prokaryotic (with no nucleus) or eukaryotic (with a nucleus).

Making More Prokaryotic Cells

Prokaryotic cells are less complex than eukaryotic cells are. Bacteria, which are prokaryotes, have ribosomes and a single, circular DNA molecule but don't have membrane-enclosed organelles. Cell division in bacteria is called *binary fission,* which means "splitting into two parts." Binary fission results in two cells that each contain one copy of the circle of DNA. A few of the bacteria in **Figure 1** are undergoing binary fission.

What You Will Learn

- Explain how cells produce more cells.
- Describe the process of mitosis.
- Explain how cell division differs in animals and plants.

Vocabulary
cell cycle
chromosome
homologous chromosomes
mitosis
cytokinesis

READING STRATEGY

Paired Summarizing Read this section silently. In pairs, take turns summarizing the material. Stop to discuss ideas that seem confusing.

cell cycle the life cycle of a cell

chromosome in a eukaryotic cell, one of the structures in the nucleus that are made up of DNA and protein; in a prokaryotic cell, the main ring of DNA

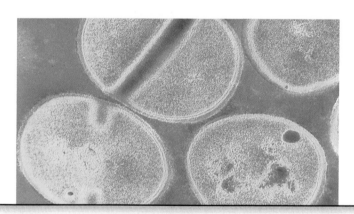

Figure 1 *Bacteria reproduce by binary fission.*

CHAPTER RESOURCES

Chapter Resource File

- **Lesson Plan**
- **Directed Reading A** BASIC **, B** SPECIAL NEEDS

Technology

- **Transparencies**
  - Bellringer
  - L12 The Cell Cycle

Workbooks

- **Interactive Textbook** Struggling Readers

- **Math Skills for Science**
  - Multiplying Whole Numbers BASIC
  - Grasping Graphing GENERAL

CONNECTION to
Math ——————— BASIC

Cell Multiplication It takes Cell A 1 h to complete its cell cycle and produce two cells. The cell cycle of Cell B takes 2 h. How many more cells would be formed from Cell A than from Cell B in 6 h?

(After 6 h, Cell A would have formed 64 cells, and Cell B would have formed 8 cells. Cell A would have formed 56 cells more than Cell B.)
LS Logical/Verbal

Eukaryotic Cells and Their DNA

Eukaryotic cells are more complex than prokaryotic cells are. The chromosomes of eukaryotic cells contain more DNA than those of prokaryotic cells do. Different kinds of eukaryotes have different numbers of chromosomes. More-complex eukaryotes do not necessarily have more chromosomes than simpler eukaryotes do. For example, fruit flies have 8 chromosomes, potatoes have 48, and humans have 46. **Figure 2** shows the 46 chromosomes of a human body cell lined up in pairs. These pairs are made up of similar chromosomes known as **homologous chromosomes** (hoh MAHL uh guhs KROH muh SOHMZ).

✓ **Reading Check** Do more-complex organisms always have more chromosomes than simpler organisms do? (*See the Appendix for answers to Reading Checks.*)

Making More Eukaryotic Cells

The eukaryotic cell cycle includes three stages. In the first stage, called *interphase,* the cell grows and copies its organelles and chromosomes. After each chromosome is duplicated, the cell enters the second stage of the cell cycle.

In the second stage, each chromosome twists, coils, and condenses into an X shape, as shown in **Figure 3.** The X shape is made up of two *chromatids,* which are held together at a region called the *centromere.* After this step, the chromatids separate. The complicated process by which chromosomes condense and separate is called **mitosis.** Mitosis ensures that each new cell receives a copy of each chromosome. Mitosis is divided into four phases, as shown on the following pages.

In the third stage, the cell splits into two cells. These cells are identical to each other and to the original cell.

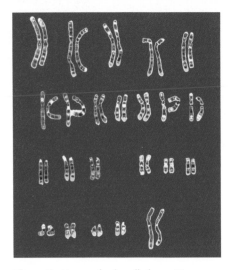

Figure 2 *Human body cells have 46 chromosomes, or 23 pairs of chromosomes.*

homologous chromosomes chromosomes that have the same sequence of genes and the same structure

mitosis in eukaryotic cells, a process of cell division that forms two new nuclei, each of which has the same number of chromosomes

Figure 3 *This duplicated chromosome consists of two chromatids. The chromatids are joined at the centromere.*

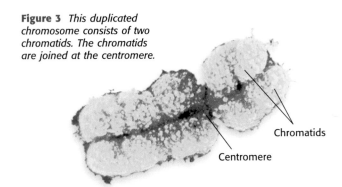

Chromatids

Centromere

CONNECTION TO Language Arts

Picking Apart Vocabulary
Brainstorm what words are similar to the parts of the term *homologous chromosome.* What can you guess about the meaning of the term's root words? Look up the roots of the words, and explain how they help describe the concept.
ACTIVITY

Is That a Fact!

Before sophisticated microscopes were available, scientists could not see cells pinching and dividing. Many scientists believed that cells came into existence spontaneously—as though crystallizing out of bodily fluids.

Biography of a Cell
Have students write and illustrate the biography of a cell. It can be humorous or serious, but it should include accurate descriptions of how materials are transported into and out of the cell and how cells reproduce. **LS** Visual/Verbal

Quiz ── GENERAL

1. **What is cell division?** (It is the process by which cells reproduce themselves.)

2. **How do prokaryotic cells make more cells?** (binary fission)

3. **How do eukaryotic cells make more cells?** (mitosis and cytokinesis)

Alternative Assessment ── GENERAL

Mitosis and Cancer
Have students research the role of mitosis in cancer and write a report or create a poster or other visual presentation on what they learn. Students' reports should include information about various cancer treatments, such as radiation, chemotherapy, and surgery. **LS** Verbal/Visual

Answer to Reading Check

During cytokinesis in plant cells, a cell plate is formed. During cytokinesis in animal cells, a cell plate does not form.

Figure 4 The Cell Cycle

Copying DNA (Interphase)
Before mitosis begins, chromosomes are copied.

Mitosis Phase 1 (Prophase)
Mitosis begins. Chromosomes condense from long strands into rodlike structures.

Mitosis Phase 2 (Metaphase)
The nuclear membrane is dissolved. Paired chromatids align at the cell's equator.

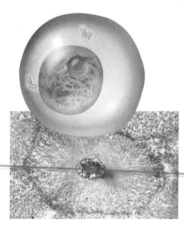
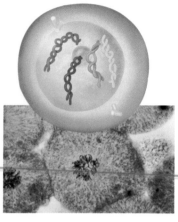

cytokinesis the division of the cytoplasm of a cell

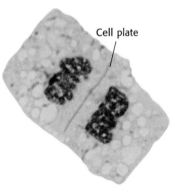

Cell plate

Figure 5 When a plant cell divides, a cell plate forms and the cell splits into two cells.

Mitosis and the Cell Cycle

Figure 4 shows the cell cycle and the phases of mitosis in an animal cell. Mitosis has four phases that are shown and described above. This diagram shows only four chromosomes to make it easy to see what's happening inside the cell.

Cytokinesis

In animal cells and other eukaryotes that do not have cell walls, division of the cytoplasm begins at the cell membrane. The cell membrane begins to pinch inward to form a groove, which eventually pinches all the way through the cell, and two daughter cells form. The division of cytoplasm is called **cytokinesis** and is shown at the last step of **Figure 4.**

Eukaryotic cells that have a cell wall, such as the cells of plants, algae, and fungi, reproduce differently. In these cells, a *cell plate* forms in the middle of the cell. The cell plate contains the materials for the new cell membranes and the new cell walls that will separate the new cells. After the cell splits into two, a new cell wall forms where the cell plate was. The cell plate and a late stage of cytokinesis in a plant cell are shown in **Figure 5.**

✓ **Reading Check** What is the difference between cytokinesis in an animal cell and cytokinesis in a plant cell?

INCLUSION Strategies

- **Developmentally Delayed** • **Hearing Impaired**
- **Learning Disabled**

Make a three-column table with these column headings: "Characteristics," "Prokaryotic Cells," and "Eukaryotic Cells." Under Characteristics, use these five row headings: "Small or large?", "Complex or simple?", "More or less DNA?", "Has organelles?", and "Number of stages in cell division." Have students copy the table and fill it in.
LS Logical/Visual

INTERNET ACTIVITY
Sequence Board ── GENERAL

For an internet activity related to this chapter, have students go to **go.hrw.com** and type in the keyword **HL5ACTW.**

Mitosis Phase 3 (Anaphase)

The chromatids separate and move to opposite sides of the cell.

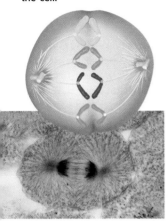

Mitosis Phase 4 (Telophase)

A nuclear membrane forms around each set of chromosomes, and the chromosomes unwind. Mitosis is complete.

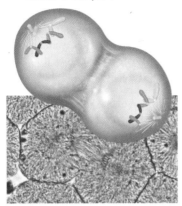

Cytokinesis

In cells that lack a cell wall, the cell pinches in two. In cells that have a cell wall, a cell plate forms between the two new cells.

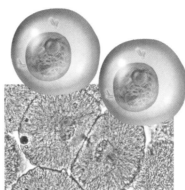

SECTION Review

Summary

- A cell produces more cells by first copying its DNA.
- Eukaryotic cells produce more cells through the four phases of mitosis.
- Mitosis produces two cells that have the same number of chromosomes as the parent cell.
- At the end of mitosis, a cell divides the cytoplasm by cytokinesis.
- In plant cells, a cell plate forms between the two new cells during cytokinesis.

Using Key Terms

1. In your own words, write a definition for each of the following terms: *cell cycle* and *cytokinesis*.

Understanding Key Ideas

2. Eukaryotic cells
   a. do not divide.
   b. undergo binary fission.
   c. undergo mitosis.
   d. have cell walls.

3. Why is it important for chromosomes to be copied before cell division?

4. Describe mitosis.

Math Skills

5. Cell A takes 6 h to complete division. Cell B takes 8 h to complete division. After 24 h, how many more copies of cell A would there be than cell B?

Critical Thinking

6. **Predicting Consequences** What would happen if cytokinesis occurred without mitosis?

7. **Applying Concepts** How does mitosis ensure that a new cell is just like its parent cell?

8. **Making Comparisons** Compare the processes that animal cells and plant cells use to make new cells. How are the processes different?

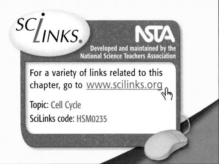

SCILINKS

NSTA
Developed and maintained by the National Science Teachers Association

For a variety of links related to this chapter, go to www.scilinks.org

Topic: Cell Cycle
SciLinks code: HSM0235

Answers to Section Review

1. Sample answer: The cell cycle describes all of the stages a cell goes through in its life. Cytokinesis is the last stage of cell reproduction when a cell's cytoplasm is split between the two new cells.

2. c

3. Chromosomes need to be copied so that the two new cells have the same genetic material as the parent cell.

4. Sample answer: Before mitosis begins, the chromosomes are copied. In phase 1, the nuclear membrane dissolves, and the chromosomes condense. In phase 2, the chromosomes line up along the equator of the cell, and homologous chromosomes pair up. In phase 3, the chromatids move to opposite sides of the cell. In phase 4, a nuclear membrane forms around the chromosomes, and the chromosomes unwind.

5. 8

6. If cytokinesis occurred without mitosis, each cell would only have half of the parent cell's genetic material or less.

7. Mitosis ensures that each new cell receives a copy of each chromosome, and hence, an exact copy of the parent cell's genetic material.

8. The processes of animal and plant cells are different because plant cells have cell walls. Cytokinesis is different in plant cells, but all other stages of mitosis are essentially the same as they are in animal cells.

CHAPTER RESOURCES

Chapter Resource File

- Section Quiz GENERAL
- Section Review GENERAL
- Vocabulary and Section Summary GENERAL
- Reinforcement Worksheet BASIC
- Critical Thinking ADVANCED

Workbooks

Science Skills
- Researching on the Web BASIC
- Organizing Your Research GENERAL

Using Scientific Methods
Inquiry Lab

The Perfect Taters Mystery

Teacher's Notes

Time Required

Two 45-minute class periods

Lab Ratings

EASY ————————————→ HARD

Teacher Prep 🧪🧪
Student Set-Up 🧪🧪
Concept Level 🧪🧪🧪
Clean Up 🧪

MATERIALS

The materials listed on the student pages are enough for one class of students. You will need one or two potatoes per class. Do not allow students to cut or peel potatoes. You will need to do this ahead of time. Allow students to choose the number of containers they will need for the experiment. They may wish to test several salt concentrations.

Safety Caution

Remind students to review all safety cautions and icons before beginning this lab activity.

Avoid including green or discolored parts of the potato in the pieces students work with. These could cause illness.

OBJECTIVES

Examine osmosis in potato cells.

Design a procedure that will give the best results.

MATERIALS

- cups, clear plastic, small
- potato pieces, freshly cut
- potato samples (A, B, and C)
- salt
- water, distilled

SAFETY

The Perfect Taters Mystery

You are the chief food detective at Perfect Taters Food Company. The boss, Mr. Fries, wants you to find a way to keep his potatoes fresh and crisp before they are cooked. His workers have tried several methods, but these methods have not worked. Workers in Group A put the potatoes in very salty water, and something unexpected happened to the potatoes. Workers in Group B put the potatoes in water that did not contain any salt, and something else happened! Workers in Group C didn't put the potatoes in any water, and that didn't work either. Now, you must design an experiment to find out what can be done to make the potatoes stay crisp and fresh.

- Before you plan your experiment, review what you know. You know that potatoes are made of cells. Plant cells contain a large amount of water. Cells have membranes that hold water and other materials inside and keep some things out. Water and other materials must travel across cell membranes to get into and out of the cell.

- Mr. Fries has told you that you can obtain as many samples as you need from the workers in Groups A, B, and C. Your teacher will have these samples ready for you to observe.

- Make a data table like the one below. List your observations in the data table. Make as many observations as you can about the potatoes tested by workers in Groups A, B, and C.

Observations	
Group A	
Group B	
Group C	

Ask a Question

❶ Now that you have made your observations, state Mr. Fries's problem in the form of a question that can be answered by your experiment.

Lab Notes

Osmosis is often a confusing and misunderstood concept in life science. Quite often, students can repeat the definition of the process but are unable to apply the concept to explain the movement of water in different osmotic environments. In this lab, students will have an opportunity to observe osmosis in a model and obtain measurable results. This lab can be done as a class demonstration if materials and space are limited. The purpose of this lab is to reinforce comprehension of osmosis and to practice the scientific method.

CHAPTER RESOURCES

Chapter Resource File

- Datasheet for Chapter Lab
- Lab Notes and Answers

Technology

Classroom Videos
- Lab Video

LabBook

- Stayin' Alive!

The graph below shows the cell cycle. Use this graph to answer the questions that follow.

The Cell Cycle

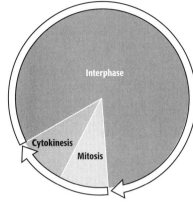

1. Which part of the cell cycle lasts longest?

A interphase

B mitosis

C cytokinesis

D There is not enough information to determine the answer.

2. Which of the following lists the parts of the cell cycle in the proper order?

F mitosis, cytokinesis, mitosis

G interphase, cytokinesis, mitosis

H interphase, mitosis, interphase

I mitosis, cytokinesis, interphase

3. Which part of the cell cycle is the briefest?

A interphase

B cell division

C cytokinesis

D There is not enough information to determine the answer.

4. Why is the cell cycle represented by a circle?

F The cell cycle is a continuous process that begins again after it finishes.

G The cell cycle happens only in cells that are round.

H The cell cycle is a linear process.

I The cell is in interphase for more than half of the cell cycle.

MATH

Read each question below, and choose the best answer.

1. A normal cell spends 90% of its time in interphase. How is 90% expressed as a fraction?

A 3/4

B 4/5

C 85/100

D 9/10

2. If a cell lived for 3 weeks and 4 days, how many days did it live?

F 7

G 11

H 21

I 25

3. How is $2 \times 3 \times 3 \times 3 \times 3$ expressed in exponential notation?

A 3×2^4

B 2×3^3

C 3^4

D 2×3^4

4. Cell A has 3 times as many chromosomes as cell B has. After cell B's chromosomes double during mitosis, cell B has 6 chromosomes. How many chromosomes does cell A have?

F 3

G 6

H 9

I 18

5. If $x + 2 = 3$, what does $x + 1$ equal?

A 4

B 3

C 2

D 1

6. If $3x + 2 = 26$, what does $x + 1$ equal?

F 7

G 8

H 9

I 10

Standardized Test Preparation

1. A

2. I

3. D

4. F

✚ TEST DOCTOR

Question 2: Students may select incorrect answers F and H if they follow the arrow but skip a step on the graph. They may select incorrect answer G if they ignore the direction of the arrow. Only answer I has the steps of the cell cycle in proper sequence.

MATH

1. D

2. I

3. D

4. H

5. C

6. H

✚ TEST DOCTOR

Question 4: Students may have trouble converting this word problem into a numerical statement because they may confuse what is happening to cell B (its chromosomes are doubling in number to 6, which means that it starts with 3) with what is happening to cell A (nothing). Students may select incorrect answer I because 3 times 6 is 18. Students who are struggling may want to create a small data table that shows what they "know" (the information given in the word problem) and what they are trying to find out (what the question asks). Word problems are a challenge for many students, and often a table or chart will help them keep the information straight.

CHAPTER RESOURCES

Chapter Resource File

• Standardized Test Preparation **GENERAL**

State Resources

For specific resources for your state, visit **go.hrw.com** and type in the keyword **HSMSTR.**

Scientific Discovery

Background

The release of energy from food is called *cellular respiration*. Cellular respiration takes place in two stages. The end result of the process is that energy is stored in the cell in the form of ATP (adenosine triphosphate) molecules.

In the microbial battery, scientists harvest some of this energy and transfer it into electricity that can be readily used.

One of the benefits of the microbial battery is its ability to make use of waste products. Ask students to consider the effect this might have on the energy demands of nations that have limited access to fossil fuels.

Science Fiction

Teaching Strategy—BASIC

This is a relatively long story, containing quite a few medical terms. Students may find it easier to read if the class discusses some of the unfamiliar terms before they start reading the story.

Science in Action

Scientific Discoveries

Electrifying News About Microbes

Your car is out of fuel, and there isn't a service station in sight. This is not a problem! Your car's motor runs on electricity supplied by trillions of microorganisms. Some chemists think that "living" batteries will someday operate everything from watches to entire cities. A group of scientists at King's College in London have demonstrated that microorganisms can convert food into usable electrical energy. The microorganisms convert foods such as table sugar and molasses most efficiently. An efficient microorganism can convert more than 90% of its food into compounds that will fuel an electric reaction. A less efficient microbe will only convert 50% of its food into these types of compounds.

Math ACTIVITY

An efficient microorganism converts 90% of its food into fuel compounds, and an inefficient microorganism converts only 50%. If the inefficient microorganism makes 60 g of fuel out of a possible 120 g of food, how much fuel would an efficient microorganism make out of the same amount of food?

Science Fiction

"Contagion" by Katherine MacLean

A quarter mile from their spaceship, the *Explorer*, a team of doctors walk carefully along a narrow forest trail. Around them, the forest looks like a forest on Earth in the fall—the leaves are green, copper, purple, and fiery red. But it isn't fall. And the team is not on Earth.

Minos is enough like Earth to be the home of another colony of humans. But Minos might also be home to unknown organisms that could cause severe illness or death among the crew of *Explorer*. These diseases might be enough like diseases on Earth to be contagious, but they might be different enough to be very difficult to treat.

Something large moves among the shadows—it looks like a man. What happens next? Read Katherine's MacLean's "Contagion" in the *Holt Anthology of Science Fiction* to find out.

Language Arts ACTIVITY

WRITING SKILL Write two to three paragraphs that describe what you think might happen next in the story.

Answer to Math Activity

An efficient microbe converts 90% of its food to fuel compounds; 90% of 120 g is 108 g of fuel compounds.

Answer to Language Arts Activity

Students' predictions will vary. Whatever a student predicts, the prediction should be reasonably related to the information that the student has from reading this introductory paragraph.

Jerry Yakel

Neuroscientist Jerry Yakel credits a sea slug for making him a neuroscientist. In a college class studying neurons, or nerve cells, Yakel got to see firsthand how ions move across the cell membrane of *Aplysia californica,* also known as a sea hare. He says, "I was totally hooked. I knew that I wanted to be a neurophysiologist then and there. I haven't wavered since."

Today, Yakel is a senior investigator for the National Institutes of Environmental Health Sciences, which is part of the U.S. government's National Institutes of Health. "We try to understand how the normal brain works," says Yakel of his team. "Then, when we look at a diseased brain, we train to understand where the deficits are. Eventually, someone will have an idea about a drug that will tweak the system in this or that way."

Yakel studies the ways in which nicotine affects the human brain. "It is one of the most prevalent and potent neurotoxins in the environment," says Yakel. "I'm amazed that it isn't higher on the list of worries for the general public."

Social Studies ACTiViTY

WRITING SKILL Research a famous or historical figure in science. Write a short report that outlines how he or she became interested in science.

go.hrw.com
To learn more about these Science in Action topics, visit **go.hrw.com** and type in the keyword **HL5ACTF.**

Current Science
Check out Current Science® articles related to this chapter by visiting go.hrw.com. Just type in the keyword **HL5CS04.**

Careers

Background

Jerry Yakel grew up in Ventura County, California. After graduating from high school, he attended a nearby community college "ostensibly to continue running track, figuring out life." Eventually, he relocated to Oregon State University, where he obtained a B.S. in 1982. He was accepted into UCLA in 1983 and received a Ph.D. in 1988.

Working for the NIH was not something Yakel originally expected to do. "Most of us trained in universities think we will work there," he says. He does enjoy some aspects of being outside the typical university setting. "In the NIH, we are supposed to take more risks in our research." He also enjoys the focus he is able to bring to his work. "I miss having students to teach, but then again I get to spend more time doing research," Yakel says. His choice of environment hasn't affected his passion. "Honestly, the type of research I [would] do actually is the same."

Answer to Social Studies Activity

Students may write about any historical figure in science. Some students may go back as far as Archimedes; others may choose Hypatia (the first woman to be a true astronomer), Benjamin Franklin, Marie Curie, Albert Einstein, Rosalind Franklin, or one of hundreds of other people. The important issues for the student are why the person is important to science and how the person became interested in science.

3

Heredity
Chapter Planning Guide

Compression guide:
To shorten instruction
because of time limitations,
omit the Chapter Lab.

OBJECTIVES	LABS, DEMONSTRATIONS, AND ACTIVITIES	TECHNOLOGY RESOURCES
PACING • 90 min pp. 54–61 **Chapter Opener**	**SE Start-up Activity**, p. 55 ◆ GENERAL	**OSP Parent Letter** ▣ **CD Student Edition on CD-ROM** **CD Guided Reading Audio CD** ▣ **TR Chapter Starter Transparency*** **VID Brain Food Video Quiz**
Section 1 Mendel and His Peas • Explain the relationship between traits and heredity. • Describe the experiments of Gregor Mendel. • Explain the difference between dominant and recessive traits.	**TE Activity** Trait Trends, p. 56 GENERAL **SE School-to-Home Activity** Describing Traits, p. 57 GENERAL **TE Demonstration** Flower Dissection, p. 58 ◆ BASIC **TE Activity** Mendelian Crosses, p. 58 ADVANCED **SE Science in Action** Math, Science, and Social Studies Activities, pp. 82–83 GENERAL	**OSP Lesson Plans** (also in print) **TR Bellringer Transparency*** **CRF SciLinks Activity*** GENERAL **CD Science Tutor**
PACING • 90 min pp. 62–67 **Section 2 Traits and Inheritance** • Explain how genes and alleles are related to genotype and phenotype. • Use the information in a Punnett square. • Explain how probability can be used to predict possible genotypes in offspring. • Describe three exceptions to Mendel's observations.	**TE Demonstration** Ratios, p. 62 ◆ BASIC **SE Quick Lab** Making a Punnett Square, p. 63 GENERAL **CRF Datasheet for Quick Lab*** **SE Quick Lab** Taking Your Chances, p. 64 ◆ GENERAL **CRF Datasheet for Quick Lab*** **TE Connection Activity** Math, p. 64 ADVANCED **SE Connection to Chemistry** Round and Wrinkled, p. 65 GENERAL **SE Model-Making Lab** Bug Builders, Inc., p. 76 ◆ GENERAL **CRF Datasheet for Chapter Lab***	**OSP Lesson Plans** (also in print) **TR Bellringer Transparency*** **TR L13 Punnett Squares** **TR** *LINK TO PHYSICAL SCIENCE* P109 The Periodic Table of the Elements*** **VID Lab Videos for Life Science** **CD Science Tutor**
PACING • 45 min pp. 68–75 **Section 3 Meiosis** • Explain the difference between mitosis and meiosis. • Describe how chromosomes determine sex. • Explain why sex-linked disorders occur in one sex more often than in the other. • Interpret a pedigree.	**TE Activity** Crosses, p. 68 GENERAL **TE Connection Activity** Math, p. 68 ADVANCED **TE Activity** Describing Meiosis, p. 71 BASIC **TE Connection Activity** Math, p. 71 GENERAL **TE Group Activity** Comparing Mitosis and Meiosis, p. 72 GENERAL **TE Connection Activity** Language Arts, p. 73 GENERAL **SE Inquiry Lab** Tracing Traits, p. 187 GENERAL **CRF Datasheet for LabBook*** **LB Long-Term Projects & Research Ideas** Portrait of a Dog* ADVANCED	**OSP Lesson Plans** (also in print) **TR Bellringer Transparency*** **TR L14 The Steps of Meiosis: A*** **TR L15 The Steps of Meiosis: B*** **TR L16 Meiosis and Dominance*** **SE Internet Activity**, p. 72 GENERAL **TE Internet Activity**, p. 75 GENERAL **CD Science Tutor**

PACING • 90 min

CHAPTER REVIEW, ASSESSMENT, AND STANDARDIZED TEST PREPARATION

CRF Vocabulary Activity* GENERAL
SE Chapter Review, pp. 78–79 GENERAL
CRF Chapter Review* GENERAL
CRF Chapter Tests A* ▣ GENERAL, **B*** ADVANCED, **C*** SPECIAL NEEDS
SE Standardized Test Preparation, pp. 80–81 GENERAL
CRF Standardized Test Preparation* GENERAL
CRF Performance-Based Assessment* GENERAL
OSP Test Generator, Test Item Listing

Online and Technology Resources

Visit **go.hrw.com** for access to Holt Online Learning, or enter the keyword **HL7 Home** for a variety of free online resources.

One-Stop
Planner® CD-ROM

This CD-ROM package includes:
• Lab Materials QuickList Software
• Holt Calendar Planner
• Customizable Lesson Plans
• Printable Worksheets
• ExamView® Test Generator
• Interactive Teacher's Edition
• Holt PuzzlePro®
• Holt PowerPoint® Resources

SKILLS DEVELOPMENT RESOURCES	SECTION REVIEW AND ASSESSMENT	CORRELATIONS
SE Pre-Reading Activity, p. 54 GENERAL **OSP** Science Puzzlers, Twisters & Teasers* GENERAL		National Science Education Standards UCP 2, 3; LS 1d, 2c
CRF Directed Reading A* ■ BASIC, B* SPECIAL NEEDS **IT** Interactive Textbook* Struggling Readers **CRF** Vocabulary and Section Summary* ■ GENERAL **SE** Reading Strategy Brainstorming, p. 56 GENERAL **TE** Support for English Language Learners, p. 57 **SE** Math Practice Understanding Ratios, p. 60 GENERAL **TE** Reading Strategy Paired Reading, p. 57 BASIC **TE** Inclusion Strategies, p. 59 ◆ **MS** Math Skills for Science What Is a Ratio?* GENERAL **SS** Science Skills Finding Useful Sources* GENERAL	**SE** Reading Checks, pp. 56 , 59, 60 GENERAL **TE** Reteaching, p. 60 BASIC **TE** Quiz, p. 60 GENERAL **TE** Alternative Assessment, p. 60 ADVANCED **SE** Section Review,* p. 61 ■ GENERAL **TE** Homework, p. 61 GENERAL **CRF** Section Quiz* ■ GENERAL	UCP 1, 2; SAI 1, 2; ST 2; SPSP 5; HNS 1, 2, 3; LS 2b, 2e
CRF Directed Reading A* ■ BASIC, B* SPECIAL NEEDS **IT** Interactive Textbook* Struggling Readers **CRF** Vocabulary and Section Summary* ■ GENERAL **SE** Reading Strategy Paired Summarizing, p. 62 GENERAL **TE** Support for English Language Learners, p. 64 **SE** Math Focus Probability, p. 65 GENERAL **MS** Math Skills for Science Punnett Square Popcorn* GENERAL **CRF** Reinforcement Worksheet Dimples and DNA* BASIC	**SE** Reading Checks, pp. 62, 64, 66 GENERAL **TE** Homework, p. 65 GENERAL **TE** Reteaching, p. 66 BASIC **TE** Quiz, p. 66 GENERAL **TE** Alternative Assessment, p. 67 GENERAL **SE** Section Review,* p. 67 ■ GENERAL **CRF** Section Quiz* ■ GENERAL	UCP 2, 3; LS 2a, 2b, 2c, 2d, 2e; *Chapter Lab:* SAI 1; HNS 2; LS 2c, 2e
CRF Directed Reading A* ■ BASIC, B* SPECIAL NEEDS **IT** Interactive Textbook* Struggling Readers **CRF** Vocabulary and Section Summary* ■ GENERAL **SE** Reading Strategy Reading Organizer, p. 68 GENERAL **SE** Connection to Language Arts Greek Roots, p. 69 GENERAL **TE** Reading Strategy Prediction Guide, p. 70 GENERAL **TE** Support for English Language Learners, p. 70 **TE** Inclusion Strategies, p. 72 **CRF** Critical Thinking A Bittersweet Solution* ADVANCED	**SE** Reading Checks, pp. 69, 70 GENERAL **TE** Reteaching, p. 74 BASIC **TE** Quiz, p. 74 GENERAL **TE** Alternative Assessment, p. 74 GENERAL **TE** Homework, p. 74 ADVANCED **SE** Section Review,* p. 75 ■ GENERAL **CRF** Section Quiz* ■ GENERAL	UCP 4, 5; SAI 1; SPSP 5; HNS 2, 3; LS 1c, 1d, 2a, 2b, 2c, 2d; *LabBook:* UCP 2; SAI 1; HNS 2; LS 2b, 2c, 2e

SCILINKS.
NSTA
www.scilinks.org
Maintained by the **National Science Teachers Association.** See Chapter Enrichment pages that follow for a complete list of topics.

Current Science®

Check out **Current Science** articles and activities by visiting the HRW Web site at **go.hrw.com**. Just type in the keyword **HL5CS05T.**

Classroom Videos

- **Lab Videos** demonstrate the chapter lab.
- **Brain Food Video Quizzes** help students review the chapter material.

Classroom CD-ROMs

- **Guided Reading Audio CD** (Also in Spanish)
- **Interactive Explorations**
- **Virtual Investigations**
- **Visual Concepts**
- **Science Tutor**

Holt Lab Generator CD-ROM

Search for any lab by topic, standard, difficulty level, or time. Edit any lab to fit your needs, or create your own labs. Use the Lab Materials QuickList software to customize your lab materials list.

Visual Resources

CHAPTER STARTER TRANSPARENCY

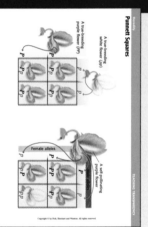

BELLRINGER TRANSPARENCIES

Section: Mendel and His Peas
You have probably noticed that different people have different characteristics, such as eye color, hair color, or whether or not their ear lobes attach directly to their head or hang down loosely. These characteristics are called traits. Where do you think people get these different traits? How do you think they are passed from one generation to the next?

Write your answers in your **science journal.**

Section: Traits and Inheritance
If you flip a coin, what are the chances that it will land on heads? tails? Suppose that you flip the coin, get heads, and then flip again. What are the chances that you will get heads again? What are the chances you will get heads two times in a row? five times?

Record your answers in your **science journal.**

TEACHING TRANSPARENCIES

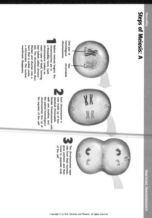

Steps of Meiosis: A

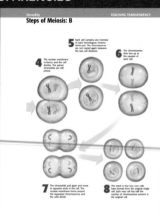

Steps of Meiosis: B

TEACHING TRANSPARENCIES

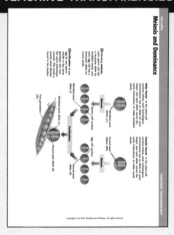

Punnett Squares

Meiosis and Dominance

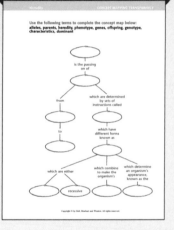

The Periodic Table of the Elements

LINK TO PHYSICAL SCIENCE

Chapter: The Periodic Table

CONCEPT MAPPING TRANSPARENCY

Use the following terms to complete the concept map below:
alleles, parents, heredity, phenotype, genes, offspring, genotype, characteristics, dominant

Planning Resources

LESSON PLANS

Lesson Plan   SAMPLE

Section: Waves

Pacing
Regular Schedule: with lab(s):2 days   without lab(s):1 days
Block Schedule: with lab(s):1 1/2 days   without lab(s):1 day

Objectives
1. Relate the seven properties of life to a living organism.
2. Describe seven themes that can help you to organize what you learn about biology.
3. Identify the tiny structures that make up all living organisms.
4. Differentiate between reproduction and heredity and between metabolism and homeostasis.

National Science Education Standards Covered
LSInter6:Cells have particular structures that underlie their functions.
LSMat1:Most cell functions involve chemical reactions.
LSBeh1:Cells store and use information to guide their functions.
UCP1: Cell functions are regulated.
SI1: Cells can differentiate and form complete multicellular organisms.
PS1: Species evolve over time.
ESS1: The great diversity of organisms is the result of more than 3.5 billion years of evolution.
ESS2: Natural selection and its evolutionary consequences provide a scientific explanation for the fossil record of ancient life forms as well as for the striking molecular similarities observed among the diverse species of living organisms.
ST1: The millions of different species of plants, animals, and microorganisms that live on Earth today are related by descent from common ancestors.
ST2: The energy for life primarily comes from the sun.
SPS1: The complexity and organization of organisms accommodates the need for obtaining, transforming, transporting, releasing, and eliminating the matter and energy used to sustain the organism.
SPSP6: As matter and energy flows through different levels of organization of living systems—cells, organs, communities—and through living systems and the physical environment, chemical elements are recombined in different ways.
HNS1: Organisms have behavioral responses to internal change and to external stimuli.

PARENT LETTER

SAMPLE

Dear Parent,

Your son's or daughter's science class will soon begin exploring the chapter entitled "The World of Physical Science." In this chapter, students will learn about how the scientific method applies to the world of physical science and the role of physical science in the world. By the end of the chapter, students should demonstrate a clear understanding of the chapter's main ideas and be able to discuss the following topics:

1. physical science as the study of energy and matter (Section 1)
2. the role of physical science in the world around them (Section 1)
3. careers that rely on physical science (Section 1)
4. the steps used in the scientific method (Section 2)
5. examples of technology (Section 2)
6. how the scientific method is used to answer questions and solve problems (Section 2)
7. how our knowledge of science changes over time (Section 2)
8. how models represent real objects or systems (Section 3)
9. examples of different ways models are used in science (Section 3)
10. the importance of the International System of Units (Section 4)
11. the appropriate units to use for particular measurements (Section 4)
12. how area and density are derived quantities (Section 4)

Questions to Ask Along the Way

You can help your son or daughter learn about these topics by asking interesting questions such as the following:

- What are some surprising careers that use physical science?
- What is a characteristic of a good hypothesis?
- When is it a good idea to use a model?
- Why do Americans measure things in terms of inches and yards and meters?

ALSO IN SPANISH

TEST ITEM LISTING

TEST ITEM LISTING
The World of Science   SAMPLE

MULTIPLE CHOICE

1. A limitation of models is that
   a. they are large enough to see.
   b. they do not act exactly like the things that they model.
   c. they are smaller than the things that they model.
   d. they model unfamiliar things.
   Answer: B   Difficulty: 1   Section: 3   Objective: 2

2. The length 10 m is equal to
   a. 100 cm.   c. 10,000 mm.
   b. 1,000 cm.   d. Both (b) and (c)
   Answer: B   Difficulty: 1   Section: 3   Objective: 2

3. To be valid, a hypothesis must be
   a. testable.   c. made into a law.
   b. supported by evidence.   d. Both (a) and (b)
   Answer: B   Difficulty: 1   Section: 3   Objective: 2

4. The statement "Sheila has a stain on her shirt" is an example of a(n)
   a. law.   c. observation.
   b. hypothesis.   d. prediction.
   Answer: B   Difficulty: 1   Section: 3   Objective: 2

5. A hypothesis is often developed out of
   a. observations.   c. laws.
   b. experiments.   d. Both (a) and (b)
   Answer: B   Difficulty: 1   Section: 3   Objective: 2

6. How many milliliters are in 3.5 kL?
   a. 3,500. mL   c. 3,500, 000. mL
   b. 0.0035 mL   d. 35,000 mL.
   Answer: B   Difficulty: 1   Section: 3   Objective: 2

7. A map of Seattle is an example of a
   a. law.   c. model.
   b. theory.   d. unit.
   Answer: B   Difficulty: 1   Section: 3   Objective: 2

8. A lab has the safety icons shown below. These icons mean that you should wear
   a. only safety goggles.   c. safety goggles and a lab apron.
   b. only a lab apron.   d. safety goggles, a lab apron, and gloves.
   Answer: B   Difficulty: 1   Section: 3   Objective: 2

9. The law of conservation of mass says the to-tal mass before a chemical change is
   a. more than the total mass after the change.
   b. less than the total mass after the change.
   c. the same as the total mass after the change.
   d. the same as the total mass after the change.
   Answer: B   Difficulty: 1   Section: 3   Objective: 2

10. In which of the following areas would you find a geochemist at work?
    a. studying the chemistry of rocks   c. studying lakes
    b. studying forestry   d. studying the atmosphere
    Answer: B   Difficulty: 1   Section: 3   Objective: 2

One-Stop Planner® CD-ROM

This CD-ROM includes all of the resources shown here and the following time-saving tools:

- *Lab Materials QuickList Software*
- *Customizable lesson plans*
- *Holt Calendar Planner*
- *The powerful ExamView® Test Generator*

Meeting Individual Needs

DIRECTED READING A

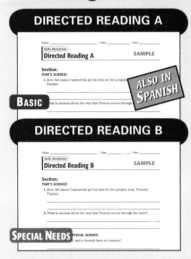

Skills Worksheet!
Directed Reading A   SAMPLE

Section:
THAT'S SCIENCE!
1. How did James Czarnowski get his idea for the penguin boat, Proteus? Explain.

BASIC   ALSO IN SPANISH

DIRECTED READING B

Skills Worksheet!
Directed Reading B   SAMPLE

Section:
THAT'S SCIENCE!
1. How did James Czarnowski get his idea for the penguin boat, Proteus? Explain.

2. What is unusual about the way that Proteus moves through the water?

SPECIAL NEEDS   PHYSICAL SCIENCE

VOCABULARY ACTIVITY

Activity
Vocabulary Activity   SAMPLE

Getting the Dirt on the Soil
After you finish reading Chapter [Unique Title], try this puzzle! Use the clues below to unscramble the vocabulary words. Write your answer in the space provided.

GENERAL

VOCABULARY AND SECTION SUMMARY

Skills Worksheet!
Vocabulary & Notes   SAMPLE

Section:
VOCABULARY
In your own words, write a definition of the following term in the space provided.
1. scientific method

2. technology

GENERAL   ALSO IN SPANISH

REINFORCEMENT

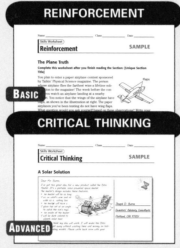

Skills Worksheet!
Reinforcement   SAMPLE

The Plane Truth
Complete this worksheet after you finish reading the Section: [Unique Section Title]

You plan to enter a paper airplane contest sponsored by Talkin' Physical Science magazine. The person whose airplane flies the farthest wins a lifetime subscription to the magazine! The week before the contest, you watch an airplane landing at a nearby

BASIC

CRITICAL THINKING

Skills Worksheet!
Critical Thinking   SAMPLE

A Solar Solution

ADVANCED

SCILINKS ACTIVITY

Activity
SciLinks Activity   SAMPLE

MARINE ECOSYSTEMS
Go to www.scilinks.com. To find links related to marine ecosystems, type in the keyword HL5000. Then, use the links to answer the questions about marine ecosystems.

GENERAL

SCIENCE PUZZLERS, TWISTERS & TEASERS

CHAPTER
5 SCIENCE PUZZLERS, TWISTERS & TEASERS
Heredity

Put on Your Rhyming Genes
1. Fill in the blanks in each of the following rhymes to complete these catchy jingles about heredity.
a. With an "X" from my mom Gail
   And a "Y" from my dad Dale
   It should be clear that I'm a _____

b. As you surely know from your reading,
   A pair of dominant or recessive alleles
   Makes you _____

GENERAL

Labs and Activities

LONG-TERM PROJECTS & RESEARCH IDEAS

PROJECT
5 STUDENT WORKSHEET   DESIGN YOUR OWN
Portrait of a Dog

Take a look at a photograph of an English bulldog. English bulldogs are short and stocky, and they have a tremendous underbite. Now look at a photograph of a greyhound. Greyhounds are tall, slender, and sleek—dogs built for speed! Although the bulldog and the greyhound are different breeds, they are members of the same species. For thousands of years humans have selectively bred dogs for certain traits and with specific tasks in mind. In fact, humans have developed more than 100 different dog breeds.

A Dog's World
1. Did you know that dachshunds were originally bred to follow foxes into foxholes? Use Internet and library resources to research a particular dog breed. What are the breed's unique characteristics? What job was the breed intended to perform? How do the breed's characteristics make it well suited for its job? Does the breed tend to have any problems? If so, why might the breed have these problems, and how can they be corrected? Write a report explaining your findings, and include illustrations of the breed you researched.

Another Research Idea
2. How would you feel if your genes had to pass a test for you to get medical coverage? Use Internet and library resources to research the controversy surrounding genetic testing. Should the results of genetic tests be made available to insurance companies? What information do insurance companies currently use when deciding to insure a person? Should an insurance company be able to refuse or cancel insurance based on the results of a genetic test? Pick one side of this controversy, and be prepared to defend your opinion in a class debate.

A Long-Term Project Idea
3. Some couples have serious health problems in their family history. These couples can meet with a genetic counselor to find out the risk of passing on the problems to their children. What kind of background is needed to be a genetic counselor? How does a genetic counselor put together and present information to prospective parents? What is the most difficult part of the job? Interview a genetic counselor, and then write a job description that explains his or her professional roles and responsibilities.

INTERNET KEYWORDS
genetic testing
genetic testing insurance
genetic testing medical coverage

LIFE SCIENCE

ADVANCED

DATASHEETS FOR QUICK LABS

TEACHER RESOURCE PAGE
Quick Lab
Reaction to Stress   DATASHEET FOR QUICK LAB   SAMPLE

Background
The graph below illustrates changes that occur in the membrane potential of a neuron during an action potential. Use the graph to answer the following questions. Refer to Figure 3 as needed.

DATASHEETS FOR CHAPTER LABS

TEACHER RESOURCE PAGE
Skills Practice Lab
Using Scientific Methods   DATASHEET FOR CHAPTER LAB   SAMPLE

Teacher's Notes
TIME REQUIRED
One 45-minute class period.

DATASHEETS FOR LABBOOK

TEACHER RESOURCE PAGE
Skills Practice Lab
Does It All Add Up?   DATASHEET FOR LABBOOK LAB   SAMPLE

Teacher's Notes
TIME REQUIRED
One 45-minute class period.

Review and Assessments

SECTION QUIZ

Assessment
Section Quiz   SAMPLE

Section:
In the space provided, write the letter of the description that best matches the term or phrase.
___ 1. building molecules that can be used as an energy source, or breaking down molecules in which energy is stored
___ 2. the process by which light energy is converted to chemical energy
___ 3. an organism that uses sunlight or inorganic substances to make organic compounds

GENERAL   ALSO IN SPANISH

SECTION REVIEW

Skills Worksheet!
Section Review   SAMPLE

Section:
KEY TERMS
1. What do paleontologists study?

2. How does a trace fossil differ from petrified wood?

GENERAL   ALSO IN SPANISH
UNDERSTANDING KEY IDEAS

CHAPTER REVIEW

Skills Worksheet!
Chapter Review   SAMPLE

USING VOCABULARY
1. Define biome in your own words.

2. Describe the characteristics of a savanna and a desert.

GENERAL   ALSO IN SPANISH

CHAPTER TEST A

Assessment
Chapter Test A   SAMPLE

MULTIPLE CHOICE
In the space provided, write the letter of the term or phrase that best completes each statement or best answers each question.
___ 1. Surface currents are formed by
   a. the moon's gravity.   c. wind.
   b. the sun's gravity.   d. increased water
___ 2. When waves come near the shore,
   a. they speed up.   c. their wavele
   b. they maintain their speed.   d. their wave
___ 3. Longshore currents transport sediment
   a. out to the open ocean.   c. only during low
   b. along the shore.   d. only during high tide.
___ 4. Which of the following does NOT control surface currents?

GENERAL   ALSO IN SPANISH

CHAPTER TEST B

Assessment
Chapter Test B   SAMPLE

MULTIPLE CHOICE
In the space provided, write the letter of the term or phrase that best completes each statement or best answers each question.
___ 1. Surface currents are formed by
   a. the moon's gravity.   c. wind.
   b. the sun's gravity.   d. increased water density.
___ 2. When waves come near the shore,
   a. they speed up.   c. their wavelength increases.
   b. they maintain their speed.   d. their wave height increases.

ADVANCED

CHAPTER TEST C

Assessment
Chapter Test C   SAMPLE

MULTIPLE CHOICE
In the space provided, write the letter of the term or phrase that best completes each statement or best answers each question.
___ 1. Surface currents are formed by
   a. the moon's gravity.   c. wind.
   b. the sun's gravity.   d. increased water density.
___ 2. When waves come near the shore,
   a. they speed up.   c. their wavelength increases.
   b. they maintain their speed.   d. their wave height increases.
___ 3. Longshore currents transport sediment
   a. out to the open ocean.   c. only during low tide.
   b. along the shore.   d. only during high tide.
___ 4. Which of the following does NOT control surface currents?

SPECIAL NEEDS

STANDARDIZED TEST PREPARATION

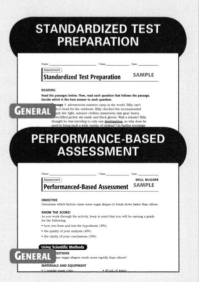

Assessment
Standardized Test Preparation   SAMPLE

READING
Read the passages below. Then, read each question that follows the passage. Decide which is the best answer to each question.

Passage 1 Adventure summer camp is the world. Billy can't wait to head for the outdoors. Billy checked the recommended supply list: light, summer clothes; sunscreen; rain gear; heavy, well-filled jacket; ski mask; and thick gloves. Wait a minute! Billy thought he was traveling to only one destination, so why does he need to bring such a wide variety of clothes? On further investiga

GENERAL

PERFORMANCE-BASED ASSESSMENT

Assessment
Performanced-Based Assessment   SKILL BUILDER   SAMPLE

OBJECTIVE
Determine which factors cause some sugar shapes to break down faster than others.

KNOW THE SCORE!
As you work through the activity, keep in mind that you will be earning a grade for the following:
• how you form and test the hypothesis (30%)
• the quality of your analysis (40%)
• the clarity of your conclusions (30%)

Using Scientific Methods
QUESTIONS
Why do some sugar shapes erode more rapidly than others?

MATERIALS AND EQUIPMENT
• 1 sugar cube   • 90 mL of water

GENERAL

This Chapter Enrichment provides relevant and interesting information to expand and enhance your presentation of the chapter material.

Section 1

Mendel and His Peas

Gregor Mendel

- In 1843, in the city of Brünn, Austria (which is now Brno, a city in the Czech Republic), Gregor Mendel (1822–1884) entered a monastery. In 1865, Mendel published the results of his garden-pea experiments. Although Mendel's ideas are wide-  spread today, few scientists learned of his work during his lifetime because there were few ways to distribute information. Mendel presented his findings in two lectures, and only 40 copies of his work were printed in his lifetime.

- When Mendel was elected abbot of the monastery in 1868, his duties prevented him from visiting other scientists or attending conferences where he could have discussed his results. Not until 1900, when Mendel's work was rediscovered by scientists in Holland, Germany, and Austria-Hungary, were his theories spread through the scientific community.

- Mendel's work was used to support Darwin's theory of evolution by natural selection and is considered to be the foundation of modern genetics. Mendel also made contributions to beekeeping, horticulture, and meteorology. In 1877, Mendel became interested in weather and began issuing weather reports to local farmers.

Is That a Fact!

- From 1856 to 1863, while studying inheritance, Mendel grew almost 30,000 pea plants!

Section 2

Traits and Inheritance

Punnett and His Squares

- Punnett squares are named after their inventor, R. C. Punnett. Punnett explored inheritance by crossing different breeds of chickens in the early 1900s, soon after Mendel's work was rediscovered.

Pollination

- Pollen can be transferred between plants by wind, insects, and a variety of animals. Some common pollinators are bees, butterflies, moths, flies, bats, and birds. Animals are attracted to the color of the flower, the patterns found on the petals, or the flower's fragrance. Pollen is an excellent food for some animals.

Is That a Fact!

- Male bees have only half the number of chromosomes that female bees have.

Section 3

Meiosis

Chromosomes

- Chromosomes are composed of genes, the sequences of DNA that provide the instructions for making all the proteins in an organism. During cell division, the duplicated chromosomes separate so that one copy of each chromosome is present in the two new cells.

Walther Flemming

- Walther Flemming (1843–1905), a German physician and anatomist, was the first to use a microscope and special dyes to study cell division. Flemming used the term *mitosis* to describe the process he observed.

Mitosis

- In mitosis, a cell divides to form two identical cells. The steps of the process are similar in almost all living organisms. In addition to enabling growth, mitosis allows organisms to replace cells that have died or malfunctioned. Mitosis can take anywhere from a few minutes to a few hours, and it may be affected by characteristics of the environment, such as light and temperature.

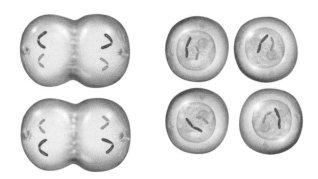

Meiosis

- Meiosis is not the same in all organisms. In humans, meiosis is very different in males and females. In males, meiosis results in four similar sperm cells. In females, however, only one functional egg is produced. The other resulting cells, which are known as *polar bodies,* are formed during the division of the original cell but do not mature.

Genetic Disorders

- A genetic disorder results from an inherited disruption in an organism's DNA. These inherited disruptions can take several forms, including a change in the number of chromosomes and the deletion or duplication of entire chromosomes or parts of chromosomes. Often, the change responsible for a disorder is the alteration of a single specific gene. However, some genetic disorders result from several of these genetic alterations occurring simultaneously. Diseases resulting from these alterations cause a wide variety of physical malfunctions and developmental problems.

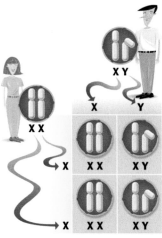

- Cystic fibrosis (CF) is a disease for which one in 31 Americans carries a recessive trait. If two of these people have children together, there is a 25% chance that any child born to them will have the disease. CF affects the intestinal, bronchial, and sweat glands. In people with CF, these glands secrete thick, sticky fluids that are difficult for the body to process, impeding breathing and digestion. Due to improvements in diagnosis and treatment, median life expectancy for those with CF has improved from under 10 years in 1960 to an estimated 40 years for those born in 1990.

- Rubinstein-Taybi syndrome (RTS) is a complex genetic disorder whose characteristics include broad thumbs and toes, mental retardation, and distinctive facial features. This wide range of characteristics is believed to be linked to any one of a number of mutations in a gene responsible for providing the body with a protein called *CBP.* CBP is thought to be vital to the body's delicate metabolism. Because CBP greatly influences body processes, people with a problem producing CBP have a wide range of difficulties. Children with RTS can benefit from proper nutrition and early intervention with therapies and special education.

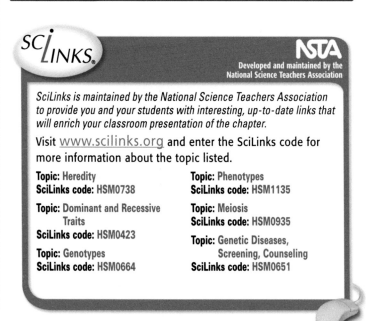

SciLinks is maintained by the National Science Teachers Association to provide you and your students with interesting, up-to-date links that will enrich your classroom presentation of the chapter.

Visit www.scilinks.org and enter the SciLinks code for more information about the topic listed.

Topic: Heredity
SciLinks code: HSM0738

Topic: Dominant and Recessive Traits
SciLinks code: HSM0423

Topic: Genotypes
SciLinks code: HSM0664

Topic: Phenotypes
SciLinks code: HSM1135

Topic: Meiosis
SciLinks code: HSM0935

Topic: Genetic Diseases, Screening, Counseling
SciLinks code: HSM0651

Overview

Tell students that this chapter will introduce heredity—the ways that traits are passed from parents to offspring. The chapter describes the ways scientists study heredity and the role of sexual reproduction.

Assessing Prior Knowledge

Students should be familiar with the following topics:

- scientific methods
- cells
- mitosis

Identifying Misconceptions

Students often hold onto misconceptions about inheritance, even after instruction. For example, they may believe that traits are inherited from only one parent or that environmentally caused characteristics may be passed on to offspring. Students tend to understand phenotype (physical traits) more easily than genotype. Finally, the process of meiosis, as it relates to the structure and location of chromosomes, is very complex. Most students require time and repeated exposure in order to comprehend all the parts and steps of meiosis. Assure students that the concepts of heredity are a foundation that will be built upon throughout their studies of life science.

3

Heredity

The Big Idea

Heredity is the passage of traits from one generation to the next.

About the PHOTO

The guinea pig in the middle has dark fur, and the other two have light orange fur. The guinea pig on the right has longer hair than the other two. Why do these guinea pigs look different from one another? The length and color of their fur was determined before they were born. These are just two of the many traits determined by genetic information. Genetic information is passed on from parents to their offspring.

PRE-READING ACTIVITY

FOLDNOTES **Key-Term Fold** Before you read the chapter, create the FoldNote entitled "Key-Term Fold" described in the **Study Skills** section of the Appendix. Write a key term from the chapter on each tab of the key-term fold. Under each tab, write the definition of the key term.

Standards Correlations

National Science Education Standards

The following codes indicate the National Science Education Standards that correlate to this chapter. The full text of the standards is at the front of the book.

Chapter Opener
UCP 2, 3; LS 1d, 2c

Section 1 Mendel and His Peas
UCP 1, 2; SAI 1, 2; ST 2; SPSP 5; HNS 1, 2, 3; LS 2b, 2e

Section 2 Traits and Inheritance
UCP 2, 3; LS 2a, 2b, 2c, 2d, 2e

Section 3 Meiosis
UCP 4, 5; SAI 1; SPSP 5; HNS 2, 3; LS 1c, 1d, 2a, 2b, 2c, 2d; *Lab Book*: UCP 2; SAI 1; HNS 2; LS 2b, 2c, 2e

Chapter Lab
SAI 1; HNS 2; LS 2c, 2e

Chapter Review
LS 1c, 2a, 2b, 2c, 2d, 2e

Science in Action
ST 2; SPSP 5

START-UP ACTIVITY

MATERIALS

FOR EACH GROUP
- boxes large, (3)
- gloves different types, (5)
- hats different types, (5)
- scarves different types, (5)

Safety Caution: Infestations of head lice are a common problem in schools. Sharing hats should be avoided during such a period. Jackets or sweatshirts could be substituted for hats in this exercise.

Answers

1. Answers may vary. There should be many different combinations. It is not likely that students will see all of the possible combinations.

2. Sample answer: eight new combinations (taken from the outfits of the two "parents") would be possible for the third person ("offspring"). This process is like inheritance because you are choosing combinations of hats, scarves, and gloves randomly. Traits are also passed from parent to offspring randomly. By combining the traits (outfits) of two "parents" (partners), there are many possible combinations of traits in the "offspring" (third person).

3. Sample answer: The number of possible genetic combinations is huge because we have so many genes.

START-UP ACTIVITY

Clothing Combos

How do the same parents have children with many different traits?

Procedure

1. Gather **three boxes**. Put **five hats** in the first box, **five gloves** in the second, and **five scarves** in the third.

2. Without looking in the boxes, select one item from each box. Repeat this process, five students at a time, until the entire class has picked "an outfit." Record what outfit each student chooses.

Analysis

1. Were any two outfits exactly alike? Did you see all possible combinations? Explain your answer.

2. Choose a partner. Using your outfits, how many different combinations could you make by giving a third person one hat, one glove, and one scarf? How is this process like parents passing traits to their children?

3. After completing this activity, why do you think parents often have children who look very different from each other?

Would You Believe . . . ?

It all started in ancient China. A fisherman caught an unusual carp. Usually these small freshwater fish are drab colored, but this one had a pale golden hue. It was too pretty to eat, so the fisherman took the fish home as a pet.

Months later, the fisherman caught another gold-tinged carp. He kept the two fish in the same bowl. When the fish reproduced, the offspring were even more brightly colored than their parents. The first goldfish had been born!

In the years that followed, people throughout China began keeping and breeding the new, orange-colored pets. Many became goldfish matchmakers, choosing only the most handsome mates

for their favorite fish. With each generation of hatchlings, the fish looked more and more distinctive. By 1500 C.E., when the first shipments of goldfish arrived in Japan, goldfish no longer resembled carp. In fact, they were so regal looking that the commoners in Japan were forbidden to keep them as pets.

Without knowing it, these early goldfish breeders were using the principles of genetics to create many new kinds of goldfish. In this chapter you will learn about heredity, the passing of traits from parents to offspring. You'll discover the principles that allowed beautiful goldfish to be bred from rather plain-looking carp.

Chapter Starter Transparency
Use this transparency to help students begin thinking about heredity.

CHAPTER RESOURCES

Technology

 Transparencies
- Chapter Starter Transparency

READING SKILLS

 Student Edition on CD-ROM

Guided Reading Audio CD
- English or Spanish

Classroom Videos
- Brain Food Video Quiz

Workbooks

Science Puzzlers, Twisters & Teasers
- Heredity GENERAL

Focus

Overview

This section introduces the genetic experiments of Gregor Mendel. Students explore how crosses between different parent plants produce different offspring. Students are also introduced to genetic probability.

 Bellringer

Present the following prompt to your students: "You have probably noticed that different people have different traits, such as eye color, hair color, and ear lobes that do or do not attach directly to their head. Where do people get these different traits?" (Many traits are inherited from parents and passed from parents to offspring through genes.)

Motivate

ACTiViTY ——————— GENERAL

Trait Trends Create a large table to record the number of students with the following traits: widow's peak, ability to roll tongue, and attached earlobes. Have pairs of students enter data for each other by adding tick marks on the table. Ask students if they can see any trends in the class data. If possible, compile data from several classes. **LS Kinesthetic/Interpersonal**

What You Will Learn

● Explain the relationship between traits and heredity.
● Describe the experiments of Gregor Mendel.
● Explain the difference between dominant and recessive traits.

Vocabulary
heredity
dominant trait
recessive trait

READING STRATEGY

Brainstorming The key idea of this section is heredity. Brainstorm words and phrases related to heredity.

heredity the passing of genetic traits from parent to offspring

Figure 1 *Gregor Mendel discovered the principles of heredity while studying pea plants.*

Mendel and His Peas

Why don't you look like a rhinoceros? The answer to this question seems simple: Neither of your parents is a rhinoceros. But there is more to this answer than meets the eye.

As it turns out, **heredity,** or the passing of traits from parents to offspring, is more complicated than you might think. For example, you might have curly hair, while both of your parents have straight hair. You might have blue eyes even though both of your parents have brown eyes. How does this happen? People have investigated this question for a long time. About 150 years ago, Gregor Mendel performed important experiments. His discoveries helped scientists begin to find some answers to these questions.

✓ **Reading Check** What is heredity? (*See the Appendix for answers to Reading Checks.*)

Who Was Gregor Mendel?

Gregor Mendel, shown in **Figure 1,** was born in 1822 in Heinzendorf, Austria. Mendel grew up on a farm and learned a lot about flowers and fruit trees.

When he was 21 years old, Mendel entered a monastery. The monks taught science and performed many scientific experiments. From there, Mendel was sent to Vienna where he could receive training in teaching. However, Mendel had trouble taking tests. Although he did well in school, he was unable to pass the final exam. He returned to the monastery and put most of his energy into research. Mendel discovered the principles of heredity in the monastery garden.

Unraveling the Mystery

From working with plants, Mendel knew that the patterns of inheritance were not always clear. For example, sometimes a trait that appeared in one generation (parents) was not present in the next generation (offspring). In the generation after that, though, the trait showed up again. Mendel noticed these kinds of patterns in several other living things, too. Mendel wanted to learn more about what caused these patterns.

To keep his investigation simple, Mendel decided to study only one kind of organism. Because he had studied garden pea plants before, they seemed like a good choice.

CHAPTER RESOURCES

Chapter Resource File

- • Lesson Plan
  - • Directed Reading A BASIC
  - • Directed Reading B SPECIAL NEEDS

Technology

- Transparencies
  - • Bellringer

Workbooks

- Interactive Textbook Struggling Readers

Answer to Reading Check
the passing of traits from parents to offspring

Self-Pollinating Peas

In fact, garden peas were a good choice for several reasons. Pea plants grow quickly, and there are many different kinds available. They are also able to self-pollinate. A *self-pollinating plant* has both male and female reproductive structures. So, pollen from one flower can fertilize the ovule of the same flower or the ovule of another flower on the same plant. The flower on the right side of **Figure 2** is self-pollinating.

Why is it important that pea plants can self-pollinate? Because eggs (in an ovule) and sperm (in pollen) from the same plant combine to make a new plant, Mendel was able to grow true-breeding plants. When a *true-breeding plant* self-pollinates, all of its offspring will have the same trait as the parent. For example, a true-breeding plant with purple flowers will always have offspring with purple flowers.

Pea plants can also cross-pollinate. In *cross-pollination*, pollen from one plant fertilizes the ovule of a flower on a different plant. There are several ways that this can happen. Pollen may be carried by insects to a flower on a different plant. Pollen can also be carried by the wind from one flower to another. The left side of **Figure 2** shows these kinds of cross-pollination.

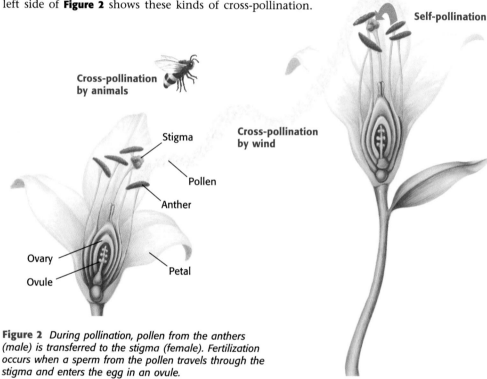

Cross-pollination by animals

Stigma

Pollen

Anther

Ovary

Ovule

Petal

Cross-pollination by wind

Self-pollination

Figure 2 *During pollination, pollen from the anthers (male) is transferred to the stigma (female). Fertilization occurs when a sperm from the pollen travels through the stigma and enters the egg in an ovule.*

Teach

READING STRATEGY — BASIC

Paired Reading Have students read the section silently. As they read, students should make notes or write questions about any section that is confusing or hard to understand. Then, have students discuss the section with a partner, and allow students to help each other understand the material from this section.
LS Verbal/Interpersonal

Using the Figure — BASIC

Flower Fertilization Discuss the physical processes involved in the fertilization of the flowers illustrated in **Figure 2**. These flowers can be fertilized by another flower or can fertilize themselves. Compare this figure with **Figure 4** on the next page, and point out that removing the anthers from the flower makes it impossible for the plant to self-pollinate. **LS** Visual/Verbal

CONNECTION to Real World — GENERAL

Rapidly Growing Organisms Mendel favored the garden pea because it grows quickly, allowing him to produce many generations within a short time span. Modern scientists favor yeast, bacteria, fruit flies, and mice for studies of heredity and genetics. Each of these organisms has a rapid rate of reproduction. However, rapidly-growing organisms can pose problems. For example, medical scientists face ongoing threats from strains of bacteria that develop resistance to common antibiotics. In some cases, medications that were once widely prescribed are no longer effective. **LS** Logical/Intrapersonal

SUPPORT FOR

English Language Learners

Language of Genetics Many terms used in this section are specialized to the area of genetics. Students who are studying this field in English for the first time may not have encountered these words before. Have students read the section silently and note any words they do not understand. Then, ask them to read it again with a partner, discussing terms on their lists and trying to elicit their meanings from the surrounding context. They should write the terms and meanings in their science journals as they are discovered. If there are any terms left undefined after the partner reading, ask students to share them with the class to see if anyone else can define them. Check journals, and have students make corrections as necessary. Potentially unknown words include: *trait, mature, generation, pass on, offspring, pollinate, self-, cross-.* **LS** Verbal/Interpersonal

Discussion — GENERAL

Scientific Methods Have students identify the use of scientific methods in Mendel's work.

- **Ask a question:** How are traits inherited?
- **Form a hypothesis:** Inheritance has a pattern.
- **Test the hypothesis:** Cross true-breeding plants and offspring.
- **Analyze the results:** Identify patterns in inherited traits.
- **Draw conclusions:** Traits are inherited in predictable patterns.
- **Communicate the results:** Publish the results for peer review.

Ask students, "Why weren't Mendel's ideas accepted for so many years?" (because of problems with the last step—other scientists could not easily read or understand his findings)
LS Logical/Verbal

Demonstration — BASIC

Flower Dissection Obtain a flower that has anthers and a stigma, such as a pea flower, a tulip, or a lily. Be careful because pollen can stain clothing and cause allergic reactions. Dissect the flower, and show students the anthers and the stigma. Ask students if this flower could self-pollinate. (yes, because it has both anthers and a stigma) Demonstrate how Mendel removed the anthers of his flowers and then used a small brush to transfer pollen from plant to plant.
English Language Learners
LS Kinesthetic

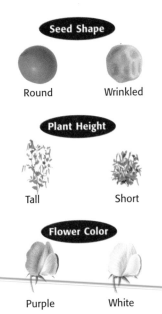

Round Wrinkled

Seed Shape

Plant Height

Tall Short

Flower Color

Purple White

Figure 3 *These are some of the plant characteristics that Mendel studied.*

Characteristics

Mendel studied only one characteristic at a time. A *characteristic* is a feature that has different forms in a population. For example, hair color is a characteristic in humans. The different forms, such as brown or red hair, are called *traits*. Mendel used plants that had different traits for each of the characteristics he studied. For instance, for the characteristic of flower color, he chose plants that had purple flowers and plants that had white flowers. Three of the characteristics Mendel studied are shown in **Figure 3**.

Mix and Match

Mendel was careful to use plants that were true breeding for each of the traits he was studying. By doing so, he would know what to expect if his plants were to self-pollinate. He decided to find out what would happen if he bred, or crossed, two plants that had different traits of a single characteristic. To be sure the plants cross-pollinated, he removed the anthers of one plant so that the plant could not self-pollinate. Then, he used pollen from another plant to fertilize the plant, as shown in **Figure 4**. This step allowed Mendel to select which plants would be crossed to produce offspring.

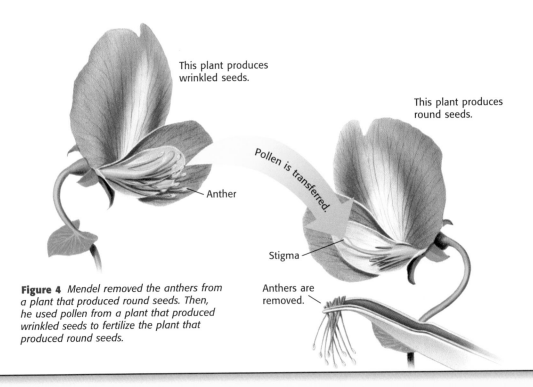

This plant produces wrinkled seeds.

This plant produces round seeds.

Pollen is transferred.

Anther

Stigma

Anthers are removed.

Figure 4 *Mendel removed the anthers from a plant that produced round seeds. Then, he used pollen from a plant that produced wrinkled seeds to fertilize the plant that produced round seeds.*

ACTIVITY — ADVANCED

Mendelian Crosses Give each student a purple bead (*P*) and a white bead (*p*), and ask students to perform a Mendelian cross. Tell students to begin the first generation with the allele combination *Pp*. Have students randomly "pollinate" with 10 other members of the class. To pollinate, one student should hide one bead in each hand. The partner should pick a hand. That hand holds the allele from one parent. Partners should switch roles and repeat this step to determine the allele from the second parent. Students should record the genotype for each pollination. Have students tally the results and determine the ratio of white-flowering plants to purple-flowering plants that results from the matches.
LS Kinesthetic/Interpersonal Co-op Learning

Mendel's First Experiments

In his first experiments, Mendel crossed pea plants to study seven different characteristics. In each cross, Mendel used plants that were true breeding for different traits for each characteristic. For example, he crossed plants that had purple flowers with plants that had white flowers. This cross is shown in the first part of **Figure 5.** The offspring from such a cross are called *first-generation plants*. All of the first-generation plants in this cross had purple flowers. Are you surprised by the results? What happened to the trait for white flowers?

Mendel got similar results for each cross. One trait was always present in the first generation, and the other trait seemed to disappear. Mendel chose to call the trait that appeared the **dominant trait.** Because the other trait seemed to fade into the background, Mendel called it the **recessive trait.** (To *recede* means "to go away or back off.") To find out what might have happened to the recessive trait, Mendel decided to do another set of experiments.

Mendel's Second Experiments

Mendel allowed the first-generation plants to self-pollinate. **Figure 5** also shows what happened when a first-generation plant with purple flowers was allowed to self-pollinate. As you can see, the recessive trait for white flowers reappeared in the second generation.

Mendel did this same experiment on each of the seven characteristics. In each case, some of the second-generation plants had the recessive trait.

✔ Reading Check Describe Mendel's second set of experiments.

dominant trait the trait observed in the first generation when parents that have different traits are bred

recessive trait a trait that reappears in the second generation after disappearing in the first generation when parents with different traits are bred

Parent Generation

Pollen transfer

First Generation
All flowers are purple.

A mature plant is allowed to self-pollinate.

Second Generation
For every three plants with purple flowers, there is one plant with white flowers.

Figure 5 *Mendel used the pollen from a plant with purple flowers to fertilize a plant with white flowers. Then, he allowed the offspring to self-pollinate.*

Answer to Reading Check

During his second set of experiments, Mendel allowed the first-generation plants, which resulted from his first set of experiments, to self-pollinate. The recessive trait reappeared in the second generation.

Answers for Table 1 Ratios

Seed color	3.00:1
Seed shape	2.96:1
Pod color	2.82:1
Pod shape	2.95:1
Flower position	3.14:1
Plant height	2.84:1

Reteaching ——— BASIC

Mendel's Experiments Have students re-enact Mendel's experiments using cups (to represent a plant), colored buttons or chips (to represent various alleles or genotypes), and colored strips of paper (to represent visible traits or phenotypes). Have students perform crosses by taking alleles from "parent" cups and creating "offspring" cups, deciding which traits would then become visible. **English Language Learners** LS Kinesthetic/Logical

Quiz ——— GENERAL

1. What did Mendel call the trait that appeared in all of his first-generation plants? (the dominant trait)

2. What is the probability of getting heads in a coin toss? (1/2)

Alternative Assessment ——— ADVANCED

Story of a Scientist Have students create a comic book or short video drama about Mendel's life and work. Tell students to highlight his use of the scientific method and his habits as a scientist. LS Interpersonal

MATH PRACTICE

Understanding Ratios

A ratio is a way to compare two numbers. Look at **Table 1.** The ratio of plants with purple flowers to plants with white flowers can be written as 705 to 224 or 705:224. This ratio can be reduced, or simplified, by dividing the first number by the second as follows:

$$\frac{705}{224} = \frac{3.15}{1}$$

which is the same thing as a ratio of 3.15:1.

For every 3 plants with purple flowers, there will be roughly 1 plant with white flowers. Try this problem:

In a box of chocolates, there are 18 nougat-filled chocolates and 6 caramel-filled chocolates. What is the ratio of nougat-filled chocolates to caramel-filled chocolates?

Ratios in Mendel's Experiments

Mendel then decided to count the number of plants with each trait that turned up in the second generation. He hoped that this might help him explain his results. Take a look at Mendel's results, shown in **Table 1.**

As you can see, the recessive trait did not show up as often as the dominant trait. Mendel decided to figure out the ratio of dominant traits to recessive traits. A *ratio* is a relationship between two different numbers that is often expressed as a fraction. Calculate the dominant-to-recessive ratio for each characteristic. (If you need help, look at the Math Practice at left.) Do you notice anything interesting about the ratios? Round to the nearest whole number. Are the ratios all the same, or are they different?

✓ **Reading Check** What is a ratio?

Table 1 Mendel's Results

Characteristic	Dominant traits		Recessive traits		Ratio
Flower color	705 purple		224 white		3.15:1
Seed color	6,002 yellow		2,001 green		?
Seed shape	5,474 round		1,850 wrinkled		?
Pod color	428 green		152 yellow		?
Pod shape	882 smooth		299 bumpy		?
Flower position	651 along stem		207 at tip		?
Plant height	787 tall		277 short		?

Answer to Math Practice

The ratio of nougat-filled chocolates to caramel-filled chocolates is 18:6, or 18/6, which can be reduced to 3/1. This fraction can be rewritten as 3:1 or 3 to 1.

Answers to questions on student page

All the ratios are about the same. They can be rounded to 3:1.

Answer to Reading Check

A ratio is a relationship between two different numbers that is often expressed as a fraction.

SECTION Review

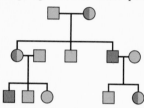

Summary

- In mitosis, chromosomes are copied once, and then the nucleus divides once. In meiosis, chromosomes are copied once, and then the nucleus divides twice.

- The process of meiosis produces sex cells, which have half the number of chromosomes. These two halves combine during reproduction.

- In humans, females have two X chromosomes. So, each egg contains one X chromosome. Males have both an X and a Y chromosome. So, each sperm cell contains either an X or a Y chromosome.

- Sex-linked disorders occur in males more often than in females. Colorblindness and hemophilia are examples of sex-linked disorders.

- A pedigree is a diagram used to trace a trait through many generations of a family.

Using Key Terms

1. Use each of the following terms in the same sentence: *meiosis* and *sex chromosomes*.

In each of the following sentences, replace the incorrect term with the correct term from the word bank.

pedigree	homologous chromosomes
meiosis	mitosis

2. During fertilization, chromosomes are copied, and then the nucleus divides twice.

3. A Punnett square is used to show how inherited traits move through a family.

4. During meiosis, sex cells line up in the middle of the cell.

Understanding Key Ideas

5. Genes are found on
   a. chromosomes.
   b. proteins.
   c. alleles.
   d. sex cells.

6. If there are 14 chromosomes in pea plant cells, how many chromosomes are present in a sex cell of a pea plant?

7. Draw the eight steps of meiosis. Label one chromosome, and show its position in each step.

Interpreting Graphics

Use this pedigree to answer the question below.

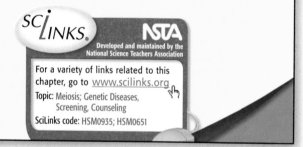

8. Is this disorder sex linked? Explain your reasoning.

Critical Thinking

9. **Identifying Relationships** Put the following in order of smallest to largest: chromosome, gene, and cell.

10. **Applying Concepts** A pea plant has purple flowers. What alleles for flower color could the sex cells carry?

SCi LINKS®

NSTA
Developed and maintained by the
National Science Teachers Association

For a variety of links related to this chapter, go to www.scilinks.org
Topic: Meiosis; Genetic Diseases, Screening, Counseling
SciLinks code: HSM0935; HSM0651

Answers to Section Review

1. Sample answer: At the end of meiosis, each sex cell will contain only one sex chromosome (either X or Y).

2. During meiosis, chromosomes are copied, and then the nucleus divides twice.

3. A pedigree is used to show how inherited traits move through a family.

4. During meiosis, homologous chromosomes line up in the middle of the cell.

5. a

6. 7

7. Answers may vary. Students' drawings should be similar to the diagram of meiosis in the student text.

8. Sample answer: yes; The disorder seems to be sex linked because the females are carriers of the disease but only males have the disease itself.

9. gene, chromosome, cell

10. Sample answer: Because the purple gene (*P*) is dominant over the white gene (*p*), the genotype of the purple-flowered pea plant could be either *PP* or *Pp*. Thus, the possible alleles carried by the sex cells would be *P* or *p*.

INTERNET ACTiViTy

Essay ——————— GENERAL

For an internet activity related to this chapter, have students goto **go.hrw.com** and type in the keyword **HL5DNAW.**

CHAPTER RESOURCES

Chapter Resource File

- Section Quiz GENERAL
- Section Review GENERAL
- Vocabulary and Section Summary GENERAL
- Critical Thinking ADVANCED

Bug Builders, Inc.

Teacher's Notes

Time Required
Two 45-minute class periods

Lab Ratings

EASY ———————————→ HARD

Teacher Prep 🧪🧪🧪
Student Set-Up 🧪🧪
Concept Level 🧪🧪🧪
Clean Up 🧪

MATERIALS

The materials listed on the student page are enough for a group of 3–4 students. For step 3, prepare 14 small paper sacks—representing paired parent alleles for each of seven characteristics—as follows:

1. Use the table in step 6 to decide the genotypes for each of the parent bugs' characteristics.
2. Cut 1 in. squares of paper to represent alleles. Use seven colors of paper—a different color for each characteristic. Cut enough squares so that each student will receive two alleles for each characteristic.
3. Label the alleles for each characteristic according to the genotypes you chose.
4. Label each pair of sacks with one of the seven characteristics. Place an equal number of alleles in each sack.
5. For each characteristic, label one sack "Mom" and the other sack "Dad." Have students draw one allele from each sack.

Safety Caution
Remind students to review all safety cautions and icons before beginning this lab activity. Students should use caution with toothpicks and should not eat any of the materials used.

Bug Builders, Inc.

Imagine that you are a designer for a toy company that makes toy alien bugs. The president of Bug Builders, Inc., wants new versions of the wildly popular Space Bugs, but he wants to use the bug parts that are already in the warehouse. It's your job to come up with a new bug design. You have studied how traits are passed from one generation to another. You will use this knowledge to come up with new combinations of traits and assemble the bug parts in new ways. Model A and Model B, shown below, will act as the "parent" bugs.

OBJECTIVES

Build models to further your understanding of inheritance.

Examine the traits of a population of offspring.

MATERIALS

- allele sacks (14) (supplied by your teacher)
- gumdrops, green and black (feet)
- map pins (eyes)
- marshmallows, large (head and body segments)
- pipe cleaners (tails)
- pushpins, green and blue (noses)
- scissors
- toothpicks, red and green (antennae)

SAFETY

Ask a Question

1. If there are two forms of each of the seven traits, then how many possible combinations are there?

Form a Hypothesis

2. Write a hypothesis that is a possible answer to the question above. Explain your reasoning.

Test the Hypothesis

3. Your teacher will display 14 allele sacks. The sacks will contain slips of paper with capital or lowercase letters on them. Take one piece of paper from each sack. (Remember: Capital letters represent dominant alleles, and lowercase letters represent recessive alleles.) One allele is from "Mom," and one allele is from "Dad." After you have recorded the alleles you have drawn, place the slips of paper back into the sack.

Model A ("Mom")
- red antennae
- 3 body segments
- curly tail
- 2 pairs of legs
- green nose
- black feet
- 3 eyes

Model B ("Dad")
- green antennae
- 2 body segments
- straight tail
- 3 pairs of legs
- blue nose
- green feet
- 2 eyes

CHAPTER RESOURCES

Chapter Resource File
- Datasheet for Chapter Lab
- Lab Notes and Answers

Technology

Classroom Videos
- Lab Video

LabBook
- Tracing Traits

Ask a Question

1. There are 128 possible combinations. (Calculation: There are two forms of each of seven characteristics, so, $2 \times 2 \times 2 \times 2 \times 2 \times 2 \times 2 = 2^7 = 128$)

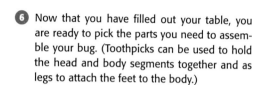

Bug Family Traits				
Trait	Model A "Mom" allele	Model B "Dad" allele	New model "Baby" genotype	New model "Baby" phenotype
Antennae color				
Number of body segments				
Tail shape				
Number of leg pairs		DO NOT WRITE IN BOOK		
Nose color				
Foot color				
Number of eyes				

4 Create a table like the one above. Fill in the first two columns with the alleles that you selected from the sacks. Next, fill in the third column with the genotype of the new model ("Baby").

5 Use the information below to fill in the last column of the table.

Genotypes and Phenotypes	
RR or *Rr*—red antennae	*rr*—green antennae
SS or *Ss*—3 body segments	*ss*—2 body segments
CC or *Cc*—curly tail	*cc*—straight tail
LL or *Ll*—3 pairs of legs	*ll*—2 pairs of legs
BB or *Bb*—blue nose	*bb*—green nose
GG or *Gg*—green feet	*gg*—black feet
EE or *Ee*—2 eyes	*ee*—3 eyes

6 Now that you have filled out your table, you are ready to pick the parts you need to assemble your bug. (Toothpicks can be used to hold the head and body segments together and as legs to attach the feet to the body.)

Analyze the Results

1 **Organizing Data** Take a poll of the traits of the offspring. What are the ratios for each trait?

2 **Examining Data** Do any of the new models look exactly like the parents? Explain.

Draw Conclusions

3 **Interpreting Information** What are the possible genotypes of the parent bugs?

4 **Making Predictions** How many different genotypes are possible in the offspring?

Applying Your Data

Find a mate for your "Baby" bug. What are the possible genotypes and phenotypes of the offspring from this match?

Analyze the Results

1. Student ratios should be similar to the ratios determined when the alleles were selected by the teacher.

2. If any students have offspring bugs that look like one of the parents, have students compare the genotype of the offspring with the genotype of the parents. The offspring and parents look alike but still have different genotypes for some traits.

Draw Conclusions

3. Student answers should reflect the data on parent alleles that were recorded in step 5.

4. Students' answers should include Punnett squares based on the parental traits. Except for the results obtained by parental genotypes that are all homozygous recessive, students will see other possibilities for genotypes and phenotypes from the same parents.

Applying Your Data

Students should create Punnett squares to show the possible genotypes and describe phenotypes that follow the rules of dominance for each characteristic.

CHAPTER RESOURCES

Workbooks

Long-Term Projects & Research Ideas
• Portrait of a Dog **ADVANCED**

Holt Lab Generator CD-ROM

Search for any lab by topic, standard, difficulty level, or time. Edit any lab to fit your needs, or create your own labs. Use the Lab Materials QuickList software to customize your lab materials list.

CLASSROOM TESTED & APPROVED

Kathy LaRoe
East Valley Middle School
East Helena, Montana

Chapter Review

Assignment Guide

Section	Questions
1	7, 13, 18
2	2, 4, 5, 8, 9, 11, 19–23
3	1, 3, 6, 10, 12, 14–17

ANSWERS

Using Key Terms

1. sex cells
2. phenotype, genotype
3. Meiosis
4. alleles

Understanding Key Ideas

5. d
6. c
7. b
8. b
9. c
10. c
11. b

USING KEY TERMS

Complete each of the following sentences by choosing the correct term from the word bank.

sex cells   genotype
sex chromosomes   alleles
phenotype   meiosis

1 Sperm and eggs are known as _____.

2 The _____ is the expression of a trait and is determined by the combination of alleles called the _____.

3 _____ produces cells with half the normal number of chromosomes.

4 Different versions of the same genes are called _____.

UNDERSTANDING KEY IDEAS

Multiple Choice

5 Genes carry information that determines

a. alleles.
b. ribosomes.
c. chromosomes.
d. traits.

6 The process that produces sex cells is

a. mitosis.
b. photosynthesis.
c. meiosis.
d. probability.

7 The passing of traits from parents to offspring is called

a. probability.
b. heredity.
c. recessive.
d. meiosis.

8 If you cross a white flower with the genotype *pp* with a purple flower with the genotype *PP*, the possible genotypes in the offspring are

a. *PP* and *pp*.
b. all *Pp*.
c. all *PP*.
d. all *pp*.

9 For the cross in item 8, what would the phenotypes be?

a. all white
b. 3 purple and 1 white
c. all purple
d. half white, half purple

10 In meiosis,

a. chromosomes are copied twice.
b. the nucleus divides once.
c. four cells are produced from a single cell.
d. two cells are produced from a single cell.

11 When one trait is not completely dominant over another, it is called

a. recessive.
b. incomplete dominance.
c. environmental factors.
d. uncertain dominance.

Short Answer

⓬ Which sex chromosomes do females have? Which do males have?

⓭ In one or two sentences, define the term *recessive trait* in your own words.

⓮ How are sex cells different from other body cells?

⓯ What is a sex-linked disorder? Give one example of a sex-linked disorder that is found in humans.

CRITICAL THINKING

⓰ **Concept Mapping** Use the following terms to create a concept map: *meiosis, eggs, cell division, X chromosome, mitosis, Y chromosome, sperm,* and *sex cells.*

⓱ **Identifying Relationships** If you were a carrier of one allele for a certain recessive disorder, how could genetic counseling help you prepare for the future?

⓲ **Applying Concepts** If a child has blond hair and both of her parents have brown hair, what does that tell you about the allele for blond hair? Explain.

⓳ **Applying Concepts** What is the genotype of a pea plant that is true-breeding for purple flowers?

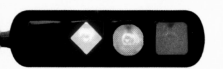

INTERPRETING GRAPHICS

Use the Punnett square below to answer the questions that follow.

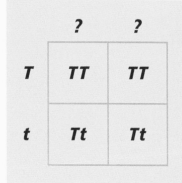

⓴ What is the unknown genotype?

㉑ If *T* represents the allele for tall pea plants and *t* represents the allele for short pea plants, what is the phenotype of each parent and of the offspring?

㉒ If each of the offspring were allowed to self-fertilize, what are the possible genotypes in the next generation?

㉓ What is the probability of each genotype in item 22?

Critical Thinking

16. An answer to this exercise can be found at the end of this book.

17. Sample answer: A genetic counselor could test my spouse to see if my spouse is also a carrier of the recessive allele. The counselor could then predict what the chances are that we could have a child with the recessive disorder.

18. The allele for blond hair is recessive.

19. *PP*

Interpreting Graphics

20. *TT*

21. All the parents and offspring are tall pea plants.

22. Students should make two new Punnett squares. Self-fertilization of *TT* (*TT* × *TT*) will yield offspring that are all *TT*. Self fertilization of *Tt* (*Tt* × *Tt*) will yield offspring that are *TT*, *Tt*, and *tt*.

23. *TT* has a 100% probability with a *TT* parent and a 25% probability with a *Tt* parent. *Tt* has a 50% probability with a *Tt* parent and a 0% probability with a *TT* parent. The genotype *tt* has a 25% probability with a *Tt* parent and a 0% probability with a *TT* parent.

---

12. Females have two X chromosomes. Males have one X and one Y chromosome.

13. Sample answer: A recessive trait is a genetic trait that is expressed only if there is not a dominant allele present.

14. Sex cells have half the number of chromosomes as other body cells.

15. Sample answer: A sex-linked disorder is a disorder that is caused by a gene on one of the sex chromosomes and so is expressed in one sex more than the other. Color blindness is a sex-linked disorder found in humans.

CHAPTER RESOURCES

Chapter Resource File

• Chapter Review **GENERAL**
• Chapter Test A **GENERAL**
• Chapter Test B **ADVANCED**
• Chapter Test C **SPECIAL NEEDS**
• Vocabulary Activity **GENERAL**

Workbooks

Study Guide
• Study Guide is also available in Spanish.

Standardized Test Preparation

Teacher's Note

To provide practice under more realistic testing conditions, give students 20 minutes to answer all of the questions in this Standardized Test Preparation.

MISCONCEPTION ALERT

Answers to the standardized test preparation can help you identify student misconceptions and misunderstandings.

READING

Passage 1

1. C
2. F
3. C

 TEST DOCTOR

Question 2: This question primarily requires the reader to re-read the sentence in which the word is used, which clearly serves to define the word. Then, the reader must look among the possible answers for the one that most closely matches the meaning given in the sentence.

Question 3: This question requires a simple deduction from the final two sentences of the passage. The uses of "if," "then," and "therefore" are clear indicators of logical reasoning. Remind students to look for these kinds of indicators for these types of test questions.

Passage 2

1. A
2. H
3. A

READING

Read the passages below. Then, answer the questions that follow each passage.

Passage 1 The different versions of a gene are called *alleles*. When two different alleles occur together, one is often expressed while the other has no obvious effect on the organism's appearance. The expressed form of the trait is dominant. The trait that was not expressed when the dominant form of the trait was present is called *recessive*. Imagine a plant that has both purple and white alleles for flower color. If the plant blooms purple, then purple is the dominant form of the trait. Therefore, white is the recessive form.

1. According to the passage, which of the following statements is true?
   A All alleles are expressed all of the time.
   B All traits for flower color are dominant.
   C When two alleles are present, the expressed form of the trait is dominant.
   D A recessive form of a trait is always expressed.

2. According to the passage, a trait that is not expressed when the dominant form is present is called
   F recessive.
   G an allele.
   H heredity.
   I a gene.

3. According to the passage, which allele for flower color is dominant?
   A white
   B pink
   C purple
   D yellow

Passage 2 Sickle cell anemia is a recessive genetic disorder. People inherit this disorder only when they inherit the disease-causing recessive allele from both parents. The disease causes the body to make red blood cells that bend into a sickle (or crescent moon) shape. The sickle-shaped red blood cells break apart easily. Therefore, the blood of a person with sickle cell anemia carries less oxygen. Sickle-shaped blood cells also tend to get stuck in blood vessels. When a blood vessel is blocked, the blood supply to organs can be cut off. But the sickle-shaped blood cells can also protect a person from malaria. Malaria is a disease caused by an organism that invades red blood cells.

1. According to the passage, sickle cell anemia is a
   A recessive genetic disorder.
   B dominant genetic disorder.
   C disease caused by an organism that invades red blood cells.
   D disease also called *malaria*.

2. According to the passage, sickle cell anemia can help protect a person from
   F blocked blood vessels.
   G genetic disorders.
   H malaria.
   I low oxygen levels.

3. Which of the following is a fact in the passage?
   A When blood vessels are blocked, vital organs lose their blood supply.
   B When blood vessels are blocked, it causes the red blood cells to bend into sickle shapes.
   C The blood of a person with sickle cell anemia carries more oxygen.
   D Healthy red blood cells never get stuck in blood vessels.

 TEST DOCTOR

Question 2: The answer to this question comes from the second-to-last sentence in the passage. Weak readers often miss details from the middle parts of passages, and standardized tests sometimes probe for this kind of mistake with such questions. One strategy for this type of question is to form a question such as "From what problem can sickle cell anemia protect a person?" and then re-read or skim the passage with this question in mind.

The Punnett square below shows a cross between two flowering plants. Use this Punnett square to answer the questions that follow.

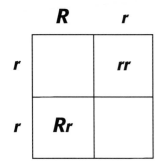

1. What is the genotype of the offspring represented in the upper left-hand box of the Punnett square?

A *RR*

B *Rr*

C *rr*

D *rrr*

2. What is the genotype of the offspring represented in the lower right-hand box of the Punnett square?

F *RR*

G *Rr*

H *rr*

I *rrr*

3. What is the ratio of *Rr* (purple-flowered plants) to *rr* (white-flowered plants) in the offspring?

A 1:3

B 2:2

C 3:1

D 4:0

MATH

Read each question below, and choose the best answer.

1. What is another way to write $4 \times 4 \times 4$?

A 4^2

B 4^3

C 3^3

D 3^4

2. Jane was making a design on top of her desk with pennies. She put 4 pennies in the first row, 7 pennies in the second row, and 13 pennies in the third row. If Jane continues this pattern, how many pennies will she put in the sixth row?

F 25

G 49

H 97

I 193

3. In which of the following lists are the numbers in order from smallest to greatest?

A 0.012, 0.120, 0.123, 1.012

B 1.012, 0.123, 0.120, 0.012

C 0.123, 0.120, 0.012, 1.012

D 0.123, 1.012, 0.120, 0.012

4. In which of the following lists are the numbers in order from smallest to greatest?

F $-12.0, -15.5, 2.2, 4.0$

G $-15.5, -12.0, 2.2, 4.0$

H $-12.0, -15.5, 4.0, 2.2$

I $2.2, 4.0, -12.0, -15.5$

5. Which of the following is equal to -11?

A $7 + 4$

B $-4 + 7$

C $-7 + 4$

D $-7 + -4$

6. Catherine earned $75 for working 8.5 h. How much did she earn per hour?

F $10.12

G $9.75

H $8.82

I $8.01

Standardized Test Preparation

INTERPRETING GRAPHICS

1. B

2. H

3. B

+ TEST DOCTOR

Questions 1 and 2: These questions require understanding of the term *genotype* and the ability to complete a Punnett square. Students who miss these questions may need to review these concepts.

Question 3: This question asks for the ratio of the genotype *Rr* to the genotype *rr*. If completed, the Punnett square would show 2 *Rr* and 2 *rr* genotypes. Thus, the ratio would be 2:2 (answer B). Students who miss this question may need to review the concept of ratios.

MATH

1. B

2. H

3. A

4. G

5. D

6. H

+ TEST DOCTOR

Question 6: This question is essentially a simple long-division problem, but students may get confused or discouraged by long division when the calculation extends for many decimal places. For this problem, students can save time if they recognize that they need only to find the answer in dollars and cents. Thus, they need to calculate to the thousandths place ($8.823) and then round their answer to the nearest cent.

Science, Technology, and Society

Background

Genetic research has spawned a flurry of debate over ethical, social, and legal issues surrounding the use of genetic information. These issues include the privacy and ownership of personal genetic information and the possibility that people will selectively breed or control the birth of their children based on genetic knowledge.

Weird Science

Teaching Strategy—GENERAL

Offer the following analogies to help students grasp the concepts discussed in this article.

- Blueprints: Show students sample construction blueprints. Explain that genes are like these plans for a building and that mutations are like mistakes in copying, reading, or building from the blueprints.

- Recipes: Show students a book of cake recipes. Genes are like recipes, and an organism is like a cake made according to a recipe. A mutation is like using a different ingredient or a different amount of an ingredient. The mutation may or may not "ruin" the "cake."

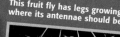

Science in Action

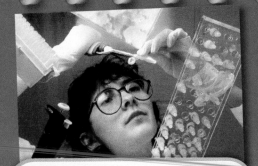

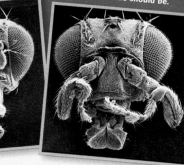

This is a normal fruit fly under a scanning electron microscope.

This fruit fly has legs growing where its antennae should be.

Science, Technology, and Society

Mapping the Human Genome

In 2003, scientists finished one of the most ambitious research projects ever. Researchers with the Human Genome Project (HGP) mapped the human body's complete set of genetic instructions, which is called the *genome*. You might be wondering whose genome the scientists are decoding. Actually, it doesn't matter—only 0.1% of each person's genetic material is unique. The researchers' goals are to identify how tiny differences in that 0.1% make each of us who we are and to begin to understand how some differences can cause disease. Scientists are already using the map to think of new ways to treat genetic diseases, such as asthma, diabetes, and kidney disease.

Social Studies ACTIVITY

WRITING SKILL Research DNA fingerprinting. Write a short report describing how DNA fingerprinting has affected the way criminals are caught.

Weird Science

Lab Rats with Wings

Drosophila melanogaster (droh SAHF i luh muh LAN uh GAS tuhr) is the scientific name for the fruit fly. This tiny insect has played a big role in helping scientists understand many illnesses. Because fruit flies reproduce every 2 weeks, scientists can alter a fruit fly gene and see the results of the experiment very quickly. Another important reason for using these "lab rats with wings" is that their genetic code is simple and well understood. Fruit flies have 12,000 genes, but humans have more than 25,000. Scientists use fruit flies to find out about diseases like cancer, Alzheimer's, and muscular dystrophy.

Language Arts ACTIVITY

WRITING SKILL The mythical creature called the *Chimera* (kie MIR uh) was said to be part lion, part goat, and part serpent. According to legend, the Chimera terrorized people for years until it was killed by a brave hero. The word *chimera* now refers to any organism that has parts from many organisms. Write a short story about the Chimera that describes what it looks like and how it came to be.

Answer to Social Studies Activity

Sample answer: DNA fingerprinting has made it much easier to match genetic material (evidence) at a crime scene to the genetic information of one particular individual. DNA can be found in hair, saliva, blood, and small skin cells. The DNA is analyzed and then compared to the DNA fingerprint of particular individuals. When the DNA fingerprints match, police can be sure that the person was at the scene of the crime.

Answer to Language Arts Activity

The Chimera (or Chimaera) was said to be a savage beast that spat fire from its mouth. In classical Greco-Roman stories, it wreaked havoc on the ancient lands until it was killed by the hero Bellerophon, who rode his winged horse Pegasus. This basic story is among the most ancient myths and appears in many texts from Homer's *Iliad* to traditional fairy tales.

Stacey Wong

Genetic Counselor If your family had a history of a particular disease, what would you do? Would you eat healthier foods, get more exercise, or visit your doctor regularly? All of those are good ideas, but Stacey Wong went a step farther. Her family's history of cancer helped her decide to become a genetic counselor. "Genetic counselors are usually part of a team of health professionals," she says, which can include physicians, nurses, dieticians, social workers, laboratory personnel, and others. "If a diagnosis is made by the geneticist," says Wong, "then I provide genetic counseling." When a patient visits a genetic counselor, the counselor asks many questions and builds a family medical history. Although counseling involves discussing what it means to have a genetic condition, Wong says "the most important part is to get to know the patient or family we are working with, listen to their concerns, gain an understanding of their values, help them to make decisions, and be their advocate."

Careers

Background

Stacey Wong was born in Oakland, California, and grew up in the nearby suburb of Alameda. She received a B.S. in cell and molecular biology from UCLA and an M.S. in genetic counseling from California State University Northridge. More information about genetic-counseling careers can be obtained from the National Society of Genetic Counselors.

Math

The probability of inheriting genetic disease *A* is 1/10,000. The probability of inheriting genetic disease *B* is also 1/10,000. What is the probability that one person would inherit both genetic diseases *A* and *B*?

go.hrw.com

To learn more about these Science in Action topics, visit **go.hrw.com** and type in the keyword **HL5HERF**.

Current Science

Check out Current Science® articles related to this chapter by visiting go.hrw.com. Just type in the keyword **HL5CS05**.

Answer to Math Activity
$1/10{,}000 \times 1/10{,}000 = 1/100{,}000{,}000$

Genes and DNA
Chapter Planning Guide

Compression guide:
To shorten instruction because of time limitations, omit the Chapter Lab.

OBJECTIVES	LABS, DEMONSTRATIONS, AND ACTIVITIES	TECHNOLOGY RESOURCES
PACING • 135 min pp. 84–89 **Chapter Opener**	**SE** Start-up Activity, p. 85 ◆ GENERAL	**OSP** Parent Letter ■ **CD** Student Edition on CD-ROM **CD** Guided Reading Audio CD ■ **TR** Chapter Starter Transparency* **VID** Brain Food Video Quiz
Section 1 What Does DNA Look Like? • List three important events that led to understanding the structure of DNA. • Describe the basic structure of a DNA molecule. • Explain how DNA molecules can be copied.	**TE** Activity Modeling Code, p. 86 GENERAL **TE** Group Activity A Place in History, p. 87 GENERAL **SE** Quick Lab Making a Model of DNA, p. 88 ◆ GENERAL **CRF** Datasheet for Quick Lab* **SE** Science in Action Math, Social Studies, and Language Arts Activities, pp. 104–105 GENERAL **SE** Model-Making Lab Base-Pair Basics, p. 98 ◆ GENERAL **CRF** Datasheet for Chapter Lab* **LB** Whiz-Bang Demonstrations Grand Strand* GENERAL	**OSP** Lesson Plans (also in print) **TR** Bellringer Transparency* **TR** L17 DNA Structure* **CRF** SciLinks Activity* GENERAL **VID** Lab Videos for Life Science **CD** Science Tutor
PACING • 45 min pp. 90–97 **Section 2 How DNA Works** • Explain the relationship between DNA, genes, and proteins. • Outline the basic steps in making a protein. • Describe three types of mutations, and provide an example of a gene mutation. • Describe two examples of uses of genetic knowledge.	**TE** Demonstration A Tight Fit, p. 90 ◆ GENERAL **TE** Connection Activity Chemistry, p. 92 ADVANCED **TE** Group Activity Skit, p. 92 GENERAL **TE** Connection Activity Math, p. 93 ◆ GENERAL **TE** Activity Complementary Code, p. 94 BASIC **SE** School-to-Home Activity An Error in the Message, p. 95 GENERAL **TE** Connection Activity Social Studies, p. 96 ADVANCED **LB** Long-Term Projects & Research Ideas The Antifreeze Protein* ADVANCED **LB** Long-Term Projects & Research Ideas Ewe Again, Dolly?* ADVANCED	**OSP** Lesson Plans (also in print) **TR** Bellringer Transparency* **TR** L18 Unraveling DNA* **TR** L19 The Making of a Protein: A* **TR** L20 The Making of a Protein: B* **TR** LINK TO EARTH SCIENCE E66 The Formation of Smog* **TR** L21 How Sickle Cell Anemia Results from a Mutation* **SE** Internet Activity, p. 92 GENERAL **CD** Interactive Explorations CD-ROM DNA Pawprints GENERAL **CD** Science Tutor

PACING • 90 min

CHAPTER REVIEW, ASSESSMENT, AND STANDARDIZED TEST PREPARATION

CRF Vocabulary Activity* GENERAL
SE Chapter Review, pp. 100–101 GENERAL
CRF Chapter Review* ■ GENERAL
CRF Chapter Tests A* ■ GENERAL, B* ADVANCED, C* SPECIAL NEEDS
SE Standardized Test Preparation, pp. 102–103 GENERAL
CRF Standardized Test Preparation* GENERAL
CRF Performance-Based Assessment* GENERAL
OSP Test Generator, Test Item Listing

Online and Technology Resources

Visit go.hrw.com for access to Holt Online Learning, or enter the keyword **HL7 Home** for a variety of free online resources.

This CD-ROM package includes:
• Lab Materials QuickList Software
• Holt Calendar Planner
• Customizable Lesson Plans
• Printable Worksheets
• ExamView® Test Generator
• Interactive Teacher's Edition
• Holt PuzzlePro®
• Holt PowerPoint® Resources

Is That a Fact!

◆ If uncoiled, the DNA in the 46 chromosomes of a human body cell is about 2 m long. Within chromosomes, this DNA is so tightly coiled that if all 46 chromosomes were lined up end to end, they would span less than 0.5 cm.

Genetic Engineering

● Genetically engineered hybrid organisms are often called *chimeras*. The word *chimera* comes from Greek mythology, in which the Chimera was a fire-breathing monster, usually depicted as a composite of a lion, a goat, and a serpent.

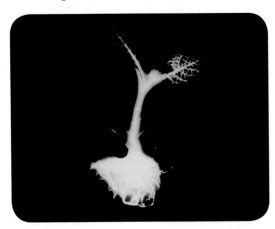

● Scientists often disagree about the ethics of genetic engineering and about the safety risks involved. Dr. Maxine Frank Singer was one of the first scientists to warn the National Academy of Science of the potential hazards of genetic engineering. Because of the efforts of Dr. Singer and her colleagues, the National Institute of Health began to develop specific guidelines for genetic research as early as 1976. These guidelines, now regularly amended, continue to regulate the production and use of DNA and genetically engineered organisms.

The Human Genome Project

● The Human Genome Project (HGP) was started in 1990 as an international collaboration of scientists with the goal of mapping the entire sequence of DNA found in humans. In April 2003, in conjunction with the anniversary of the historic publication by Watson and Crick of DNA's molecular structure, the HGP announced that its work was mostly done. The HGP had completed mapping 99% of the human genetic code. Some mystery remained about the area of chromosomes called the *centromere*.

● Many potential benefits are predicted to result from the Human Genome Project, and some benefits have already been realized. Scientists working on the HGP have developed faster methods of determining the sequences within DNA samples. Also, scientists have improved methods of finding and tracking the functions of specific genes within cells. Such advances have made it easier to study the genetics of all kinds of organisms and to find the genetic indicators of specific kinds of cancer and other diseases.

DNA Fingerprints

● DNA fingerprints are frequently used in criminal investigations. The DNA can come from hair, skin cells, blood, or other body fluids left at the crime scene by the perpetrator. Scientists use enzymes to make copies of specific DNA sections from different locations on different chromosomes. The copied fragments are separated by size and other characteristics on a gel, and they are stained to yield a unique set of dark bands on the gel. This set of bands is known as a *DNA fingerprint*. The fingerprint is then compared with the DNA fingerprint of the suspect to help determine innocence or guilt.

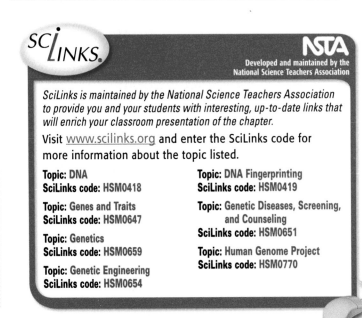

SciLinks is maintained by the National Science Teachers Association to provide you and your students with interesting, up-to-date links that will enrich your classroom presentation of the chapter.

Visit www.scilinks.org and enter the SciLinks code for more information about the topic listed.

Topic: DNA
SciLinks code: HSM0418

Topic: Genes and Traits
SciLinks code: HSM0647

Topic: Genetics
SciLinks code: HSM0659

Topic: Genetic Engineering
SciLinks code: HSM0654

Topic: DNA Fingerprinting
SciLinks code: HSM0419

Topic: Genetic Diseases, Screening, and Counseling
SciLinks code: HSM0651

Topic: Human Genome Project
SciLinks code: HSM0770

Overview

Tell students that this chapter is about DNA—the substance that makes up genes—and about how DNA works within cells to direct the growth and functioning of every organism.

Assessing Prior Knowledge

Students should be familiar with the following topics:

• cell structure

• mitosis and meiosis

• basic rules of heredity

• chromosomes

Identifying Misconceptions

The roles of DNA, RNA, and proteins in cells are very complex, and many puzzles remain. Students may tend to simplify their concept of the "rules" as they learn them. Students may remain unconvinced of the role of chance and probability in heredity. Also, students may have difficulty linking their knowledge of the functions of DNA at the cellular level to what they have learned and will learn about the functioning of tissues and organs within an entire organism.

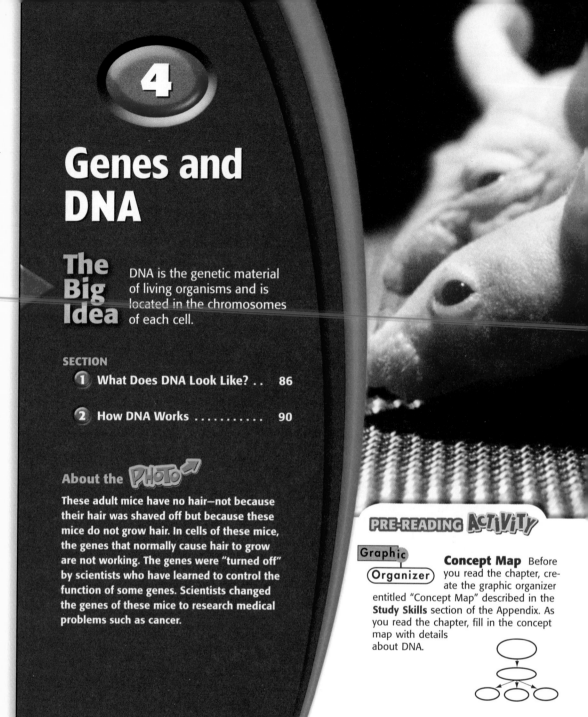

4

Genes and DNA

The Big Idea

DNA is the genetic material of living organisms and is located in the chromosomes of each cell.

About the PHOTO

These adult mice have no hair—not because their hair was shaved off but because these mice do not grow hair. In cells of these mice, the genes that normally cause hair to grow are not working. The genes were "turned off" by scientists who have learned to control the function of some genes. Scientists changed the genes of these mice to research medical problems such as cancer.

PRE-READING ACTIVITY

Graphic Organizer

Concept Map Before you read the chapter, create the graphic organizer entitled "Concept Map" described in the **Study Skills** section of the Appendix. As you read the chapter, fill in the concept map with details about DNA.

Standards Correlations

National Science Education Standards

The following codes indicate the National Science Education Standards that correlate to this chapter. The full text of the standards is at the front of the book.

Chapter Opener
UCP 5; SAI 1, 2; ST 2; LS 2e

Section 1 What Does DNA Look Like?
UCP 2, 5; SAI 1, 2; ST 1, 2; SPSP 5; HNS 1, 2, 3; LS 1a, 2d, 5a

Section 2 How DNA Works
UCP 1, 4, 5; SAI 1, 2; ST 2; SPSP 4, 5; LS 1c, 1e, 1f, 2b, 2c, 2d, 2e, 5b

Chapter Lab
UCP 2, 5; SAI 1, 2; HNS 1; LS 1a

Chapter Review
UCP 1, 2, 5; SAI 1, 2; ST 2; SPSP 4; HNS 2, 3; LS 1a, 1c, 1e, 1f, 2c, 2d, 2e, 5a, 5b

Science In Action
UCP 1, 2, 5; ST 2; SPSP 4 ,5; HNS 1, 2, 3; LS 1f

START-UP ACTIVITY

MATERIALS

FOR EACH GROUP
- magnifying lens
- paper, tracing (1 sheet)
- paper, white (1 sheet for each student)
- pencil or piece of charcoal
- tape, transparent

Safety Caution: Remind students to review all safety cautions and icons before beginning this lab activity. Charcoal is nontoxic, but it can stain clothes.

Teacher's Notes: The loop pattern is found in about 65% of the population, the whorl in about 30%, and the arch in about 5%.

Answers

1. The number of fingerprint types will vary for each class. No two students should have the same fingerprint (those of identical twins may be similar but still unique). Accept any reasonable explanation that incorporates variation in inherited traits among populations.

START-UP ACTIVITY

Fingerprint Your Friends

One way to identify people is by taking their fingerprints. Does it really work? Are everyone's fingerprints unique? Try this activity to find out.

Procedure

1. Rub the tip of a **pencil** back and forth across a **piece of tracing paper.** Make a large, dark mark.
2. Rub the tip of one of your fingers on the pencil mark. Then place a small **piece of transparent tape** over the darkened area on your finger.
3. Remove the tape, and stick it on **a piece of white paper.** Repeat steps 1–3 for the rest of your fingers.
4. Look at the fingerprints with a **magnifying lens.** What patterns do you see? Is the pattern the same on every finger?

Analysis

1. Compare your fingerprints with those of your classmates. Do any two people in your class have the same prints? Try to explain your findings.

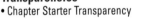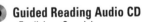

What If . . . ?

Imagine that you are wrongly accused of   A technique known as DNA finger-

Chapter Starter Transparency
Use this transparency to help students begin thinking about genes and DNA.

CHAPTER RESOURCES

Technology

Transparencies
- Chapter Starter Transparency

READING SKILLS

Student Edition on CD-ROM

Guided Reading Audio CD
- English or Spanish

Classroom Videos
- Brain Food Video Quiz

Workbooks

Science Puzzlers, Twisters & Teasers
- Genes and DNA GENERAL

Focus

Overview

This section introduces students to the structure and function of DNA and to the process of DNA replication.

📡 Bellringer

To test prior knowledge, have students answer the following questions:

1. Give an example of the difference between traits and characteristics. (Sample answer: Eye color is a characteristic, while having blue eyes is a trait.)

2. Where are genes found in cells? (in chromosomes; in cells that have nuclei, chromosomes are within the nucleus)

Motivate

ACTIVITY ——— GENERAL

Modeling Code Create a code by pairing each letter of the alphabet with a numeral. For example, the numeral 1 could represent the letter *a*. Have students encode a brief message. Then, have students exchange and decode the message. Explain that a code is simply another way to represent information and that there are many types of codes. The genetic code is based on sequences of the four nucleotide bases of DNA. English Language Learners

LS Logical

What Does DNA Look Like?

For many years, the structure of a DNA molecule was a puzzle to scientists. In the 1950s, two scientists deduced the structure while experimenting with chemical models. They later won a Nobel Prize for helping solve this puzzle!

Inherited characteristics are determined by genes, and genes are passed from one generation to the next. Genes are parts of chromosomes, which are structures in the nucleus of most cells. Chromosomes are made of protein and DNA. **DNA** stands for *deoxyribonucleic acid* (dee AHKS ee RIE boh noo KLEE ik AS id). DNA is the genetic material—the material that determines inherited characteristics. But what does DNA look like?

The Pieces of the Puzzle

Scientists knew that the material that makes up genes must be able to do two things. First, it must be able to give instructions for building and maintaining cells. Second, it must be able to be copied each time a cell divides, so that each cell contains identical genes. Scientists thought that these things could be done only by complex molecules, such as proteins. They were surprised to learn how much the DNA molecule could do.

Nucleotides: The Subunits of DNA

DNA is made of subunits called nucleotides. A **nucleotide** consists of a sugar, a phosphate, and a base. The nucleotides are identical except for the base. The four bases are *adenine, thymine, guanine,* and *cytosine.* Each base has a different shape. Scientists often refer to a base by the first letter of the base, *A, T, G,* and *C.* **Figure 1** shows models of the four nucleotides.

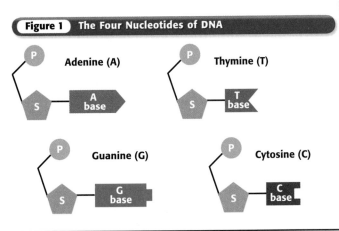

Figure 1 The Four Nucleotides of DNA

Adenine (A)
Thymine (T)
Guanine (G)
Cytosine (C)

What You Will Learn

● List three important events that led to understanding the structure of DNA.
● Describe the basic structure of a DNA molecule.
● Explain how DNA molecules can be copied.

Vocabulary

DNA
nucleotide

READING STRATEGY

Prediction Guide Before reading this section, write the title of each heading in this section. Next, under each heading, write what you think you will learn.

DNA **d**eoxyribo**n**ucleic **a**cid, a molecule that is present in all living cells and that contains the information that determines the traits that a living thing inherits and needs to live

nucleotide in a nucleic-acid chain, a subunit that consists of a sugar, a phosphate, and a nitrogenous base

---

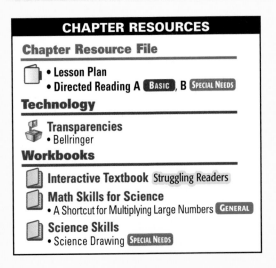

CHAPTER RESOURCES

Chapter Resource File

- Lesson Plan
- Directed Reading A **BASIC**, B **SPECIAL NEEDS**

Technology

Transparencies
- Bellringer

Workbooks

Interactive Textbook **Struggling Readers**

Math Skills for Science
- A Shortcut for Multiplying Large Numbers **GENERAL**

Science Skills
- Science Drawing **SPECIAL NEEDS**

Chargaff's Rules

In the 1950s, a biochemist named Erwin Chargaff found that the amount of adenine in DNA always equals the amount of thymine. And he found that the amount of guanine always equals the amount of cytosine. His findings are known as *Chargaff's rules*. At the time of his discovery, no one knew the importance of these findings. But Chargaff's rules later helped scientists understand the structure of DNA.

✓ **Reading Check** Summarize Chargaff's rules. (*See the Appendix for answers to Reading Checks.*)

Franklin's Discovery

More clues about the structure of DNA came from scientists in Britain. There, chemist Rosalind Franklin, shown in **Figure 2,** was able to make images of DNA molecules. She used a process known as *X-ray diffraction* to make these images. In this process, X rays are aimed at the DNA molecule. When an X ray hits a part of the molecule, the ray bounces off. The pattern made by the bouncing rays is captured on film. Franklin's images suggested that DNA has a spiral shape.

Watson and Crick's Model

At about the same time, two other scientists were also trying to solve the mystery of DNA's structure. They were James Watson and Francis Crick, shown in **Figure 3.** After seeing Franklin's X-ray images, Watson and Crick concluded that DNA must look like a long, twisted ladder. They were then able to build a model of DNA by using simple materials from their laboratory. Their model perfectly fit with both Chargaff's and Franklin's findings. The model eventually helped explain how DNA is copied and how it functions in the cell.

CONNECTION TO Chemistry

WRITING SKILL **Linus Pauling** Many scientists contributed to the discovery of DNA's structure. In fact, some scientists competed to be the first to make the discovery. One of these competitors was a chemist named Linus Pauling. Research and write a paragraph about how Pauling's work helped Watson and Crick.

Figure 2 *Rosalind Franklin used X-ray diffraction to make images of DNA that helped reveal the structure of DNA.*

Figure 3 *This photo shows James Watson (left) and Francis Crick (right) with their model of DNA.*

Answer to Connection to Chemistry
Linus Pauling was an innovator in the use of models to deduce chemical behavior. Whereas some scientists belittled the practice of "playing" with chemical models, Pauling inspired other scientists, such as Watson and Crick, to try this strategy. Watson and Crick's deduction of DNA's ladder structure was partly brought about by manipulating models of nucleotides.

Close

Reteaching ———— BASIC

DNA's Complementary Strands

To help students understand how the term *complementary* relates to the structure of DNA, point out that the term means "completing." Using **Figure 4** and **Figure 5,** explain that complementary base pairs join to *complete* each rung on the spiral-staircase structure of DNA. Then, point out that complementary strands of DNA join to complete one DNA molecule.

LS Visual/Verbal

Quiz ———— GENERAL

1. When is DNA copied? (every time a cell divides)

2. Name the four types of nucleotides. (adenine, thymine, guanine, and cytosine)

Alternative Assessment ———— GENERAL

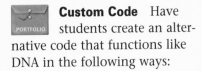

Custom Code Have students create an alternative code that functions like DNA in the following ways:

- The code is based on four letters or symbols.

- Coded information can be split up and then reassembled.

Have students draw and explain their coding system. **LS** Logical

Quick Lab

Making a Model of DNA

1. Gather assorted simple materials that you could use to build a basic model of DNA. You might use **clay, string, toothpicks, paper, tape, plastic foam,** or **pieces of food.**

2. Work with a partner or a small team to build your model. Use your book and other resources to check the details of your model.

3. Show your model to your classmates. Give your classmates feedback about the scientific aspects of their models.

DNA's Double Structure

The shape of DNA is shown in **Figure 4.** As you can see, a strand of DNA looks like a twisted ladder. This shape is known as a *double helix* (DUB uhl HEE LIKS). The two sides of the ladder are made of alternating sugar parts and phosphate parts. The rungs of the ladder are made of a pair of bases. Adenine on one side of a rung always pairs with thymine on the other side. Guanine always pairs with cytosine.

Notice how the double helix structure matches Chargaff's observations. When Chargaff separated the parts of a sample of DNA, he found that the matching bases were always present in equal amounts. To model how the bases pair, Watson and Crick tried to match Chargaff's observations. They also used information from chemists about the size and shape of each of the nucleotides. As it turned out, the width of the DNA ladder matches the combined width of the matching bases. Only the correct pairs of bases fit within the ladder's width.

Making Copies of DNA

The pairing of bases allows the cell to *replicate*, or make copies of, DNA. Each base always bonds with only one other base. Thus, pairs of bases are *complementary* to each other, and both sides of a DNA molecule are complementary. For example, the sequence CGAC will bond to the sequence GCTG.

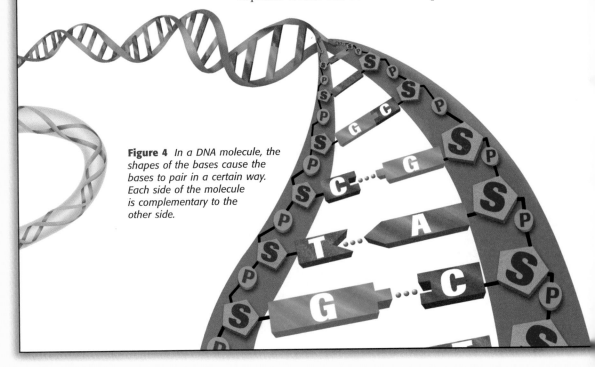

Figure 4 *In a DNA molecule, the shapes of the bases cause the bases to pair in a certain way. Each side of the molecule is complementary to the other side.*

Quick Lab

MATERIALS

FOR EACH GROUP

- variety of materials, such as clay, string, toothpicks, paper, tape, plastic foam, beads or buttons and pipe cleaners or wire.
- food or candy items could be another option

Teacher's Note: Display student models within the school. Have students reevaluate or improve upon them later.

Safety Caution: Advise students to keep the area around them uncluttered. Students should exercise caution with sharp objects. Any food items used should not be eaten and should be disposed of.

Answers

2. Student models should resemble **Figure 4** in basic structure but may vary in size, color, and construction.

3. Students should suggest ways to make each model more accurate.

How Copies Are Made

During replication, as shown in **Figure 5**, a DNA molecule is split down the middle, where the bases meet. The bases on each side of the molecule are used as a pattern for a new strand. As the bases on the original molecule are exposed, complementary nucleotides are added to each side of the ladder. Two DNA molecules are formed. Half of each of the molecules is old DNA, and half is new DNA.

When Copies Are Made

DNA is copied every time a cell divides. Each new cell gets a complete copy of all the DNA. The job of unwinding, copying, and re-winding the DNA is done by proteins within the cell. So, DNA is usually found with several kinds of proteins. Other proteins help with the process of carrying out the instructions written in the code of the DNA.

✓ Reading Check How often is DNA copied?

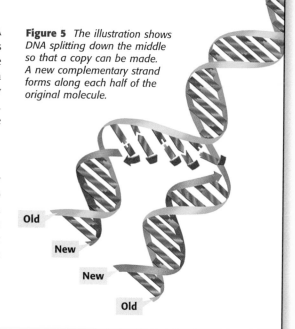

Figure 5 *The illustration shows DNA splitting down the middle so that a copy can be made. A new complementary strand forms along each half of the original molecule.*

Old

New

New

Old

SECTION Review

Summary

- DNA is the material that makes up genes. It carries coded information that is copied in each new cell.
- The DNA molecule looks like a twisted ladder. The two halves are long strings of nucleotides. The rungs are complementary pairs of bases.
- Because each base has a complementary base, DNA can be replicated accurately.

Using Key Terms

1. Use the term *DNA* in a sentence.

2. In your own words, write a definition for the term *nucleotide*.

Understanding Key Ideas

3. List three important events that led to understanding the structure of DNA.

4. Which of the following is NOT part of a nucleotide?
   a. base
   b. sugar
   c. fat
   d. phosphate

Math Skills

5. If a sample of DNA contained 20% cytosine, what percentage of guanine would be in this sample? What percentage of adenine would be in the sample? Explain.

Critical Thinking

6. **Making Inferences** Explain what is meant by the statement "DNA unites all organisms."

7. **Applying Concepts** What would the complementary strand of DNA be for the sequence of bases below?

   C T T A G G C T T A C C A

8. **Analyzing Processes** How are copies of DNA made? Draw a picture as part of your answer.

Developed and maintained by the National Science Teachers Association

For a variety of links related to this chapter, go to www.scilinks.org

Topic: DNA; Genes and Traits
SciLinks code: HSM0418; HSM0647

Answer to Reading Check

every time a cell divides

CHAPTER RESOURCES

Chapter Resource File

- Section Quiz GENERAL
- Section Review GENERAL
- Vocabulary and Section Summary GENERAL
- SciLinks Activity GENERAL
- Datasheet for Quick Lab

Technology

- Transparencies
  - L17 DNA Structure

SECTION
2

Focus

Overview

This section shows how DNA is a part of chromosomes, how DNA is used as a template for making proteins, and how errors in DNA can lead to mutations and genetic disorders.

Bellringer

Have students unscramble the following words and use them both in one sentence:

tpsoneir (proteins)

neesg (genes)

(Sample answer: Genes contain instructions for making proteins.)

Motivate

Demonstration — GENERAL

A Tight Fit To illustrate the way that DNA is *supercoiled* within chromosomes and cells, hold up a long rubber band or thick piece of string. Begin to twist each end in opposite directions until coils form. Continue twisting until the band is highly compacted. Then, challenge students to fit 2 m of fine thread into a thimble or an empty gelatin capsule. **English Language Learners**

LS Kinesthetic

Answer to Reading Check

a string of nucleotides that give the cell information about how to make a specific trait

---

How DNA Works

Almost every cell in your body contains about 2 m of DNA. How does all of the DNA fit in a cell? And how does the DNA hold a code that affects your traits?

DNA is found in the cells of all organisms, including bacteria, mosquitoes, and humans. Each organism has a unique set of DNA. But DNA functions the same way in all organisms.

Unraveling DNA

DNA is often wound around proteins, coiled into strands, and then bundled up even more. In a cell that lacks a nucleus, each strand of DNA forms a loose loop within the cell. In a cell that has a nucleus, the strands of DNA and proteins are bundled into chromosomes, as shown in **Figure 1**.

The structure of DNA allows DNA to hold information. The order of the bases on one side of the molecule is a code that carries information. A *gene* consists of a string of nucleotides that give the cell information about how to make a specific trait. There is an enormous amount of DNA, so there can be a large variety of genes.

Reading Check What makes up a gene? (*See the Appendix for answers to Reading Checks.*)

What You Will Learn

- Explain the relationship between DNA, genes, and proteins.
- Outline the basic steps in making a protein.
- Describe three types of mutations, and provide an example of a gene mutation.
- Describe two examples of uses of genetic knowledge.

Vocabulary
RNA
ribosome
mutation

READING STRATEGY

Reading Organizer As you read this section, make a flowchart of the steps of how DNA codes for proteins.

Figure 1 Unraveling DNA

a A typical skin cell has a diameter of about 0.0025 cm. The DNA in the nucleus of each cell codes for proteins that determine traits such as skin color.

b The DNA in the nucleus is part of a material called *chromatin*. Long strands of chromatin are usually bundled loosely within the nucleus.

WEIRD SCIENCE

In 2003, the Human Genome Project had successfully mapped 99% of the 3 billion base pairs that make up a set of human DNA. But the project has raised new questions as well. For example, only about 3% of those base pairs are used in making proteins; the other 97% are regulatory sequences, nonfunctioning genes, and sequences with no known function.

Additionally, scientists originally expected to find over 50,000 human genes because human cells produce at least that many proteins. Instead, latest estimates indicate that there are about 25,000 human genes, and many genes code for multiple proteins. In this and other ways, human genes appear to be unique among organisms.

The diagram below shows an original sequence of DNA and three possible mutations. Use the diagram to answer the questions that follow.

Original sequence

Mutation A

Mutation B

Mutation C

1. In which mutation was an original base pair replaced?
   A Mutation A
   B Mutation B
   C Mutation C
   D There is not enough information to determine the answer.

2. In which mutation was a new base pair added?
   F Mutation A
   G Mutation B
   H Mutation C
   I There is not enough information to determine the answer.

3. In which mutation was an original base pair removed?
   A Mutation A
   B Mutation B
   C Mutation C
   D There is not enough information to determine the answer.

MATH

Read each question below, and choose the best answer.

1. Mary was making a design on top of her desk with marbles. She put 3 marbles in the first row, 7 marbles in the second row, 15 marbles in the third row, and 31 marbles in the fourth row. If Mary continues this pattern, how many marbles will she put in the seventh row?
   A 46
   B 63
   C 127
   D 255

2. Bobby walked 3 1/2 km on Saturday, 2 1/3 km on Sunday, and 1 km on Monday. How many kilometers did Bobby walk on those 3 days?
   F 5 1/6
   G 5 5/6
   H 6 1/6
   I 6 5/6

3. Marie bought a new aquarium for her goldfish. The aquarium is 60 cm long, 20 cm wide, and 30 cm high. Which equation could be used to find the volume of water needed to fill the aquarium to 25 cm deep?

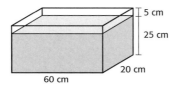

   A $V = 30 \times 60 \times 20$
   B $V = 25 \times 60 \times 20$
   C $V = 30 \times 60 \times 20 - 5$
   D $V = 30 \times 60 \times 25$

4. How is the product of $6 \times 6 \times 6 \times 4 \times 4 \times 4$ expressed in scientific notation?
   F $6^4 \times 3^6$
   G $6^3 \times 4^3$
   H $3^6 \times 3^4$
   I 24^6

Standardized Test Preparation

CHAPTER RESOURCES

Chapter Resource File
• Standardized Test Preparation GENERAL

State Resources
 For specific resources for your state, visit **go.hrw.com** and type in the keyword **HSMSTR**.

1. B
2. F
3. C

 TEST DOCTOR

Question 1: The student must recognize that, in Mutation B, the only change from the original sequence is a different base-pair in the middle of the sequence—a replacement. Mutation A is an insertion, and Mutation C is a deletion.

MATH
1. D
2. I
3. B
4. G

 TEST DOCTOR

Question 1: The problem requires students to predict the next three values in a patterned sequence of numbers. The pattern is as follows:

3, 7, 15, 31, . . .

The logic of the pattern is to multiply each number by 2 and then add 1 to get the next number. Thus,

1	3
2	$(3 \times 2) + 1 = 7$
3	$(7 \times 2) + 1 = 15$
4	$(15 \times 2) + 1 = 31$
5	$(31 \times 2) + 1 = 63$
6	$(63 \times 2) + 1 = 127$
7	$(127 \times 2) + 1 = 255$

Question 3: The problem asks for the equation to find the volume of water in the aquarium, which is a rectangular box. The equation for the volume of a rectangular box is *length × width × height* (in any order). The problem and the diagram indicate that the depth of water needed is only 25 cm, so the value to use for *height* is 25 cm. Answer B uses the correct values in the order *height × length × width*.

Scientific Debate

Background

The U.S. Food and Drug Administration began approving genetically modified organisms (GMOs) for consumer use in the 1990s. Some consumer groups have protested and boycotted such foods. Several countries around the world have banned the creation, sale, or importation of GMOs. Some consumer groups have asked that all GMO foods be clearly labeled. The majority of GMO foods being sold in the United States are made with corn or soybeans that contain bacterial genes.

Scientists have mixed opinions about GMOs. However, most scientists recognize that the potential to create new and unknown types of organisms should be undertaken with careful scientific scrutiny, should involve ethical considerations, and should be regulated by governments.

Science Fiction

ACTiViTY ——— ADVANCED

Further Reading If students liked this story, encourage them to read more of McKillip's stories, such as the following:

• *Fool's Run,* Warner, 1987

• *Something Rich and Strange,* Bantam, 1994

• *Winter Rose,* Ace, 1996

Science in Action

Scientific Debate

Supersquash or Frankenfruit?

Some food that you buy may have been developed in a new way. Food producers may use genetic engineering to make food crops easier to grow or sell, more nutritious, or resistant to pests and disease. More than half of the packaged foods sold in the United States are likely to contain ingredients from genetically modified organisms.

The U.S. government has stated that research shows that these foods are safe. But some scientists are concerned that genes introduced into crop plants could cause new environmental or health problems. For example, people who are allergic to peanuts might also be allergic to tomato plants that contain peanut genes.

Math ACTiViTY

Write a survey about genetically altered foods. Ask your teacher to approve your questions. Ask at least 15 people to answer your survey. Create graphs to summarize your results.

Science Fiction

"Moby James" by Patricia A. McKillip

Rob Trask and his family live on a space station. Rob thinks that his real brother was sent back to Earth. The person who claims to be his brother, James, is really either some sort of mutated plant or a mutant pair of dirty sweat socks.

Now, Rob has another problem—his class is reading Herman Melville's novel *Moby Dick.* As he reads the novel, Rob becomes convinced that his brother is a great white mutant whale—Moby James. To see how Rob solves his problems, read "Moby James" in the *Holt Anthology of Science Fiction.*

Language Arts ACTiViTY

WRITING SKILL Read "Moby James" by Patricia A. McKillip. Then, write your own short science-fiction story about a mutant organism. Be sure to incorporate some science into your science fiction.

Answer to Math Activity

Check that student surveys ask questions for which answers can be easily tallied, such as "Do you think that genetically modified foods should be labeled in the store?" Check that students have kept records and summarized their results accurately. Give them feedback about how well their graphs communicate the data they gathered.

Answer to Language Arts Activity

Instead of collecting and grading students' stories, you may want to have them read their stories to each other or to a family member, and then ask for feedback about how much science is included in their fiction.

Lydia Villa-Komaroff

Genetic Researcher When Lydia Villa-Komaroff was young, science represented "a kind of refuge" for her. She grew up in a very large family that lived in a very small house. "I always wanted to find things out. I was one of those kids who took things apart."

In college, Villa-Komaroff became very interested in the process of embryonic development—how a simple egg grows into a complex animal. This interest led her to study genes and the way that genes code for proteins. For example, insulin is a protein that is normally produced by the human body. Often, people who suffer from diabetes lack the insulin gene, so their bodies can't make insulin. These people may need to inject insulin into their blood as a drug treatment.

Before the research by Villa-Komaroff's team was done, insulin was difficult to produce. Villa-Komaroff's team isolated the human gene that codes for insulin. Then, the scientists inserted the normal human insulin gene into the DNA of bacteria. This inserted gene caused the bacteria to produce insulin. This technique was a new and more efficient way to produce insulin. Now, most of the insulin used for diabetes treatment is made in this way. Many genetic researchers dream of making breakthroughs like the one that Villa-Komaroff made in her work with insulin.

Social Studies ACTIVITY

WRITING SKILL Do some research about several women, such as Marie Curie, Barbara McClintock, or Maxine Frank Singer, who have done important scientific research. Write a short biography about one of these women.

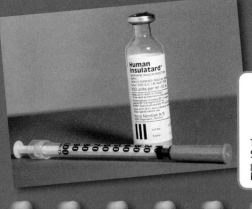

To learn more about these Science in Action topics, visit **go.hrw.com** and type in the keyword **HL5DNAF**.

Current Science

Check out Current Science® articles related to this chapter by visiting **go.hrw.com**. Just type in the keyword **HL5CS06**.

Answer to Social Studies Activity

Suggest that students do research in the library or on the Internet for information. Additional women scientists to consider are as follows:

- Jewel Plummer Cobb
- Ruth Fulton Benedict
- Emma Perry Carr
- Rosalyn Yalow

Check student biographies for accuracy, and comment on any interesting facts.

People in Science

Background

Lydia Villa-Komaroff grew up in Santa Fe, New Mexico, in a household that loved to tell family stories. One favorite was the story of Villa-Komaroff's grandfather, Encarnacion Villa, and his brush with the Mexican revolutionary Pancho Villa. Encarnacion was going to be killed by Pancho Villa's soldiers when he refused to join their fight. But when Pancho Villa heard the captive's name, he ordered his release but told him he must have many sons. Pancho Villa probably could not imagine that a granddaughter of his former captive would someday become the third Mexican-American woman to earn a Ph.D. in the United States and would go on to make many important contributions to science.

When Lydia Villa-Komaroff and her colleagues inserted the human gene that directs the production of insulin into the DNA of bacteria, they were using recombinant DNA technology. In recombinant DNA technology, researchers identify which segment of DNA is the gene that directs the production of the desired substance, cut this section out of the DNA with special enzymes, and make copies, or clones. The researchers then take one of these clones and insert it, again using special enzymes, into the correct spot on the host DNA. The researchers look for a location on the host DNA that will ensure that the host organism will read the DNA and produce the substance.

The Evolution of Living Things
Chapter Planning Guide

Compression guide:
To shorten instruction because of time limitations, omit Section 3.

OBJECTIVES	LABS, DEMONSTRATIONS, AND ACTIVITIES	TECHNOLOGY RESOURCES
PACING • 90 min pp. 106–115 **Chapter Opener**	SE **Start-up Activity,** p. 107 ◆ GENERAL	OSP **Parent Letter** ■ CD **Student Edition on CD-ROM** CD **Guided Reading Audio CD** ■ TR **Chapter Starter Transparency*** VID **Brain Food Video Quiz**
Section 1 Change over Time • Identify two kinds of evidence that show that organisms have evolved. • Describe one pathway through which a modern whale could have evolved from an ancient mammal. • Explain how comparing organisms can provide evidence that they have ancestors in common.	SE **Connection to Geology** Sedimentary Rock, p. 111 ◆ GENERAL TE **Connection Activity** Math, p. 111 ADVANCED TE **Connection Activity** Art, p. 112 ADVANCED TE **Connection Activity** Geography, p. 113 ADVANCED	OSP **Lesson Plans** (also in print) TR **Bellringer Transparency*** TR **LINK TO EARTH SCIENCE** E8 The Rock Cycle* TR **L22 Evidence of Whale Evolution: A*** TR **L23 Evidence of Whale Evolution: B*** TR **L24 Comparing Skeletal Structures*** CD **Science Tutor**
PACING • 90 min pp. 116–121 **Section 2 How Does Evolution Happen?** • List four sources of Charles Darwin's ideas about evolution. • Describe the four parts of Darwin's theory of evolution by natural selection. • Relate genetics to evolution.	TE **Demonstration** Form and Function, p. 117 ◆ GENERAL TE **Connection Activity** Social Studies, p. 117 ADVANCED TE **Connection Activity** Geography, p. 118 GENERAL SE **Quick Lab** Population Growth Versus Food Supply, p. 119 ◆ GENERAL CRF **Datasheet for Quick Lab*** TE **Activity** Natural Selection, p. 120 BASIC SE **Inquiry Lab** Survival of the Chocolates, p. 126 GENERAL CRF **Datasheet for Chapter Lab***	OSP **Lesson Plans** (also in print) TR **Bellringer Transparency*** TR **L25 Four Parts of Natural Selection*** CRF **SciLinks Activity*** GENERAL VID **Lab Videos for Life Science** CD **Science Tutor**
PACING • 45 min pp. 122–125 **Section 3 Natural Selection in Action** • Give three examples of natural selection in action. • Outline the process of speciation.	TE **Connection Activity** Real World, p. 123 GENERAL TE **Group Activity** Amazing Adaptations, p. 123 ADVANCED SE **Science in Action** Math, Social Studies, and Language Arts Activities, p. 132–133 GENERAL LB **Whiz-Bang Demonstrations** Adaptation Behooves You* ◆ GENERAL LB **Long-Term Projects & Research Ideas** Evolution's Explosion* ADVANCED	OSP **Lesson Plans** (also in print) TR **Bellringer Transparency*** TR **L26 Evolution of the Galápagos Finches*** TE **Internet Activity,** p. 123 GENERAL CD **Science Tutor**

PACING • 90 min

CHAPTER REVIEW, ASSESSMENT, AND STANDARDIZED TEST PREPARATION

CRF **Vocabulary Activity*** GENERAL
SE **Chapter Review,** pp. 128–129 GENERAL
CRF **Chapter Review*** ■ GENERAL
CRF **Chapter Tests A*** ■ GENERAL, **B*** ADVANCED, **C*** SPECIAL NEEDS
SE **Standardized Test Preparation,** pp. 130–131 GENERAL
CRF **Standardized Test Preparation*** GENERAL
CRF **Performance-Based Assessment*** GENERAL
OSP **Test Generator, Test Item Listing**

Online and Technology Resources

 Holt Online Learning

Visit **go.hrw.com** for access to Holt Online Learning, or enter the keyword **HL7 Home** for a variety of free online resources.

 One-Stop Planner® CD-ROM

This CD-ROM package includes:
• Lab Materials QuickList Software
• Holt Calendar Planner
• Customizable Lesson Plans
• Printable Worksheets
• ExamView® Test Generator
• Interactive Teacher's Edition
• Holt PuzzlePro®
• Holt PowerPoint® Resources

SKILLS DEVELOPMENT RESOURCES	SECTION REVIEW AND ASSESSMENT	CORRELATIONS
SE Pre-Reading Activity, p. 106 `GENERAL` **OSP** Science Puzzlers, Twisters & Teasers* `GENERAL`		National Science Education Standards UCP 2, 5; SAI 1, 2; LS 1a, 5a
CRF Directed Reading A* ■ `BASIC`, B* `SPECIAL NEEDS` **IT** Interactive Textbook* `Struggling Readers` **CRF** Vocabulary and Section Summary* ■ `GENERAL` **SE** Reading Strategy Paired Summarizing, p. 108 `GENERAL` **TE** Connection to Earth Science Rock Layers, p. 110 `GENERAL` **TE** Support for English Language Learners, p. 112 **SE** Math Practice The Weight of Whales, p. 113 `GENERAL` **TE** Inclusion Strategies, p. 113	**SE** Reading Checks, pp. 108, 110, 112, 114 `GENERAL` **TE** Reteaching, p. 114 `BASIC` **TE** Quiz, p. 114 `GENERAL` **TE** Alternative Assessment, p. 114 `ADVANCED` **TE** Homework, p. 115 `GENERAL` **SE** Section Review,* p. 115 ■ `GENERAL` **CRF** Section Quiz* ■ `GENERAL`	UCP 2, 4, 5; SAI 2; HNS 2; LS 2e, 3a, 3d, 4a, 5a, 5b, 5c
CRF Directed Reading A* ■ `BASIC`, B* `SPECIAL NEEDS` **IT** Interactive Textbook* `Struggling Readers` **CRF** Vocabulary and Section Summary* ■ `GENERAL` **SE** Reading Strategy Brainstorming, p. 116 `GENERAL` **TE** Connection to Geography Galápagos, p. 117 `GENERAL` **TE** Support for English Language Learners, p. 117 **TE** Reading Strategy Prediction Guide, p. 118 `GENERAL` **MS** Math Skills for Science Multiplying Whole Numbers* `GENERAL` **CRF** Reinforcement Worksheet Bicentennial Celebration* `BASIC`	**SE** Reading Checks, pp. 117, 119, 120 `GENERAL` **TE** Homework, p. 116 `GENERAL` **TE** Homework, p. 118 `ADVANCED` **TE** Reteaching, p. 120 `BASIC` **TE** Quiz, p. 120 `GENERAL` **TE** Alternative Assessment, p. 120 `ADVANCED` **SE** Section Review,* p. 121 ■ `GENERAL` **CRF** Section Quiz* ■ `GENERAL`	UCP 1, 2, 4, 5; SAI 1, 2; SPSP 2, 5; HNS 1, 2, 3; LS 2a, 2b, 2d, 2e, 3d, 5a, 5b; *Chapter Lab:* UCP 2, 4; SAI 1, 2
CRF Directed Reading A* ■ `BASIC`, B* `SPECIAL NEEDS` **IT** Interactive Textbook* `Struggling Readers` **CRF** Vocabulary and Section Summary* ■ `GENERAL` **SE** Reading Strategy Prediction Guide, p. 122 `GENERAL` **TE** Support for English Language Learners, p. 123 **TE** Inclusion Strategies, p. 124 ♦ **CRF** Critical Thinking Taking the Earth's Pulse* `ADVANCED`	**SE** Reading Checks, pp. 123, 124 `GENERAL` **TE** Reteaching, p. 124 `BASIC` **TE** Quiz, p. 124 `GENERAL` **TE** Alternative Assessment, p. 124 `ADVANCED` **SE** Section Review,* p. 125 ■ `GENERAL` **CRF** Section Quiz* ■ `GENERAL`	UCP 1, 3, 4; SPSP 4, 5; LS 2a, 2e, 3d, 4d, 5b

SciLINKS.
NSTA
www.scilinks.org
Maintained by the **National Science Teachers Association.** See Chapter Enrichment pages that follow for a complete list of topics.

Current Science®
Check out *Current Science* articles and activities by visiting the HRW Web site at **go.hrw.com.** Just type in the keyword **HL5CS07T.**

 Classroom Videos
• **Lab Videos** demonstrate the chapter lab.
• **Brain Food Video Quizzes** help students review the chapter material.

 Classroom CD-ROMs
• **Guided Reading Audio CD** (Also in Spanish)
• **Interactive Explorations**
• **Virtual Investigations**
• **Visual Concepts**
• **Science Tutor**

 Holt Lab Generator CD-ROM
Search for any lab by topic, standard, difficulty level, or time. Edit any lab to fit your needs, or create your own labs. Use the Lab Materials QuickList software to customize your lab materials list.

Visual Resources

CHAPTER STARTER TRANSPARENCY

What If . . . ?

The time is 50 million years ago. The place is a swamp in North America. Imagine yourself trekking through the steamy swamp, sidestepping snakes and spiders. Suddenly, out of the trees dashes a 182 kg giant with a huge head, a thick neck, and long, muscular legs.

What is this beast? A velociraptor? A giant sloth? A prehistoric bear? None of the above. It's a *Diatryma*, a kind of flightless bird that was common during the Cenozoic era of prehistory, 57 to 55 million years ago! *Diatryma* stood over 2 m tall and had an enormous beak and sharp claws.

Scientists know about *Diatryma* from many fossils dug up in Wyoming, New Mexico, and New Jersey. *Diatryma* was probably forced out of existence by large mammals. Though the monster bird is long gone, smaller versions of it live in poultry coops around the world. *Diatryma's* fossils indicate that it was a distant cousin of the present-day chicken!

BELLRINGER TRANSPARENCIES

Section: Change Over Time

The cockroach originated on Earth over 250 million years ago and is thriving today all over the world. A giant deer that was 2 m tall first appeared less than 1 million years ago and became extinct around 11,000 years ago. Why do you think one animal thrived and the other one perished?

Record your answer in your **science journal**.

Section: How Does Evolution Happen?

The following are characteristics that almost all humans have in common: upright walking, hair, fingerprints, binocular vision, speech. List the advantages and disadvantages of each characteristic. Do you think the advantages are greater than the disadvantages? Why or why not?

Record your responses in your **science journal**.

TEACHING TRANSPARENCIES

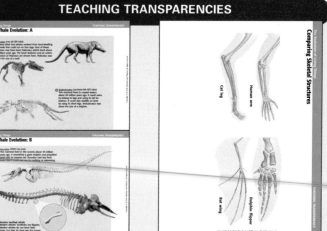

Evidence of Whale Evolution: A

Evidence of Whale Evolution: B

Comparing Skeletal Structures

TEACHING TRANSPARENCIES

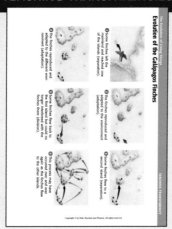

Four Parts of Natural Selection

Evolution of the Galápagos Finches

The Rock Cycle

LINK TO EARTH SCIENCE

Chapter: Rocks: Mineral Mixtures

CONCEPT MAPPING TRANSPARENCY

Use the following terms to complete the concept map below: evolution, evidence, extinct species, living species, common ancestors, DNA, time, fossil record, body structures

Planning Resources

LESSON PLANS

Lesson Plan SAMPLE

Section: Waves

Pacing

Regular Schedule: with lab(s):2 days without lab(s):3 days
Block Schedule: with lab(s):1 1/2 days without lab(s):1 day

Objectives

1. Relate the seven properties of life to a living organism.
2. Describe seven themes that can help you to organize what you learn about biology.
3. Identify the tiny structures that make up all living organisms.
4. Differentiate between reproduction and heredity and between metabolism and homeostasis.

National Science Education Standards Covered

LSInter4:Cells have particular structures that underlie their functions.
LSMat1:Most cell functions involve chemical reactions.
LSBeh1:Cells store and use information to guide their functions.
UCP1:Cell functions are regulated.
SI1: Cells can differentiate and form complete multicellular organisms.
PS1:Species evolve over time.
ESS1: The great diversity of organisms is the result of more than 3.5 billion years of evolution.
ESS2: Natural selection and its evolutionary consequences provide a scientific explanation for the fossil record of ancient life forms as well as for the striking molecular similarities observed among the diverse species of living organisms.
ST1:The millions of different species of plants, animals, and microorganisms that live on Earth today are related by descent from common ancestors.
ST2: The energy for life primarily comes from the sun.
SPSP1: The complexity and organization of organisms accommodates the need for obtaining, transforming, transporting, releasing, and eliminating the matter and energy used to sustain the organism.
SPSP6: As matter and energy flows through different levels of organization of living systems—cells, organs, communities—and between living systems and the physical environment, chemical elements are recombined in different ways.
HNS1: Organisms have behavioral responses to internal changes and to external stimuli.

PARENT LETTER

SAMPLE

Dear Parent,

Your son's or daughter's science class will soon begin exploring the chapter entitled "The World of Physical Science." In this chapter, students will learn about how the scientific method applies to the world of physical science and the role of physical science in the world. By the end of the chapter, students should demonstrate a clear understanding of the chapter's main ideas and be able to discuss the following topics:

1. physical science as the study of energy and matter (Section 1)
2. the role of physical science in the world around them (Section 1)
3. careers that rely on physical science (Section 1)
4. the steps used in the scientific method (Section 2)
5. examples of technology (Section 2)
6. how the scientific method is used to answer questions and solve problems (Section 2)
7. how our knowledge of science changes over time (Section 2)
8. how models represent real objects or systems (Section 3)
9. examples of different ways models are used in science (Section 3)
10. the importance of the International System of Units (Section 4)
11. the appropriate units to use for particular measurements (Section 4)
12. how area and density are derived quantities (Section 4)

Questions to Ask Along the Way

You can help your son or daughter learn about these topics by asking interesting questions such as the following:

- What are some surprising careers that use physical science?
- What is a characteristic of a good hypothesis?
- When is it a good idea to use a model?
- Why do Americans measure things in terms of inches and yards and meters?

ALSO IN SPANISH

TEST ITEM LISTING

TEST ITEM LISTING
The World of Science SAMPLE

MULTIPLE CHOICE

1. A limitation of models is that
   a. they are large enough to see.
   b. they do not act exactly like the things that they model.
   c. they are smaller than the things that they model.
   d. they model unfamiliar things.
   Answer: B Difficulty: 1 Section: 3 Objective: 2

2. The length 10 m is equal to
   a. 100 cm. c. 10,000 mm.
   b. 1,000 cm. d. Both (b) and (c)
   Answer: B Difficulty: 1 Section: 3 Objective: 2

3. To be valid, a hypothesis must be
   a. testable. c. made into a law.
   b. supported by evidence. d. Both (a) and (b)
   Answer: D Difficulty: 1 Section: 2 Objective: 2 1

4. The statement "Sheila has a stain on her shirt" is an example of a(n)
   a. law. c. observation.
   b. hypothesis. d. prediction.
   Answer: C Difficulty: 1 Section: 2 Objective: 2

5. A hypothesis is often developed out of
   a. observations. c. laws.
   b. experiments. d. Both (a) and (b)
   Answer: B Difficulty: 1 Section: 2 Objective: 2

6. How many milliliters are in 3.5 kL?
   a. 3,500 mL c. 3,500, 000 mL
   b. 0.0035 mL d. 35,000 mL
   Answer: B Difficulty: 1 Section: 3 Objective: 2

7. A map of Seattle is an example of a
   a. law. c. model.
   b. theory. d. unit.
   Answer: C Difficulty: 1 Section: 3 Objective: 2

8. A lab has the safety icons shown below. These icons mean that you should wear
   a. only safety goggles. c. safety goggles and a lab apron.
   b. only a lab apron. d. safety goggles, a lab apron, and gloves.
   Answer: D Difficulty: 1 Section: 1 Objective: 2

9. The law of conservation of mass says the not at least before a chemical change is
   a. more than the total mass after the change.
   b. less than the total mass after the change.
   c. the same as the total mass after the change.
   d. not the same as the total mass after the change.
   Answer: C Difficulty: 1 Section: 1 Objective: 2

10. In which of the following, areas might you find a geochemist at work?
    a. studying the chemistry of rocks c. studying biology
    b. studying forestry d. studying the atmosphere
    Answer: A Difficulty: 1 Section: 1 Objective: 2

One-Stop Planner® CD-ROM

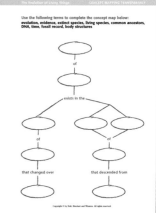

This CD-ROM includes all of the resources shown here and the following time-saving tools:

- **Lab Materials QuickList Software**
- **Customizable lesson plans**
- **Holt Calendar Planner**
- **The powerful ExamView® Test Generator**

Meeting Individual Needs

DIRECTED READING A

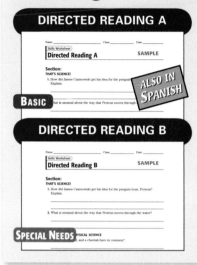

BASIC

DIRECTED READING B

SPECIAL NEEDS

VOCABULARY ACTIVITY

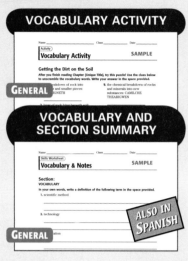

GENERAL

VOCABULARY AND SECTION SUMMARY

GENERAL

REINFORCEMENT

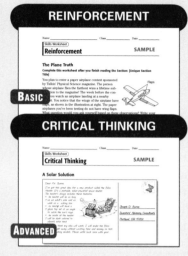

BASIC

CRITICAL THINKING

ADVANCED

SCILINKS ACTIVITY

GENERAL

SCIENCE PUZZLERS, TWISTERS & TEASERS

GENERAL

Labs and Activities

WHIZ-BANG DEMONSTRATIONS

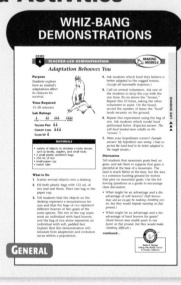

GENERAL

LONG-TERM PROJECTS & RESEARCH IDEAS

ADVANCED

DATASHEETS FOR QUICK LABS

DATASHEETS FOR CHAPTER LABS

DATASHEETS FOR LABBOOK

Review and Assessments

SECTION QUIZ

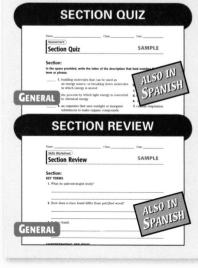

GENERAL

SECTION REVIEW

GENERAL

CHAPTER REVIEW

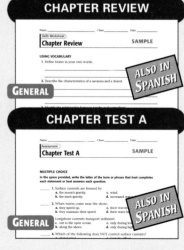

GENERAL

CHAPTER TEST A

GENERAL

CHAPTER TEST B

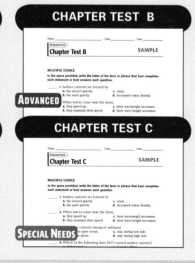

ADVANCED

CHAPTER TEST C

SPECIAL NEEDS

STANDARDIZED TEST PREPARATION

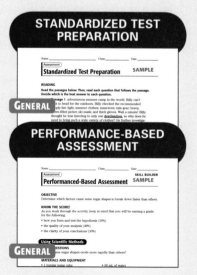

GENERAL

PERFORMANCE-BASED ASSESSMENT

GENERAL

This Chapter Enrichment provides relevant and interesting information to expand and enhance your presentation of the chapter material.

Section 1

Change over Time

Evolution of Whales and Other Mammals

• Scientists think that all mammals evolved from a shrewlike ancestor. This ancestor survived the mass extinction that wiped out the dinosaurs about 65 million years ago. This hypothesis is supported by fossils formed during and after the time of the dinosaurs.

• The first ocean-dwelling mammals appeared in the fossil record about 50 million years ago. Scientists think that these mammals were the ancestors of whales and shared an ancestor with the artiodactyl group (even-toed, hoofed mammals). However, other types of aquatic mammals, such as dugongs, manatees, and sea lions, probably evolved separately and from later branches of the mammal lineage.

• In many ways, whales are more similar to their hoofed mammal relatives than they are to fish. Similarities include internal structures, behavior, and DNA. Also, whales swim by moving their tails up and down, in a motion similar to a gallop and to the swimming of an otter, whereas fish move their tails sideways.

Homologous Structures

• *Homologous structures* are anatomical features that have similar evolutionary and embryological origins and exhibit similar anatomical patterns. For example, bird wings, human arms, whale flippers, and deer forelimbs are all homologous. However, bird wings and butterfly wings are *analogous structures* because they function similarly but are anatomically dissimilar.

• Cellular components and biochemicals may also be homologous. For example, hemoglobin molecules from different vertebrate species have similar amino-acid sequences. But hemocyanin, which transports oxygen in crabs, has a very different sequence and is therefore analogous to hemoglobin; that is, the two molecules have a similar function but different structure.

Is That a Fact!

◆ The California halibut belongs to the family Bothidae, also known as the *left-eyed flounders*. Despite the name, about 40% of California halibut adults have both eyes on the right side of their body.

Convergent Evolution

• When scientists study the fossils, skeletons, and DNA of species thought to be related, the scientists sometimes find that the organisms are not related at all. For example, the jerboa and the kangaroo rat look almost identical, but scientists have concluded that they have different ancestors. 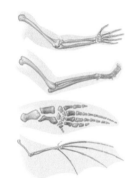 Such cases illustrate *convergent evolution*, where different species developed similar adaptations to similar environmental conditions and roles.

Frozen Fossils

• In some cases, scientists can obtain DNA from ancient tissues that have not completely decomposed or fossilized. Two Japanese geneticists are hoping to create a mammoth-elephant hybrid by using tissue from a Siberian mammoth that died and was frozen thousands of years ago. However, the chances of finding intact DNA are small, and the genetic structures of mammoths and elephants are not fully compatible.

Is That a Fact!

◆ The human appendix is a *vestigial organ,* or an organ that performs little or no apparent function but that is thought to have had a function in ancestors. The appendix is a narrow tube attached to the large intestine. In chimpanzees, gorillas, and orangutans, the appendix is an intestinal sac that helps them digest tough plant material.

Section 2

How Does Evolution Happen?

Alfred Russel Wallace

- Alfred Wallace (1823–1913) was born in England. He came from a poor family and had no formal scientific education. Though originally interested in botany, he began to study insects with the encouragement of British naturalist Henry Walter Bates, whom Wallace met when he was about 20 years old. Bates and Wallace explored the Amazon from 1848 to 1852 and found much evidence to support a theory of evolution by natural selection.

- From 1854 to 1862, Wallace traveled in the Malay Archipelago to find more evidence of evolution. In 1855, he published a preliminary essay, "On the Law Which Has Regulated the Introduction of New Species." Meanwhile, nearly 20 years after Charles Darwin's voyage on the HMS *Beagle,* Darwin was still mulling over his data. In 1858, Wallace mailed an essay to Darwin that explained Wallace's theory that natural selection pressures species to change.

- In July 1858, Wallace's essay was presented along with a paper by Darwin at a meeting of the Linnean Society in London. In the following year, after nearly two decades of delay (because of his doubts and repeated analysis), Darwin published *On the Origin of Species by Means of Natural Selection.*

Charles Lyell

- Charles Lyell (1797–1875), the eldest of 10 children, was born in Scotland and raised in England. He traveled with his father, who was a naturalist, to collect butterflies and aquatic insects. Lyell continued this informal research throughout college. Lyell's research in geology led him to the belief that natural processes occurring over millions of years have shaped Earth's features. This idea was known as *uniformitarianism.* Lyell's work influenced Darwin's formulation of the theory of natural selection.

Section 3

Natural Selection in Action

Adaptive Coloration

- Penguins, puffins, killer whales, and blue sharks are just some of the ocean animals that have white bellies and black or dark blue dorsal surfaces. This type of coloration is called *countershading.* When seen from below, the white underside helps the animal blend into the lighter sky above the water. When viewed from above, the dark coloration makes the animal difficult to see against the ocean depths.

Sexual Selection

- *Sexual selection* is the term for the selection of traits that is brought about by a specific pattern of mating. In many sexual organisms, members of one sex must compete with each other for access to mates. Biologists think this behavior results when one sex's investment in the next generation is greater than the other sex's. At an extreme, the "choosiness" of one sex may drive the evolution of traits that confer no apparent advantage to the opposite sex. The long tails and colorful plumage of many male birds are considered examples of such "runaway sexual selection."

SciLinks is maintained by the National Science Teachers Association to provide you and your students with interesting, up-to-date links that will enrich your classroom presentation of the chapter.

Visit www.scilinks.org and enter the SciLinks code for more information about the topic listed.

Topic: Species and Adaptation
SciLinks code: HSM1433

Topic: Fossil Record
SciLinks code: HSM0615

Topic: Galápagos Islands
SciLinks code: HSM0631

Topic: Darwin and Natural Selection
SciLinks code: HSM0378

Overview

Tell students that this chapter will introduce them to *evolution* —the process by which populations on Earth change over time. Evolution helps explain the variations and adaptations that we see in organisms around us and in evidence of the past.

Assessing Prior Knowledge

Students should be familiar with the following topics:

- scientific methods and models
- heredity and genetics

Identifying Misconceptions

Students may have heard that evolution is "just a theory." But in academic biology, evolution (defined as the process by which species change over time) is accepted in the way that "cell theory" is now accepted. Furthermore, the theory of evolution by natural selection (integrated with modern genetic knowledge) is considered to be strongly supported and widely accepted. Specific models, mechanisms, rates, and other aspects of evolution continue to be investigated and debated among scientists, but few biologists doubt that evolution happens.

The Evolution of Living Things

The Big Idea

Biological evolution explains how populations change over time.

About the

Can you find two eyes and a mouth in this photo? The eyes and mouth belong to an adult flounder. Adult flounders swim on their sides and have both eyes on one side of their body. These characteristics allow flounders to lie flat and still see all of their surroundings. Flounders also look like the sandy bottoms of coastal areas. These adaptations help flounders survive in their environment.

PRE-READING ACTIVITY

Graphic Organizer

Concept Map Before you read the chapter, create the graphic organizer entitled "Concept Map" described in the **Study Skills** section of the Appendix. As you read the chapter, fill in the concept map with details about evolution and natural selection.

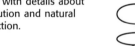

Standards Correlations

National Science Education Standards

The following codes indicate the National Science Education Standards that correlate to this chapter. The full text of the standards is at the front of the book.

Chapter Opener
UCP 2, 5; SAI 1, 2; LS 1a, 5a

Section 1 Change over Time
UCP 2, 4, 5; SAI 2; HNS 2; LS 2e, 3a, 3d, 4a, 5a, 5b, 5c

Section 2 How Does Evolution Happen?
UCP 1, 2, 4, 5; SAI 1, 2; SPSP 2, 5; HNS 1, 2, 3; LS 2a, 2b, 2d, 2e, 3d, 5a, 5b

Section 3 Natural Selection in Action
UCP 1, 3, 4; SPSP 4, 5; LS 2a, 2e, 3d, 4d, 5b

Chapter Lab
UCP 2, 4; SAI 1, 2

Chapter Review
SAI 2; SPSP 4; HNS 1, 2, 3; LS 2e, 3d, 4a, 5a, 5b, 5c

Science in Action
SPSP 2, 4, 5; HNS 1, 3

MATERIALS

FOR EACH PAIR
- cloth, white, approximately 20 cm × 20 cm
- marshmallows, colored (all same color), miniature (25)
- marshmallows, white, miniature (25)

Teacher's Note: Newspaper can be used as an alternative to marshmallows in this activity. Instead of using marshmallows, punch 25 holes from the classified section of a newspaper and 25 holes from newsprint in multiple colors, such as the Sunday comics. Instead of using cloth, use the newspaper for the background. Spread the holes on the paper, and have the "hunter" pick up as many as he or she can in 15 s. Tally the results.

Answers

1. Answers may vary, but students are likely to pick up more colored marshmallows than white ones.

2. Sample answer: The marshmallows represent organisms that could be eaten; the cloth represents the area where they live.

3. Sample answer: Many organisms in the wild blend into their surroundings by having colors or patterns that make them hard to see. This might help them hide from things trying to eat them. A weakness of this model is that it's very simple—a real "wild" environment would be more than two colors and would contain a variety of organisms.

START-UP ACTIVITY

Out of Sight, Out of Mind

In this activity, you will see how traits can affect the success of an organism in a particular environment.

Procedure

1. Count out **25 colored marshmallows** and **25 white marshmallows.**

2. Ask your partner to look away while you spread the marshmallows out on a **white cloth.** Do not make a pattern with the marshmallows. Now, ask your partner to turn around and pick the first marshmallow that he or she sees.

3. Repeat step 2 ten times.

Analysis

1. How many white marshmallows did your partner pick? How many colored marshmallows did he or she pick?

2. What did the marshmallows and the cloth represent in your investigation? What effect did the color of the cloth have?

3. When an organism blends into its environment, the organism is *camouflaged.* How does this activity model camouflaged organisms in the wild? What are some weaknesses of this model?

Chapter Starter Transparency
Use this transparency to help students begin thinking about changes in species over time.

CHAPTER RESOURCES

Technology

 **Transparencies**
- Chapter Starter Transparency

READING SKILLS

 Student Edition on CD-ROM

Guided Reading Audio CD
- English or Spanish

Classroom Videos
- Brain Food Video Quiz

Workbooks

Science Puzzlers, Twisters & Teasers
- The Evolution of Living Things GENERAL

SECTION
1

Focus

Overview

This section introduces the concept of evolution as change over time in populations of organisms. Students will survey evidence used to understand evolution and determine ancestry, including the fossil record and comparisons of organisms' physical and genetic traits.

Bellringer

Have students respond to the following prompt: "The cockroach originated on Earth more than 250 million years ago and is thriving today all over the world. A giant deer (more than 2 m tall!) evolved less than 1 million years ago and became extinct around 11,000 years ago. Why do you think one animal thrived and the other perished?"
(Accept all reasonable answers.)

Motivate

Discussion ── GENERAL

Adaptation Ask students if a polar bear could live comfortably in Hawaii. Ask if a fish could survive in a forest. Why or why not? Discuss various characteristics of animals, such as physical adaptations, that make the animals well suited for a specific environment. **LS** Verbal

What You Will Learn

● Identify two kinds of evidence that show that organisms have evolved.

● Describe one pathway through which a modern whale could have evolved from an ancient mammal.

● Explain how comparing organisms can provide evidence that they have ancestors in common.

Vocabulary

adaptation   fossil
species   fossil record
evolution

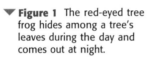
READING STRATEGY

Paired Summarizing Read this section silently. In pairs, take turns summarizing the material. Stop to discuss ideas that seem confusing.

Change over Time

If someone asked you to describe a frog, you might say that a frog has long hind legs, has bulging eyes, and croaks. But what color skin would you say that a frog has?

Once you start to think about frogs, you realize that frogs differ in many ways. These differences set one kind of frog apart from another. The frogs in **Figures 1, 2,** and **3** look different from each other, yet they may live in the same areas.

Differences Among Organisms

As you can see, each frog has a different characteristic that might help the frog survive. A characteristic that helps an organism survive and reproduce in its environment is called an **adaptation.** Adaptations may be physical, such as a long neck or striped fur. Or adaptations may be behaviors that help an organism find food, protect itself, or reproduce.

Living things that have the same characteristics may be members of the same species. A **species** is a group of organisms that can mate with one another to produce fertile offspring. For example, all strawberry poison arrow frogs are members of the same species and can mate with each other to produce more strawberry poison arrow frogs. Groups of individuals of the same species living in the same place make up a *population.*

✔ *Reading Check* How can you tell that organisms are members of the same species? (*See the Appendix for answers to Reading Checks.*)

▼ **Figure 1** The red-eyed tree frog hides among a tree's leaves during the day and comes out at night.

◄ **Figure 2** The bright coloring of the strawberry poison arrow frog warns predators that the frog is poisonous.

Figure 3 The smokey ▶ jungle frog blends into the forest floor.

CHAPTER RESOURCES

Chapter Resource File

- **Lesson Plan**
- **Directed Reading A** BASIC
- **Directed Reading B** SPECIAL NEEDS

Technology

Transparencies
- Bellringer

Workbooks

Interactive Textbook Struggling Readers

Answer to Reading Check

Organisms are members of the same species if they mate with each other and produce fertile offspring.

Adaptation

Populations constantly undergo natural selection. After two groups have separated, natural selection may act on each group in different ways. Over many generations, the separated groups may evolve different sets of traits. If the environmental conditions for each group differ, the adaptations in the groups will also differ.

Division

Over many generations, two separated groups of a population may become very different. Even if a geographical barrier is removed, the groups may not be able to interbreed anymore. At this point, the two groups are no longer the same species.

Figure 4 shows another way that populations may stop interbreeding. Leopard frogs and pickerel frogs probably had the same ancestor species. Then, at some point, some of these frogs began to mate at different times during the year.

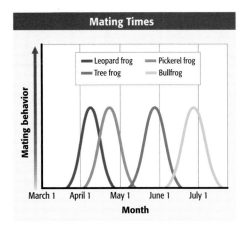

Figure 4 *The leopard frog and the pickerel frog are similar species. However, leopard frogs do not search for mates at the same time of year that pickerel frogs do.*

SECTION Review

Summary

● Natural selection explains how populations adapt to changes in their environment. A variety of examples of such adaptations can be found.

● Natural selection also explains how one species may evolve into another. Speciation occurs as populations undergo separation, adaptation, and division.

Using Key Terms

1. In your own words, write a definition for the term *speciation*.

Understanding Key Ideas

2. Two populations have evolved into two species when
   a. the populations are separated.
   b. the populations look different.
   c. the populations can no longer interbreed.
   d. the populations adapt.

3. Explain why the number of tuskless elephants in Uganda may be increasing.

Math Skills

4. A female cockroach can produce 80 offspring at a time. If half of the offspring produced by a certain female are female and each female produces 80 offspring, how many cockroaches are there in the third generation?

Critical Thinking

5. **Forming Hypotheses** Most kinds of cactus have leaves that grow in the form of spines. The stems or trunks become thick, juicy pads or barrels. Explain how these cactus parts might have evolved.

6. **Making Comparisons** Suggest an organism other than an insect that might evolve an adaptation to human activities.

SCLINKS

NSTA
Developed and maintained by the
National Science Teachers Association

For a variety of links related to this chapter, go to www.scilinks.org

Topic: Species and Adaptation
SciLinks code: HSM1433

Is That a Fact!

Some species that have adapted to live in total darkness no longer even have eyes! Just as whales have evolved into legless forms, these species have completely adapted to life without light, and some have evolved forms lacking eyes altogether. There are blind cave fish, eels, salamanders, worms, shrimp, crayfish, spiders, beetles, and crickets.

CHAPTER RESOURCES

Chapter Resource File

- Section Quiz GENERAL
- Section Review GENERAL
- Vocabulary and Section Summary GENERAL
- Critical Thinking ADVANCED

Technology

Transparencies
- L26 Evolution of the Galápagos Finches

Survival of the Chocolates

Teacher's Notes

Time Required

One or two 45-minute class periods

Lab Ratings

EASY ———————————→ HARD

Teacher Prep 🧪
Student Set-Up 🧪🧪
Concept Level 🧪🧪
Clean Up 🧪

Safety Caution

Safety concerns will vary with each design.

Preparation Notes

Be prepared for a variety of experimental designs. For example, students may wish to test which color will crack easiest under physical stress or which color will dissolve more quickly in water. This lab is an opportunity to reinforce scientific methods and practice designing experiments. Encourage students to brainstorm a variety of possible hypotheses and ways of testing the hypotheses. Have students identify scientific methods in their experiments.

Survival of the Chocolates

Imagine a world populated with candy, and hold that delicious thought in your head for just a moment. Try to apply the idea of natural selection to a population of candy-coated chocolates. According to the theory of natural selection, individuals who have favorable adaptations are more likely to survive. In the "species" of candy-coated chocolates you will study in this experiment, the characteristics of individual chocolates may help them "survive." For example, shell strength (the strength of the candy coating) could be an adaptive advantage. Plan an experiment to find out which characteristics of the chocolates are favorable "adaptations."

OBJECTIVES

Form a hypothesis about the fate of the candy-coated chocolates.

Predict what will happen to the candy-coated chocolates.

Design and conduct an experiment to test your hypothesis.

MATERIALS

- chocolates, candy-coated, small, in a variety of colors (about 100)
- items to be determined by the students and approved by the teacher

SAFETY

Ask a Question

① What might "survival" mean for a candy-coated chocolate? What are some ways you can test which chocolates are the "strongest" or "most fit" for their environment? Also, write down any other questions that you could ask about the "survival" of the chocolates.

Form a Hypothesis

② Form a hypothesis, and make a prediction. For example, if you chose to study candy color, your prediction might be similar to this: If the ___ colored shell is the strongest, then fewer of the chocolates with this color of shell will ___ when ___.

 Holt Lab Generator CD-ROM

Search for any lab by topic, standard, difficulty level, or time. Edit any lab to fit your needs, or create your own labs. Use the Lab Materials QuickList software to customize your lab materials list.

 **Karma Houston-Hughes**
Kyrene Middle School
Tempe, Arizona

CHAPTER RESOURCES

Chapter Resource File

- Datasheet for Chapter Lab
- Lab Notes and Answers

Technology

- Classroom Videos
  - Lab Video

Test the Hypothesis

3 Design a procedure to determine which type of candy-coated chocolate is most likely to survive. In your plan, be sure to include materials and tools you may need to complete this procedure.

4 Check your experimental design with your teacher before you begin. Your teacher will supply the candy and assist you in gathering materials and tools.

5 Record your results in a data table. Be sure to organize your data in a clear and understandable way.

Analyze the Results

1 **Describing Events** Write a report that describes your experiment. Be sure to include tables and graphs of the data you collected.

Draw Conclusions

2 **Evaluating Data** In your report, explain how your data either support or do not support your hypothesis. Include possible errors and ways to improve your procedure.

Applying Your Data

Can you think of another characteristic of the chocolates that can be tested to determine which type is best adapted to survive? Explain your idea, and describe how you might test it.

CHAPTER RESOURCES

Workbooks

📔 **Whiz-Bang Demonstrations**
• Adaptation Behooves You GENERAL

📔 **Long-Term Projects & Research Ideas**
• Evolution's Explosion ADVANCED

Form a Hypothesis

2. Answers may vary. The example statement is only an example for format. Students may wish to investigate a characteristic other than candy shell hardness. Help them make a prediction about their own experiment. Check that all students have formed testable hypotheses.

Test the Hypothesis

4. Answers may vary. Check that students have planned a controlled experiment and that each factor is accounted for. Also, check that they have planned for all materials they will need.

5. Answers may vary. Students should conduct their own experiment and record all procedures, observations, and results. Students should use data tables to record results where appropriate.

Analyze the Results

1. Reports may vary but should describe all parts of the experiment and present the results with tables, diagrams, or graphs as appropriate.

Draw Conclusions

2. Reports may vary but should include a conclusion that the hypothesis was supported or not. Check that student conclusions are directly related to the hypothesis and were logically drawn from the experimental results.

Chapter Review

Assignment Guide

Section	Questions
1	2–4, 6, 8, 9, 12, 13, 21, 22
2	5, 10, 11, 14, 15, 17, 23
3	1, 7, 16, 18, 19, 20

ANSWERS

Using Key Terms

1. speciation
2. natural selection
3. species
4. fossil record
5. selective breeding
6. adaptation
7. generation time

Understanding Key Ideas

8. a
9. b
10. b
11. c

USING KEY TERMS

Complete each of the following sentences by choosing the correct term from the word bank.

adaptation
evolution
generation time
species
speciation
fossil record
selective breeding
natural selection

1. When a single population evolves into two populations that cannot interbreed anymore, ___ has occurred.

2. Darwin's theory of ___ explained the process by which organisms become well-adapted to their environment.

3. A group of organisms that can mate with each other to produce offspring is known as a(n) ___.

4. The ___ provides information about organisms that have lived in the past.

5. In ___, humans select organisms with desirable traits that will be passed from one generation to another.

6. A(n) ___ helps an organism survive better in its environment.

7. Populations of insects and bacteria can evolve quickly because they usually have a short ___.

UNDERSTANDING KEY IDEAS

Multiple Choice

8. Fossils are commonly found in
   a. sedimentary rock.
   b. all kinds of rock.
   c. granite.
   d. loose sand.

9. The fact that all organisms have DNA as their genetic material is evidence that
   a. all organisms undergo natural selection.
   b. all organisms may have descended from a common ancestor.
   c. selective breeding takes place every day.
   d. genetic resistance rarely occurs.

10. Charles Darwin puzzled over differences in the ___ of the different species of Galápagos finches.
    a. webbed feet
    b. beaks
    c. bone structure of the wings
    d. eye color

11. Darwin observed variations among individuals within a population, but he did not realize that these variations were caused by
    a. interbreeding.
    b. differences in food.
    c. differences in genes.
    d. selective breeding.

12. Sample answer: Living organisms can be compared in terms of body structures with other living organisms and with organisms from the fossil record. Also, the DNA of living organisms can be compared.

Raymond Pierotti

Canine Evolution Raymond Pierotti thinks that it's natural that he became an evolutionary biologist. He grew up exploring the desert around his home in New Mexico. He was fascinated by the abundant wildlife surviving in the bleak landscape. "One of my earliest memories is getting coyotes to sing with me from my backyard," he says.

Pierotti now studies the evolutionary relationships between wolves, coyotes, and domestic dogs. Some of his ideas come from the traditions of the Comanches. According to the Comanche creation story, humans came from wolves. Although Pierotti doesn't believe that humans evolved from wolves, he sees the creation story as a suggestion that humans and wolves have evolved together. "Wolves are very similar to humans in many ways," says Pierotti. "They live in family groups and hunt together. It is possible that wolves actually taught humans how to hunt in packs, and there are ancient stories of wolves and humans hunting together and sharing the food. I think it was this relationship that inspired the Comanche creation stories."

Social Studies ACTIVITY

WRITING SKILL Research a story of creation that comes from a Greek, Roman, or Native American civilization. Write a paragraph summarizing the myth, and share it with a classmate.

To learn more about these Science in Action topics, visit **go.hrw.com** and type in the keyword **HL5EVOF**.

Current Science

Check out Current Science® articles related to this chapter by visiting **go.hrw.com**. Just type in the keyword **HL5CS07**.

Answer to Social Studies Activity
Student summaries may vary. Have students share their summaries with each other or with the entire class, and then discuss similarities between the myths.

People in Science

ACTIVITY ———— GENERAL

Have every student write or present a report on a breed of dog. The report should focus on the origin and evolution of the breed, with particular attention paid to the culture that bred it and why those characteristics were chosen. The report could also explore whether these breeds make good household pets and why. Students can easily find information on dog breeds on the Internet by searching for either the name of a breed or for "dog breeds" and visiting any of several sites that collect information on different breeds.

The History of Life on Earth
Chapter Planning Guide

Compression guide:
To shorten instruction because of time limitations, omit Section 3.

OBJECTIVES	LABS, DEMONSTRATIONS, AND ACTIVITIES	TECHNOLOGY RESOURCES
PACING • 90 min pp. 134–141 **Chapter Opener**	**SE** Start-up Activity, p. 135 ◆ GENERAL	**OSP** Parent Letter ■ **CD** Student Edition on CD-ROM **CD** Guided Reading Audio CD ■ **TR** Chapter Starter Transparency* **VID** Brain Food Video Quiz
Section 1 Evidence of the Past • Explain how fossils can be formed and how their age can be estimated. • Describe the geologic time scale and the way that scientists use it. • Compare two ways that conditions for life on Earth have changed over time.	**TE** Activity Newspaper Layers, p. 137 ◆ GENERAL **SE** Connection to Social Studies A Place in Time, p. 138 ◆ GENERAL **TE** Group Activity Detailed Geologic Timeline, p. 138 ADVANCED **SE** Quick Lab Making a Geologic Timeline, p. 139 ◆ GENERAL **CRF** Datasheet for Quick Lab* **TE** Activity Rock Collectors, p. 139 GENERAL **SE** Skills Practice Lab The Half-Life of Pennies, p. 189 ◆ GENERAL **CRF** Datasheet for LabBook*	**OSP** Lesson Plans (also in print) **TR** Bellringer Transparency* **TR** L27 Using Half-Lives to Date Fossils* **TR** L117 The Geologic Time Scale* **TR** L29 Moving Continents and Tectonic Plates* **CD** Science Tutor
PACING • 45 min pp. 142–147 **Section 2 Eras of the Geologic Time Scale** • Outline the major developments that allowed life to exist on Earth. • Describe the types of organisms that arose during the four major divisions of the geologic time scale.	**TE** Connection Activity Earth Science, p. 143 ◆ GENERAL **TE** Activity Using Maps, p. 143 ◆ GENERAL **TE** Group Activity Ancient Plants, p. 144 GENERAL **TE** Connection Activity Real World, p. 144 ◆ GENERAL **LB** Long-Term Projects & Research Ideas A Horse is a Horse* ADVANCED	**OSP** Lesson Plans (also in print) **TR** Bellringer Transparency* **SE** Internet Activity, p. 143 GENERAL **CRF** SciLinks Activity* GENERAL **CD** Interactive Explorations CD-ROM Rock On! GENERAL **CD** Science Tutor
PACING • 90 min pp. 148–153 **Section 3 Humans and Other Primates** • Describe two characteristics that all primates share. • Describe three major groups of hominids.	**TE** Activity Exploring Vision, p. 149 GENERAL **TE** Activity Primate Characteristics, p. 150 ◆ BASIC **TE** Group Activity Comparing Hominids, p. 150 ◆ GENERAL **SE** School-to-Home Activity Thumb Through This, p. 151 GENERAL **TE** Connection Activity Art, p. 151 ◆ GENERAL **TE** Activity Classifying Primates, p. 153 ADVANCED **SE** Inquiry Lab Mystery Footprints, p. 154 ◆ GENERAL **CRF** Datasheet for Chapter Lab* **SE** Science in Action Math, Social Studies, and Language Arts Activities, pp. 160–161 GENERAL	**OSP** Lesson Plans (also in print) **TR** Bellringer Transparency* **TR** L30 Comparison of Primate Skeletons* **VID** Lab Videos for Life Science **CD** Science Tutor

PACING • 90 min

CHAPTER REVIEW, ASSESSMENT, AND STANDARDIZED TEST PREPARATION

CRF Vocabulary Activity* GENERAL
SE Chapter Review, pp. 156–157 GENERAL
CRF Chapter Review* ■ GENERAL
CRF Chapter Tests A* ■ GENERAL, B* ADVANCED, C* SPECIAL NEEDS
SE Standardized Test Preparation, pp. 158–159 GENERAL
CRF Standardized Test Preparation* GENERAL
CRF Performance-Based Assessment* GENERAL
OSP Test Generator, Test Item Listing

Online and Technology Resources

 go.hrw.com **Holt Online Learning**

Visit **go.hrw.com** for access to Holt Online Learning, or enter the keyword **HL7 Home** for a variety of free online resources.

 One-Stop Planner® CD-ROM

This CD-ROM package includes:
• Lab Materials QuickList Software
• Holt Calendar Planner
• Customizable Lesson Plans
• Printable Worksheets
• ExamView® Test Generator
• Interactive Teacher's Edition
• Holt PuzzlePro®
• Holt PowerPoint® Resources

SKILLS DEVELOPMENT RESOURCES	SECTION REVIEW AND ASSESSMENT	CORRELATIONS
SE Pre-Reading Activity, p. 134 GENERAL **OSP** Science Puzzlers, Twisters & Teasers GENERAL		National Science Education Standards UCP 2, 3, SAI 1, 2; SPSP 5; HNS 3
CRF Directed Reading A* ■ BASIC, B* SPECIAL NEEDS **IT** Interactive Textbook* Struggling Readers **CRF** Vocabulary and Section Summary* ■ GENERAL **SE** Reading Strategy Reading Organizer, p. 136 GENERAL **SE** Math Practice Fractions of Fractions, p. 137 GENERAL **TE** Support for English Language Learners, p. 137 **TE** Inclusion Strategies, p. 140 **SE** Connection to Geology Mid-Atlantic Ridge, p. 141 GENERAL **MS** Math Skills for Science Radioactive Decay and the Half-Life* GENERAL **MS** Math Skills for Science Geologic Time Scale* GENERAL **CRF** Reinforcement Worksheet Earth Timeline* BASIC	**SE** Reading Checks, pp. 137, 139, 140 GENERAL **TE** Homework, p. 139 GENERAL **TE** Reteaching, p. 140 BASIC **TE** Quiz, p. 140 GENERAL **TE** Alternative Assessment, p. 141 GENERAL **SE** Section Review,* p. 141 ■ GENERAL **CRF** Section Quiz* ■ GENERAL	UCP 1, 2, 4; SAI 1, 2; HNS 1, 2, 3; LS 1a, 3d, 5b, 5c; *LabBook:* UCP 1, 3; SAI 1; LS 5c
CRF Directed Reading A* ■ BASIC, B* SPECIAL NEEDS **IT** Interactive Textbook* Struggling Readers **CRF** Vocabulary and Section Summary* ■ GENERAL **SE** Reading Strategy Mnemonics, p. 142 GENERAL **TE** Support for English Language Learners, p. 143 **SE** Connection to Oceanography Prehistoric Marine Organisms, p. 144 GENERAL **TE** Inclusion Strategies, p. 144 **SE** Math Focus Relative Scale, p. 146 GENERAL **TE** Connection to Math Another Time Scale, p. 146 ADVANCED **MS** Math Skills for Science Subtraction Review* GENERAL **CRF** Reinforcement Worksheet Condensed History* BASIC	**SE** Reading Checks, pp. 142, 145, 146 GENERAL **TE** Reteaching, p. 146 BASIC **TE** Quiz, p. 146 GENERAL **TE** Alternative Assessment, p. 146 GENERAL **SE** Section Review,* p. 147 ■ GENERAL **CRF** Section Quiz* ■	UCP 1, 2, 3, 4; SAI 1; LS 1a, 1b, 3d, 5a, 5b, 5c
CRF Directed Reading A* BASIC, B* SPECIAL NEEDS **IT** Interactive Textbook* Struggling Readers **CRF** Vocabulary and Section Summary* ■ GENERAL **SE** Reading Strategy Discussion, p. 148 GENERAL **TE** Support for English Language Learners, p. 149 **CRF** Critical Thinking Fossil Revelations* ADVANCED	**SE** Reading Checks, pp. 149, 150, 153 GENERAL **TE** Homework, p. 152 GENERAL **TE** Reteaching, p. 152 BASIC **TE** Quiz, p. 152 GENERAL **TE** Alternative Assessment, p. 152 ADVANCED **SE** Section Review,* p. 153 ■ GENERAL **CRF** Section Quiz* ■ GENERAL	UCP 2, 4, 5; SAI 1, 2; ST 1, 2; HNS 2, 3; LS 1a, 3d, 5a, 5b, 5c; *Chapter Lab:* UCP 2, 5; SAI 1; HNS 2

SCiLINKS.
NSTA
www.scilinks.org
Maintained by the **National Science Teachers Association.** See Chapter Enrichment pages that follow for a complete list of topics.

Current Science®
Check out *Current Science* articles and activities by visiting the HRW Web site at **go.hrw.com.** Just type in the keyword **HL5CS08T.**

 Classroom Videos
• **Lab Videos** demonstrate the chapter lab.
• **Brain Food Video Quizzes** help students review the chapter material.

 Classroom CD-ROMs
• **Guided Reading Audio CD** (Also in Spanish)
• **Interactive Explorations**
• **Virtual Investigations**
• **Visual Concepts**
• **Science Tutor**

 Holt Lab Generator CD-ROM
Search for any lab by topic, standard, difficulty level, or time. Edit any lab to fit your needs, or create your own labs. Use the Lab Materials QuickList software to customize your lab materials list.

6 Chapter Resources

Visual Resources

CHAPTER STARTER TRANSPARENCY

BELLRINGER TRANSPARENCIES

Section: Evidence of the Past
Imagine that you haven't cleaned your room for 30 years and you finally decide to sort through the 2 m pile of stuff on your floor. What might you find on the top of the pile? in the middle? on the bottom?

Write your responses in your **science journal.**

Section: Eras of the Geologic Time Scale
Suppose that electrical energy had never been developed. How would your life differ from what it is like now? What do you do every day that requires electricity?

Write your answers in your **science journal.**

TEACHING TRANSPARENCIES

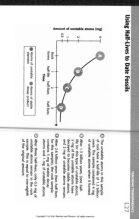

Using Half-Lives to Date Fossils

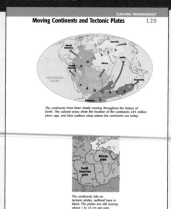

Moving Continents and Tectonic Plates L29

The continents have been slowly moving throughout the history of Earth. The colored areas show the location of the continents 245 million years ago, and blue outlines show where the continents are today.

The continents ride on tectonic plates, outlined here in black. The plates are still moving about 1 to 10 cm per year.

TEACHING TRANSPARENCIES

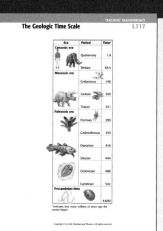

The Geologic Time Scale L117

Era	Period	Time*
Cenozoic era		
	Quaternary	1.8
	Tertiary	65.5
Mesozoic era		
	Cretaceous	146
	Jurassic	200
	Triassic	251
Paleozoic era		
	Permian	299
	Carboniferous	359
	Devonian	416
	Silurian	444
	Ordovician	488
	Cambrian	542
Precambrian time		
		4,600

*Indicates how many millions of years ago the period began

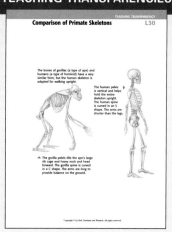

Comparison of Primate Skeletons L30

The bones of gorillas (a type of ape) and humans (a type of hominid) have a very similar form, but the human skeleton is adapted for walking upright.

The human pelvis is vertical and helps hold the entire skeleton upright. The human spine is curved in an S shape. The arms are shorter than the legs.

The gorilla pelvis tilts the ape's large rib cage and heavy neck and head forward. The gorilla spine is curved in a C shape. The arms are long to provide balance on the ground.

The Tectonic Plates; Close-up of a Tectonic Plate

LINK TO EARTH SCIENCE

Chapter: Plate Tectonics

CONCEPT MAPPING TRANSPARENCY

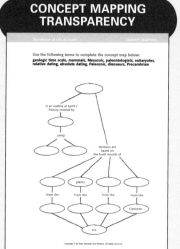

Use the following terms to complete the concept map below: **geologic time scale, mammals, Mesozoic, paleontologists, eukaryotes, relative dating, absolute dating, Paleozoic, dinosaurs, Precambrian**

Planning Resources

LESSON PLANS

Lesson Plan SAMPLE

Section: Waves

Pacing
Regular Schedule: with lab(s):2 days   without lab(s):2 days
Block Schedule: with lab(s):1 1/2 days   without lab(s):1 day

Objectives
1. Relate the seven properties of life to a living organism.
2. Describe seven themes that can help you to organize what you learn about biology.
3. Identify the tiny structures that make up all living organisms.
4. Differentiate between reproduction and heredity and between metabolism and homeostasis.

National Science Education Standards Covered
LSInter6:Cells have particular structures that underlie their functions.
LSMat1:Most cell functions involve chemical reactions.
LSBeh1:Cells store and use information to guide their functions.
UCP1:Cell functions are regulated.
SI1: Cells can differentiate and form complete multicellular organisms.
PS1:Species evolve over time.
ESS1: The great diversity of organisms is the result of more than 3.5 billion years of evolution.
ESS2: Natural selection and its evolutionary consequence provide a scientific explanation for the fossil record of ancient life forms as well as for the striking molecular similarities observed among the diverse species of living organisms.
ST1: The millions of different species of plants, animals, and microorganisms that live on Earth today are related by descent from common ancestors.
ST2: The energy for life primarily comes from the sun.
SPSP1: The complexity and organization of organisms accommodates the need for obtaining, transforming, transporting, releasing, and eliminating the matter and energy used to sustain the organism.
SPSP6: As matter and energy flow through different levels of organization of living systems—cells, organs, communities—and between living systems and the physical environment, chemical elements are recombined in different ways.
HNS1: Organisms have behavioral responses to internal changes and to external stimuli.

PARENT LETTER

Dear Parent, SAMPLE

Your son's or daughter's science class will soon begin exploring the chapter entitled "The World of Physical Science." In this chapter, students will learn about how the scientific method applies to the world of physical science and the role of physical science in the world. By the end of the chapter, students should demonstrate a clear understanding of the chapter's main ideas and be able to discuss the following topics:

1. physical science as the study of energy and matter (Section 1)
2. the role of physical science in the world around them (Section 1)
3. careers that rely on physical science (Section 1)
4. the steps used in the scientific method (Section 2)
5. examples of technology (Section 2)
6. how the scientific method is used to answer questions and solve problems (Section 2)
7. how our knowledge of science changes over time (Section 2)
8. how models represent real objects or systems (Section 3)
9. examples of different ways models are used in science (Section 3)
10. the importance of the International System of Units (Section 4)
11. the appropriate units to use for particular measurements (Section 4)
12. how area and density are derived quantities (Section 4)

Questions to Ask Along the Way

You can help your son or daughter learn about these topics by asking interesting questions such as the following:

• What are some surprising careers that use physical science?
• What is a characteristic of a good hypothesis?
• When is it a good idea to use a model?
• Why do Americans measure things in terms of inches and yards and meters?

ALSO IN SPANISH

TEST ITEM LISTING

TEST ITEM LISTING
The World of Science SAMPLE

MULTIPLE CHOICE

1. A limitation of models is that
   a. they are large enough to use
   b. they do not act exactly like the things that they model.
   c. they are smaller than the things that they model.
   d. they model unfamiliar things.
   Answer: B   Difficulty: 1   Section: 1   Objective: 2

2. The length 10 m is equal to
   a. 100 cm.   c. 10,000 mm.
   b. 1,000 cm.   d. Both (b) and (c.)
   Answer: B   Difficulty: 1   Section: 3   Objective: 2

3. To be valid, a hypothesis must be
   a. testable.   c. made into a law.
   b. supported by evidence.   d. Both (a) and (b.)
   Answer: D   Difficulty: 1   Section: 1   Objective: 2 1

4. The statement 'Sheila has a stain on her shirt' is an example of a(n)
   a. law.   c. observation.
   b. hypothesis.   d. prediction.
   Answer: B   Difficulty: 1   Section: 3   Objective: 3

5. A hypothesis is often developed out of
   a. observations.   c. laws.
   b. experiments.   d. Both (a) and (b)
   Answer: D   Difficulty: 1   Section: 3   Objective: 3

6. How many milliliters are in 3.5 kL?
   a. 3,500 mL   c. 3,500,000 mL
   b. 0.0035 mL   d. 35,000 mL
   Answer: D   Difficulty: 1   Section: 3   Objective: 2

7. A map of Seattle is an example of a
   a. law.   c. model.
   b. theory.   d. unit.
   Answer: B   Difficulty: 1   Section: 3   Objective: 3

8. A lab has the safety icons shown below. These icons mean that you should wear
   a. only safety goggles.   c. safety goggles and a lab apron
   b. only a lab apron.   d. safety goggles, a lab apron, and gloves.
   Answer: B   Difficulty: 1   Section: 1   Objective: 2

9. The law of conservation of mass says the lot of mass before a chemical change is
   a. more than the total mass after the change.
   b. less than the total mass after the change.
   c. the same as the total mass after the change.
   d. not the same as the total mass after the change.
   Answer: B   Difficulty: 1   Section: 3   Objective: 2

10. In which of the following areas might you find a geochemist at work?
    a. studying the chemicals of rocks   c. studying fishes
    b. studying forestry   d. studying the atmosphere
    Answer: B   Difficulty: 1   Section: 3   Objective: 2

One-Stop Planner® CD-ROM

This CD-ROM includes all of the resources shown here and the following time-saving tools:

• *Lab Materials QuickList Software*
• *Customizable lesson plans*
• *Holt Calendar Planner*
• *The powerful ExamView® Test Generator*

For a preview of available worksheets covering math and science skills, see pages T12–T19. All of these resources are also on the One-Stop Planner®.

Meeting Individual Needs

DIRECTED READING A

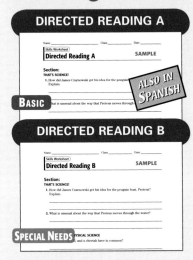

Skills Worksheet
Directed Reading A SAMPLE

Section:
THAT'S SCIENCE!
1. How did James Czarnowski get his idea for the penguin
Explain.

ALSO IN SPANISH

BASIC What is unusual about the way that Proteus moves through

DIRECTED READING B

Skills Worksheet
Directed Reading B SAMPLE

Section:
THAT'S SCIENCE!
1. How did James Czarnowski get his idea for the penguin boat, Proteus?
Explain.

2. What is unusual about the way that Proteus moves through the water?

SPECIAL NEEDS PHYSICAL SCIENCE
and, and a cheetah have in common?

VOCABULARY ACTIVITY

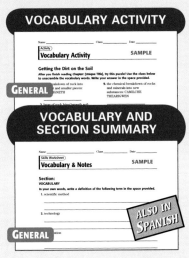

Activity
Vocabulary Activity SAMPLE

Getting the Dirt on the Soil
After you finish reading Chapter [Unique Title], try this puzzle! Use the clues below to unscramble the vocabulary words. Write your answer in the space provided.

GENERAL eakdown of rock into
and smaller pieces:
GNETH

9. the chemical breakdown of rocks
and minerals into new
substances: CAMILCHE
THEARIGWEN

2. layer of rock lying beneath soil

VOCABULARY AND SECTION SUMMARY

Skills Worksheet
Vocabulary & Notes SAMPLE

Section:
VOCABULARY
In your own words, write a definition of the following term in the space provided.

1. scientific method

2. technology

ALSO IN SPANISH

GENERAL tion

REINFORCEMENT

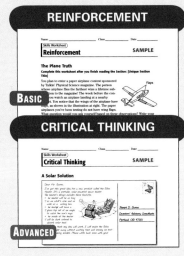

Skills Worksheet
Reinforcement SAMPLE

The Plane Truth
Complete this worksheet after you finish reading the Section: [Unique Section Title]

You plan to enter a paper airplane contest sponsored by Talkin' Physical Science magazine. The person whose airplane flies the farthest wins a lifetime subscription to the magazine! The week before the contest, you watch an airplane landing at a nearby airport. You notice that the wings of the airplane have flaps, as shown in the illustration at right. The paper airplanes you've been testing do not have wing flaps. What question would you ask yourself based on these observations? Write your

Flaps

BASIC

CRITICAL THINKING

Skills Worksheet
Critical Thinking SAMPLE

A Solar Solution

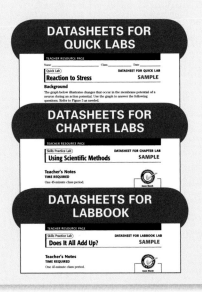

Dear Mr. Burns,
I've got this great idea for a new product called the Solar Heater. It's a portable, solar-powered space heater. The heater's design includes these features...

Joseph D. Burns
Consumer Advisory Consultant
Portland, OR 97201

Thank you also call work. I will make the Solar
Heater self-keep without putting time and money on test-
making models. Please write back soon with your

ADVANCED

SCILINKS ACTIVITY

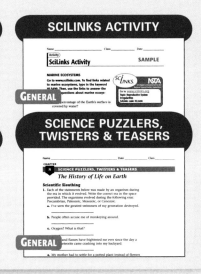

Activity
SciLinks Activity SAMPLE

MARINE ECOSYSTEMS
Go to www.scilinks.com. To find links related to marine ecosystems, type in the keyword HL5400. Then, use the links to answer the questions about marine ecosys—

GENERAL percentage of the Earth's surface is covered by water?

SciLINKS
Topic: Reproductive System
Irregularities
SciLinks code: HL5496

SCIENCE PUZZLERS, TWISTERS & TEASERS

CHAPTER
SCIENCE PUZZLERS, TWISTERS & TEASERS
The History of Life on Earth

Scientific Sleuthing
1. Each of the statements below was made by an organism during the era in which it evolved. Write the correct era in the space provided. The organisms evolved during the following eras: Precambrian, Paleozoic, Mesozoic, or Cenozoic.
a. I've seen the greatest swimmers of my generation destroyed.

b. People often accuse me of monkeying around.

c. Oxygen? What is that?

GENERAL and flames have frightened me ever since the day a
meteorite came crashing into my backyard.

e. My mother had to settle for a potted plant instead of flowers.

Labs and Activities

LONG-TERM PROJECTS & RESEARCH IDEAS

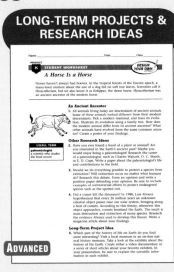

PROJECT
STUDENT WORKSHEET
A Horse Is a Horse
DESIGN YOUR OWN

Horses haven't always had hooves. In the tropical forests of the Eocene epoch, a many-toed creature about the size of a dog fed on soft tree leaves. Scientists call it *Hyracotherium*, but we also know it as *Eohippus*, the dawn horse. *Hyracotherium* was an ancient ancestor of the modern horse.

An Ancient Ancestor
1. All animals living today are descendants of ancient animals. Some of these animals looked different from their modern descendants. Pick a modern mammal, and trace its evolution. Illustrate its evolution using a family tree. How does the modern animal differ from its ancient ancestor? What other animals have evolved from the same common ancestor? Create a poster of your findings.

USEFUL TERM
paleontologist
a scientist who studies the fossil record

Other Research Ideas
2. Have you ever found a fossil of a plant or animal? Are you interested in the Earth's ancient past? Maybe you would enjoy being a paleontologist! Research the career of a paleontologist, such as Charles Walcott, O. C. Marsh, or E. D. Cope. Write a paper about the paleontologist's life and contributions to the field.

3. Should we do everything possible to protect a species from extinction? Will extinction occur no matter what humans do? Research this debate. Form an opinion and write a position paper defending your opinion. Be sure to include examples of controversial efforts to protect endangered species such as the spotted owl.

4. Did a comet kill the dinosaurs? In 1980, Luis Alvarez hypothesized that every 26 million years an unknown celestial object passes near our solar system, bringing along a host of comets. According to this theory, whenever this object approaches, comets bombard the Earth. The result is mass destruction and extinction of many species. Research the evidence Alvarez used to develop this theory. Write a magazine article about your findings.

Long-Term Project Idea
5. Which part of the history of life on Earth do you find most interesting? Visit a local museum or an on-line natural history museum. Take a look at the exhibits about the history of the Earth. Create either a video documentary or a series of short articles about your favorite exhibits. In your presentation, be sure to explain the scientific information in each exhibit.

ADVANCED

DATASHEETS FOR QUICK LABS

TEACHER RESOURCE PAGE
Quick Lab DATASHEET FOR QUICK LAB
Reaction to Stress SAMPLE

Background
The graph below illustrates changes that occur in the membrane potential of a neuron during an action potential. Use the graph to answer the following questions. Refer to Figure 3 as needed.

DATASHEETS FOR CHAPTER LABS

TEACHER RESOURCE PAGE
DATASHEET FOR CHAPTER LAB
Using Scientific Methods SAMPLE

Teacher's Notes
TIME REQUIRED
One 45-minute class period.

DATASHEETS FOR LABBOOK

TEACHER RESOURCE PAGE
DATASHEET FOR LABBOOK LAB
Does It All Add Up? SAMPLE

Teacher's Notes
TIME REQUIRED
One 45-minute class period.

Review and Assessments

SECTION QUIZ

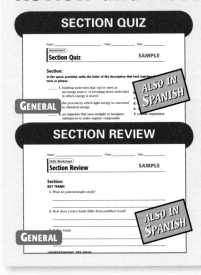

Assessment
Section Quiz SAMPLE

Section:
In the space provided, write the letter of the description that best matches
term or phrase.
1. building molecules that can be used as
an energy source, or breaking down molecules
in which energy is stored

ALSO IN SPANISH

the process by which light energy is converted
to chemical energy

GENERAL s. an organism that uses sunlight or inorganic
substances to make organic compounds

f. cellular respiration

SECTION REVIEW

Skills Worksheet
Section Review SAMPLE

Section:
KEY TERMS
1. What do paleontologist study?

2. How does a trace fossil differ from petrified wood?

GENERAL fossil.

ALSO IN SPANISH

UNDERSTANDING KEY IDEAS

CHAPTER REVIEW

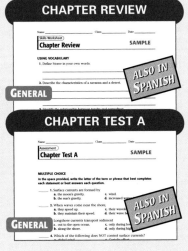

Skills Worksheet
Chapter Review SAMPLE

USING VOCABULARY
1. Define biome in your own words.

2. Describe the characteristics of a savanna and a desert.

ALSO IN SPANISH

GENERAL Identify the relationship between trophic and sunlight

CHAPTER TEST A

Assessment
Chapter Test A SAMPLE

MULTIPLE CHOICE
In the space provided, write the letter of the term or phrase that best completes
each statement or best answers each question.
1. Surface currents are formed by
a. the moon's gravity. c. wind.
b. the sun's gravity. d. increased wa

2. When waves come near the shore,
a. they speed up. c. their wave
b. they maintain their speed. d. their wave

3. Longshore currents transport sediment
a. out to the open ocean. c. only during
b. along the shore. d. only during

GENERAL 4. Which of the following does NOT control surface currents?

ALSO IN SPANISH

CHAPTER TEST B

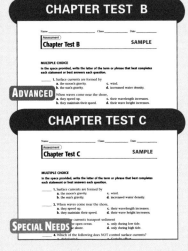

Assessment
Chapter Test B SAMPLE

MULTIPLE CHOICE
In the space provided, write the letter of the term or phrase that best completes
each statement or best answers each question.
1. Surface currents are formed by
a. the moon's gravity. c. wind.
b. the sun's gravity. d. increased water density.

When waves come near the shore,
a. they speed up. c. their wavelength increases.
b. they maintain their speed. d. their wave height increases.

ADVANCED

CHAPTER TEST C

Assessment
Chapter Test C SAMPLE

MULTIPLE CHOICE
In the space provided, write the letter of the term or phrase that best completes
each statement or best answers each question.
1. Surface currents are formed by
a. the moon's gravity. c. wind.
b. the sun's gravity. d. increased water density.

When waves come near the shore,
a. they speed up. c. their wavelength increases.
b. they maintain their speed. d. their wave height increases.

Longshore currents transport sediment
a. only during low tide.
shore. d. only during high tide.

SPECIAL NEEDS 4. Which of the following does NOT control surface currents?

STANDARDIZED TEST PREPARATION

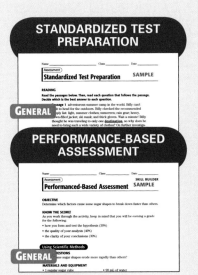

Assessment
Standardized Test Preparation SAMPLE

READING
Read the passages below. Then, read each question that follows the passage. Decide which is the best answer to each question.

age 1 adventurous summer camp in the world. Billy can't
ould last light, summer clothes; sunscreen; rain gear; heavy,
ews-filled jacket; ski mask; and thick gloves. Wait a minute! Billy
thought he was traveling to only one destination, so why does he
need to bring such a wide variety of clothes? On further investiga-

GENERAL

PERFORMANCE-BASED ASSESSMENT

Assessment
SKILL BUILDER
Performanced-Based Assessment SAMPLE

OBJECTIVE
Determine which factors cause some sugar shapes to break down faster than others.

KNOW THE SCORE!
Work through the activity, keeping in mind that you will be earning a grade
for the following:
• how you form and test the hypothesis (30%)
• the quality of your analysis (40%)
• the quality of your conclusion (30%)

Using Scientific Methods
QUESTIONS
sugar shapes erode more rapidly than others?

MATERIALS AND EQUIPMENT
1 regular sugar cube • 90 mL of water

GENERAL

This Chapter Enrichment provides relevant and interesting information to expand and enhance your presentation of the chapter material.

Section 1

Evidence of the Past

Paul Sereno

- Paul Sereno has traveled around the world to study and document dinosaur fossils. He teaches at the University of Chicago and also involves his students in searching museum collections and combing deserts for new fossils. Sereno's teams have made many important finds. One of the first was in 1988 in Argentina, where his team unearthed the skeletons of a primitive 12-foot-long dinosaur called *Herrerasaurus*. The fossils in that area shed light on how and when the Age of Reptiles began. Sereno has continued to map the dinosaur family tree by studying fossils in the Sahara, in Niger, and in Morocco.

Fossils

- Fossils may be mere traces of organisms. Preserved footprints, feces, gnaw marks, and dug-out holes can all be considered fossils. Also, traces or remains of organisms can be preserved in materials other than sedimentary rock, such as amber, tar, or lava.

- Despite what many people think, fossils are not difficult to find. Nearly every state in the United States contains an abundance of fossils. However, scientists think that only a tiny fraction of the countless organisms that lived on Earth has been preserved as fossils. Many organisms have lived and died without leaving evidence of their existence in the fossil record.

Is That a Fact!

- ◆ The oldest fossils known are structures called *stromatolites* that are more than 3.5 billion years old. These structures are bands of sedimentary rock that are very similar to layered mats formed today by colonies of bacteria and cyanobacteria.

Law of Superposition

- The law of superposition states that in a series of undisturbed sedimentary rock layers, each layer is older than the one above it and younger than the one below it. This law is based on an observation made by Nicolaus Steno, a Danish physician, in 1669.

Methods of Absolute Dating

- Radioisotope dating is the most widely used method for dating a fossil. This method analyzes samples of igneous rock found within the same rock formation as the fossil. The method differs depending on the type of chemical isotope analyzed. The older the rocks are, the less accurate the dating. Isotopes with shorter half-lives provide a more accurate range of possible ages for younger rocks and fossils. Radiocarbon dating by accelerator mass spectrometry (AMS) has become a preferred method to date with high accuracy carbon-based fossils less than 60,000 years old.

Is That a Fact!

- ◆ The beginning of the Paleozoic era is sometimes called the *Cambrian explosion*. Within the first 100 million years of this period, a large variety of multicellular organisms appeared for the first time on Earth, including most of the major groups of animals.

Modern Mass Extinction

- Because of natural selection, there will always be some extinctions of species within any given time period. Mass extinctions, however, are periods of acceleration of the average rate of extinction. Many scientists think that our planet has entered another era of mass extinction and that human activities are prompting these extinctions. Species all over the Earth are threatened by habitat destruction, pollution, and invasive nonnative species. During the last 200 years, more than 50 species of birds, more than 75 species of mammals, and hundreds of other species have become extinct.

Section 2

Eras of the Geologic Time Scale

Experiment About the Origin of Life

- In 1953, American scientist Stanley Miller devised a famous experiment to simulate life-forming conditions on the early Earth. He mixed together hydrogen, ammonia, and methane (to represent the air) and water (to represent the oceans) in a flask. When he applied electricity to the mixture, amino acids were produced. His experiment demonstrated that the building blocks of life could be created on Earth through simple chemistry. Scientists have since found amino acids in meteorites, confirming that conditions favorable for their formation also exist elsewhere.

Dinosaur Whodunit

- Scientists continue to debate various hypotheses about the cause of the mass extinction that wiped out the dinosaurs at the end of the Cretaceous period of the Mesozoic era. The prime suspect for many scientists is an asteroid that created the 185 km wide Chicxulub crater in the Yucatán area of the Gulf of Mexico. Seismology studies support this hypothesis. However, a sample of rock from the core of this crater contains evidence that the Chicxulub asteroid did not result in sudden climate change. An alternative hypothesis is that a series of asteroid impacts eventually caused climate changes that led to the mass extinction.

Is That a Fact!

- Dinosaurs are not the biggest animals ever to have lived on Earth. Blue whales are bigger than the largest known dinosaur.

Section 3

Humans and Other Primates

Clues to Migration Route

- Scientists think that people passed through the Nile Valley of Egypt when they migrated from Africa, perhaps as early as 100,000 years ago. The first evidence supporting this idea was an abundance of fossil tools and other artifacts in the Nile Valley area. Then, in 1994, the team of Belgian archaeologist Pierre Vermeersch found an ancient—but clearly human—skeleton in the area. The skeleton appears to have been a child that was ritually buried over 80,000 years ago. The skull and teeth show similarities to those of equally old human remains from East Africa and the Middle East. These similarities show a link between the African and the Middle Eastern populations.

Dawn of Language

- Scientists Matt Cartmill and Richard Kay examined fossil hominid skulls and measured the hole through which the hypoglossal nerve passes in its course from the brain to the tongue. The hypoglossal nerve enables precise control over the tongue movements needed for speech. A large hole suggests a larger nerve. Chimpanzees have much smaller holes in their skulls than do modern humans. Because australopithecine skulls have small holes, like the skulls of chimpanzees, Cartmill and Kay think that australopithecines were unable to form words.

SciLinks is maintained by the National Science Teachers Association to provide you and your students with interesting, up-to-date links that will enrich your classroom presentation of the chapter.

Visit www.scilinks.org and enter the SciLinks code for more information about the topic listed.

Topic: Evidence of the Past
SciLinks code: HSM0545

Topic: Geologic Time Scale
SciLinks code: HSM0669

Topic: Fossil Record
SciLinks code: HSM0615

Topic: Birds and Dinosaurs
SciLinks code: HSM0169

Topic: Mass Extinctions
SciLinks code: HSM0916

Topic: Human Evolution
SciLinks code: HSM0769

Overview

In this chapter, students will learn about the evidence of the history of life on earth. Students will study the geologic time scale and theories about the evolution of hominids.

Assessing Prior Knowledge

Students should be familiar with the following topics:

- cells
- the basic chemistry of life
- classification
- evolution

Identifying Misconceptions

As students learn the material in this chapter, they may have misconceptions about the length of time living organisms have been on Earth and the length of time needed for geologic processes. For example, mass extinctions are "sudden" on a geologic time scale but may take thousands of years. Furthermore, students may have misconceptions about how long humans have been on Earth. Students may also be unaware of the large amount of evidence scientists have gathered in order to determine the time and order of events in Earth's history.

6

The History of Life on Earth

The Big Idea

Geologic evidence allows us to understand the evolution of life on Earth.

About the PHOTO

What is 23,000 years old and 9 ft tall? The partial remains of the woolly mammoth in this picture! The mammoth was found in the frozen ground in Siberia in 1999. Scientists think that several types of woolly mammoths roamed the northern hemisphere until about 4,000 years ago.

PRE-READING ACTIVITY

FOLDNOTES **Layered Book** Before you read the chapter, create the Foldnote entitled "Layered Book" described in the **Study Skills** section of the Appendix. Label the tabs of the layered book with "Precambrian time," "Paleozoic era," "Mesozoic era," and "Cenozoic era." As you read the chapter, write information you learn about each category under the appropriate tab.

Standards Correlations

National Science Education Standards

The following codes indicate the National Science Education Standards that correlate to this chapter. The full text of the standards is at the front of the book.

Chapter Opener
UCP 2, 3; SAI 1, 2; SPSP 5; HNS 3

Section 1 Evidence of the Past
UCP 1, 2, 4; SAI 1, 2; HNS 1, 2, 3; LS 1a, 3d, 5b, 5c;
LabBook: UCP 1, 3; SAI 1; LS 5c

Section 2 Eras of the Geologic Time Scale
UCP 1, 2, 3, 4; SAI 1; LS 1a, 1b, 3d, 5a, 5b, 5c

Section 3 Humans and Other Primates
UCP 2, 4, 5; SAI 1, 2; ST 1, 2; HNS 2, 3; LS 1a, 3d, 5a, 5b, 5c

Chapter Lab
UCP 2, 5; SAI 1; HNS 2

Chapter Review
LS 1a, 1b, 3d, 5a, 5b, 5c

Science in Action
UCP 2; ST 2; SPSP 5; HNS 1, 3

How Did Life Begin?

Scientists think that life developed from simple chemicals in the oceans and in the atmosphere. Energy from radiation and storms could have caused these chemicals to react. Some of these reactions formed the complex molecules that made life possible. Eventually, these molecules may have joined to form structures such as cells.

The early atmosphere of the Earth did not contain oxygen gas. The first organisms did not need oxygen to survive. These organisms were *prokaryotes* (proh KAR ee OHTS), or single-celled organisms that lack a nucleus.

Photosynthesis and Oxygen

There is evidence that *cyanobacteria,* a new kind of prokaryotic organism, appeared more than 3 billion years ago. Some cyanobacteria are shown in **Figure 2.** Cyanobacteria use sunlight to produce their own food. Along with doing other things, this process releases oxygen. The first cyanobacteria began to release oxygen gas into the oceans and air.

Eventually, some of the oxygen formed a new layer of gas in the upper atmosphere. This gas, called *ozone,* absorbs harmful radiation from the sun, as shown in **Figure 3.** Before ozone formed, life existed only in the oceans and underground. The new ozone layer reduced the radiation on Earth's surface.

Multicellular Organisms

After about 1 billion years, organisms that were larger and more complex than prokaryotes appeared in the fossil record. These organisms, known as *eukaryotes* (yoo KAR ee OHTS), contain a nucleus and other complex structures in their cells. Eventually, eukaryotic cells may have evolved into organisms that are composed of many cells.

INTERNET ACTIVITY

For another activity related to this chapter, go to **go.hrw.com** and type in the keyword **HL5HISW.**

Figure 2 *Cyanobacteria are the simplest living organisms that use the sun's energy to produce their own food.*

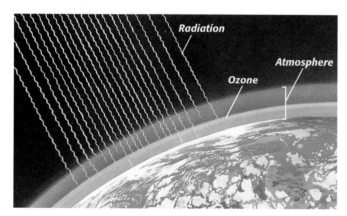

Radiation

Atmosphere

Ozone

Figure 3 *Oxygen in the atmosphere formed a layer of ozone, which helps to absorb harmful radiation from the sun.*

CONNECTION ACTIVITY
Earth Science —— GENERAL

Ancient Mountains Provide a large wall map of the world, and provide map pins or tacks in three colors. Have students locate the following mountain ranges on a map. Have students place pins on the map for each range to match the eras when each range was formed. Use the following list for reference:

Blue (Paleozoic):
• Caledonian (Scandinavia), Acadian (New York), Appalachian (eastern North America), Ural (Russia)

Green (Mesozoic):
• Palisades (New Jersey), Rockies (western North America)

Red (Cenozoic):
• Andes (South America), Alps (Europe), Himalayas (Asia)
LS Visual/Kinesthetic

Teach, continued

Group ACTIVITY — GENERAL

Ancient Plants Organize the class into five groups, and assign each group one of the following groups of paleozoic plants: club mosses, ferns, horsetails, ginkos, or conifers.

Have each group use encyclopedias or botany books to look up the plant group and prepare a poster about it. Have students include diagrams of key features of the plant group and pictures of fossils and living examples of the group. **LS** Interpersonal/Visual
Co-op Learning

CONNECTION ACTIVITY
Real World — GENERAL

Fossil Fuels The huge plants that grew in forests during the Paleozoic era later became coal. Ask students to research the locations of the world's coal deposits and to mark them on a world map. (Most of the known coal reserves are in Australia, China, Germany, Poland, Great Britain, India, Russia, South Africa, the United States, and Canada.)
LS Visual

Answer to Connection to Oceanography

Descriptions may vary.

Figure 4 *Organisms that first appeared in the Paleozoic era include reptiles, amphibians, fishes, worms, and ferns.*

Paleozoic era the geologic era that followed Precambrian time and that lasted from 542 million to 251 million years ago

The Paleozoic Era

The **Paleozoic era** (PAY lee OH ZOH ik ER uh) began about 542 million years ago and ended about 251 million years ago. Considering the length of Precambrian time, you can see that the Paleozoic era was relatively recent. Rocks from the Paleozoic era are rich in fossils of animals such as sponges, corals, snails, clams, squids, and trilobites. Fishes, the earliest animals with backbones, appeared during this era, and sharks became abundant. **Figure 4** shows an artist's depiction of life in the Paleozoic era.

The word *Paleozoic* comes from Greek words that mean "ancient life." When scientists first named this era, they thought it held the earliest forms of life. Scientists now think that earlier forms of life existed, but less is known about those life-forms. Before the Paleozoic era, most organisms lived in the oceans and left few fossils.

Life on Land

During the 300 million years of the Paleozoic era, plants, fungi, and air-breathing animals slowly colonized land. By the end of the era, forests of giant ferns, club mosses, horsetails, and conifers covered much of the Earth. All major plant groups except for flowering plants appeared during this era. These plants provided food and shelter for animals.

Fossils indicate that crawling insects were some of the first animals to live on land. They were followed by large salamander-like animals. Near the end of the Paleozoic era, reptiles and winged insects appeared.

The largest mass extinction known took place at the end of the Paleozoic era. By 251 million years ago, as many as 90% of marine species had become extinct. The mass extinction wiped out entire groups of marine organisms, such as trilobites. The oceans were completely changed.

CONNECTION TO Oceanography

Prehistoric Marine Organisms Find a variety of pictures and descriptions of marine organisms from the Cambrian period of the Paleozoic era. Choose three organisms that you find interesting. Draw or write a description of each organism. Find out whether scientists think the organism is related to any living group of organisms, and add this information to your description.

INCLUSION Strategies

- *Hearing Impaired* - *Learning Disabled*
- *Visually Impaired*

Demonstrate the superposition of geologic layers. Have student teams each use a different color of modeling clay to create a 3 in diameter circle, representing a piece of land. Ask teams to use other pieces of clay to add organisms to the land. Choose one team's model to represent early organisms, and place it where all students can see it. Then, choose a different team's model, and place it on top of the first, squashing the bottom organisms. Continue in this manner until all circles have been stacked. Slice a cross section through the stack for all to see. **LS** Kinesthetic

English Language Learners

The Mesozoic Era

The **Mesozoic era** (MES oh ZOH ik ER uh) began about 251 million years ago and lasted about 185.5 million years. *Mesozoic* comes from Greek words that mean "middle life." Scientists think that the surviving reptiles evolved into many different species after the Paleozoic era. Therefore, the Mesozoic era is commonly called the *Age of Reptiles*.

Life in the Mesozoic Era

Dinosaurs are the most well known reptiles that evolved during the Mesozoic era. Dinosaurs dominated the Earth for about 150 million years. A great variety of dinosaurs lived on Earth. Some had unique adaptations, such as ducklike bills for feeding or large spines on their bodies for defense. In addition to dinosaurs roaming the land, giant marine lizards swam in the ocean. The first birds also appeared during the Mesozoic era. In fact, scientists think that some of the dinosaurs became the ancestors of birds.

The most important plants during the early part of the Mesozoic era were conifers, which formed large forests. Flowering plants appeared later in the Mesozoic era. Some of the organisms of the Mesozoic era are illustrated in **Figure 5.**

The Extinction of Dinosaurs

At the end of the Mesozoic era, 65.5 million years ago, dinosaurs and many other animal and plant species became extinct. What happened to the dinosaurs? According to one hypothesis, a large meteorite hit the Earth and generated giant dust clouds and enough heat to cause worldwide fires. The dust and smoke from these fires blocked out much of the sunlight and caused many plants to die out. Without enough plants to eat, the plant-eating dinosaurs died out. And the meat-eating dinosaurs that fed on the plant-eating dinosaurs died. Global temperatures may have dropped for many years. However, some mammals and birds survived.

 **Reading Check** What kind of event happened at the end of both the Paleozoic and Mesozoic eras?

Figure 5 *The Mesozoic era was dominated by dinosaurs. The era ended with the mass extinction of many species.*

Mesozoic era the geologic era that lasted from 251 million to 65.5 million years ago; also called the *Age of Reptiles*

Answer to Reading Check

a mass extinction

Reteaching — BASIC

Comparing Organisms Have students compare the characteristics of each of the Paleozoic, Mesozoic, and Cenozoic organisms described in this section with those of a living descendant (if one exists) of each of the organisms. Students can organize the information in the form of a chart. **LS Visual**

Quiz — GENERAL

On index cards, write the names of several types of organisms that appeared in each the four major divisions of geologic time mentioned in this section. Then, on paper strips, write the names of the geologic time divisions, and place the strips on a table-top. Direct students to classify each organism named on a card by placing the card under the appropriate paper strip.

Alternative Assessment — GENERAL

Diorama Organize students into groups of three or four. Groups should use boxes with covers and art materials to make a diorama of one of the four major divisions of geologic time mentioned in this section. **LS Interpersonal/Kinesthetic**

Answer to Reading Check

"recent life"

Figure 6 *Many types of mammals evolved during the Cenozoic era.*

The Cenozoic Era

The **Cenozoic era** (SEN uh ZOH ik ER uh) began about 65 million years ago and continues today. *Cenozoic* comes from Greek words that mean "recent life." Scientists have more information about the Cenozoic era than about any of the previous eras. Fossils from the Cenozoic era formed recently in geologic time, so they are found in rock layers closer to the Earth's surface. The closer the fossils are to the surface, the easier they are to find.

During the Cenozoic era, many kinds of mammals, birds, insects, and flowering plants appeared. Some organisms that appeared in the Cenozoic era are shown in **Figure 6.**

✓ Reading Check What does *Cenozoic* mean?

The Age of Mammals

The Cenozoic era is sometimes called the *Age of Mammals.* Mammals have dominated the Cenozoic era the way reptiles dominated the Mesozoic era. Early Cenozoic mammals were small, forest dwellers. Larger mammals appeared later in the era. Some of these larger mammals had long legs for running, teeth that were specialized for eating different kinds of food, and large brains. Cenozoic mammals have included mastodons, saber-toothed cats, camels, giant ground sloths, and small horses.

MATH FOCUS

Relative Scale It's hard to imagine 4.6 billion years. One way is to use a *relative scale*. For example, we can represent all of Earth's history by using the 12 h shown on a clock. The scale would begin at noon, representing 4.6 billion years ago, and end at midnight, representing the present. Because 12 h represent 4.6 billion years, 1 h represents about 383 million years. (Hint: 4.6 billion ÷ 12 = 383 million) So, what time on the clock represents the beginning of the Paleozoic era, 543 million years ago?

Step 1: Write the ratio.

$$\frac{x}{543{,}000{,}000 \text{ years}} = \frac{1 \text{ h}}{383{,}000{,}000 \text{ years}}$$

Step 2: Solve for *x*.

$$x = \frac{543{,}000{,}000 \text{ years} \times 1 \text{ h}}{383{,}000{,}000 \text{ years}} = 1.42 \text{ h}$$

Step 3: Convert the answer to the clock scale.

$$1.42 \text{ h} = 1 \text{ h} + (0.42 \times 60 \text{ min/h})$$
$$1.42 \text{ h} = 1 \text{ h } 25 \text{ min}$$

So, the Paleozoic era began 1 h 25 min before midnight, at about 10:35.

Now It's Your Turn

1. Use this method to calculate the relative times at which the Mesozoic and Cenozoic eras began.

Answer to Math Focus

Mesozoic:

12 h − [(348 ÷ 383) × 60] min = 11:21

Cenozoic:

12 h − [(65 ÷ 383) × 60] min = 11:50

CONNECTION to Math — ADVANCED

Another Time Scale Have students calculate the length of the major divisions of geologic time relative to a 365-day calendar. They should state the month and day that each of the eras began. Use the Math Focus as an example, and provide a calendar for reference. Also, have students calculate the day that humans appeared (about 150,000 years ago). (Precambrian: Jan. 1; Paleozoic: Nov. 16; Mesozoic: Dec. 12; Cenozoic: Dec. 26; humans appeared: Dec. 31) **LS Logical**

A Variety of Early Hominids

Many australopithecines and other types of hominids lived at the same time. Some australopithecines had slender bodies. They had humanlike jaws and teeth but had small, apelike skulls. They probably lived in forests and grasslands and ate a vegetarian diet. Scientists think that some of these types of hominids may have been the ancestors of modern humans.

Some early hominids had large bodies and massive teeth and jaws. They had a unique skull structure and relatively small brains. Most of these types of hominids lived in tropical forests and probably ate tough plant material, such as roots. Scientists do not think that these large-bodied hominids are the ancestors of modern humans.

Global Hominids

About 2.4 million years ago, a new group of hominids appeared. These hominids were similar to the slender australopithecines but were more humanlike. These new hominids had larger and more complex brains, rounder skulls, and flatter faces than early hominids. They showed advanced tool-making abilities and walked upright.

These new hominids were members of the group *Homo,* which includes modern humans. Fossil evidence indicates that several members of the *Homo* group existed at the same time and on several continents. Members of this group were probably scavengers that ate a variety of foods. Some of these hominids may have adapted to climate change by migrating and changing the way they lived.

An early member of this new group was *Homo habilis* (HOH moh HAB uh luhs), which lived about 2.4 million years ago. About 1.8 million years ago, a hominid called *Homo erectus* (HOH moh i REK tuhs) appeared. This type of hominid could grow as tall as modern humans do. A museum creation of a member of *Homo erectus* is shown in **Figure 5.** No one knows what early hominids looked like. Scientists construct models based on skulls and other evidence.

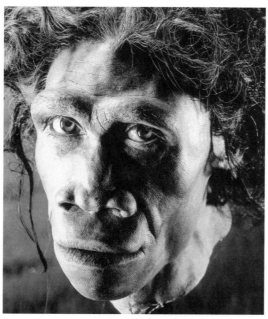

Figure 5 *Fossils of a hominid known as* Homo erectus *have been found in Africa, Europe, and Asia.*

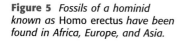

Reteaching — BASIC

PORTFOLIO **Timeline** Have students make a timeline that shows the order of appearance of the primates discussed in the chapter. When students have finished their timelines, have them review the timeline of another student. **LS** Visual

Quiz — GENERAL

Among primates, what is distinctive about hominids?
(The main characteristic that distinguishes hominids from other primates is walking upright on two legs as their main way of moving around.)

Alternative Assessment — ADVANCED

Hominid Poster Have students construct a poster with a detailed timeline of the appearance of different types of primates and hominids. Ask students to include pictures and information about the distinguishing characteristics of each group. Encourage students to conduct additional research to find the latest discoveries. **LS** Visual/Logical

Recent Hominids

As recently as 30,000 years ago, two types of hominids may have lived in the same areas at the same time. Both had the largest brains of any hominids and made advanced tools, clothing, and art. Scientists think that modern humans may have descended from one of these two types of hominids.

Neanderthals

One recent hominid is known as *Neanderthal* (nee AN duhr TAWL). Neanderthals lived in Europe and western Asia. They may have lived as early as 230,000 years ago. They hunted large animals, made fires, and wore clothing. They also may have cared for the sick and elderly and buried their dead with cultural rituals. About 30,000 years ago, Neanderthals disappeared. No one knows what caused their extinction.

Early and Modern Humans

Modern humans are classified as the species **Homo sapiens** (HOH moh SAY pee UHNZ). The earliest *Homo sapiens* existed in Africa 100,000 to 160,000 years ago. The group migrated out of Africa sometime between 40,000 and 100,000 years ago. Compared with Neanderthals, *Homo sapiens* has a smaller and flatter face, and has a skull that is more rounded. Of all known hominids, only *Homo sapiens* still exists.

Early *Homo sapiens* created large amounts of art. Early humans produced sculptures, carvings, paintings, and clothing such as that shown in **Figure 6.** The preserved villages and burial grounds of early humans show that they had an organized and complex society.

Homo sapiens the species of hominids that includes modern humans and their closest ancestors and that first appeared about 100,000 to 160,000 years ago

Figure 6 *These photos show museum recreations of early* Homo sapiens.

Homework — GENERAL

Writing **Future Scientists** Have students write a page from an anthropologist's journal that will be written 100,000 years in the future. Tell students that the anthropologist is studying an archaeological site that contains the remains or traces of people from today. Suggest that students describe the scientist's thoughts and hypotheses about the site.
LS Visual   **PORTFOLIO**

Science Bloopers

A skull of a *Homo sapiens* who had dental problems was found in Zambia. There was a hole in one side of the skull and signs of a partially healed abscess. This skull was made famous by a writer who imagined that the hole was caused by a bullet shot from an interplanetary visitor's gun 120,000 years ago.

Drawing the Hominid Family Tree

Scientists review their hypotheses when they learn something new about a group of organisms and their related fossils. As more hominid fossils are discovered, there are more features to compare. Sometimes, scientists add details to the relationships they see between each group. Sometimes, new groups of hominids are recognized. Human evolution was once thought to be a line of descent from ancient primates to modern humans. But scientists now speak of a "tree" or even a "bush" to describe the evolution of various hominids in the fossil record.

✓ Reading Check What is likely to happen when a new hominid fossil is discovered?

Answer to Reading Check
Sample Answer: Scientists will review their ideas about the evolution of hominids.

SECTION Review

Summary

- Humans, apes, and monkeys are primates. Almost all primates have opposable thumbs and binocular vision.

- Hominids, a subgroup of primates, include humans and their humanlike ancestors. The oldest known hominid fossils may be 7 million years old.

- Early hominids included australopithecines and the *Homo* group.

- Early *Homo sapiens* did not differ very much from present-day humans. *Homo sapiens* is the only type of hominid living today.

Using Key Terms

1. Use each of the following words in the same sentence: *primate, hominid,* and *Homo sapiens.*

Understanding Key Ideas

2. The unique characteristics of primates are
   a. bipedalism and thumbs.
   b. opposable thumbs.
   c. opposable thumbs and binocular vision.
   d. opposable toes and thumbs.

3. Describe the major evolutionary developments from early hominids to modern humans.

4. Compare members of the *Homo* group with australopithecines.

Critical Thinking

5. **Forming Hypotheses** Suggest some reasons why Neanderthals might have become extinct.

6. **Making Inferences** Imagine you are a scientist excavating an ancient campsite. What might you infer about the people who used the site if you found the charred bones of large animals and various stone blades among human fossils?

Interpreting Graphics

The figure below shows a possible ancestral relationships between humans and some modern apes. Use this figure to answer the questions that follow.

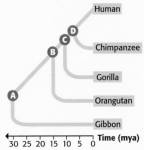

7. Which letter represents the ancestor of all the apes?

8. To which living ape are gorillas most closely related?

For a variety of links related to this chapter, go to www.scilinks.org

Topic: Human Evolution
SciLinks code: HSM0769

Answers to Section Review

1. Sample answer: *Homo sapiens* is the only living type of hominid but not the only living type of primate.

2. c

3. walking upright, larger brains, changed diet, using tools, and culture

4. Sample answer: Compared to australopithecines, *Homo* were larger, had larger brains and different skull shapes, moved out of Africa and into other continents, and used tools.

5. Sample answer: They may have been killed off by larger animals, or they may have run out of food and starved to extinction.

6. Sample answer: It is possible that the people had hunted animals for food.

7. A

8. chimpanzee

ACTiViTy ——— ADVANCED

Classifying Primates Have students find out the family or genus of the apes and hominids mentioned in this section.

- Apes: family Pongidae (great apes; includes orangutans, gorillas, chimpanzees)

- Hominids: family Hominidae

- Australopithecines: genus *Australopithecus* (slender) and genus *Paranthropus* (robust)

- Homo group: genus *Homo* (includes species *Homo habilis, Homo erectus, Homo neanderthalensis,* and *Homo sapiens*)

LS Verbal

CHAPTER RESOURCES

Chapter Resource File

- Section Quiz GENERAL
- Section Review GENERAL
- Vocabulary and Section Summary GENERAL
- Critical Thinking ADVANCED

Mystery Footprints

Teacher's Notes

Time Required

Two 45-minute class periods

Lab Ratings

EASY ———————→ HARD

Teacher Prep 🧪🧪🧪
Student Set-Up 🧪🧪
Concept Level 🧪🧪
Clean Up 🧪🧪

Preparation Notes

To set up this lab, you will need to either find a sandy area outside or construct a long, shallow sandbox out of wood or cardboard. You may prefer to perform this activity outside because it is likely to be messy. Ask a boy and a girl (preferably students who are not in your science class) or two adults, one male and one female, to walk through the sand with their bare feet. The sand should be about 16 cm deep, and the area to be walked through should be long enough that three or four footprints can be seen in the sand. Slightly moistened sand will hold the best footprints. You may want to make the footprints more permanent by using plaster of Paris. If you do not have access to sand, look for a type of soil that will hold a footprint.

OBJECTIVES

Form a hypothesis to explain observations of traces left by other organisms.

Design and **conduct** an experiment to test one of these hypotheses.

Analyze and **communicate** the results in a scientific way.

MATERIALS

• ruler, metric or meterstick
• sand, slightly damp
• large box, at least 1 m² or large enough to contain 3 or 4 footprints

SAFETY

Mystery Footprints

Sometimes, scientists find clues preserved in rocks that are evidence of the activities of organisms that lived thousands of years ago. Evidence such as preserved footprints can provide important information about an organism. Imagine that your class has been asked by a group of scientists to help study some human footprints. These footprints were found embedded in rocks in an area just outside of town.

Ask a Question

① Your teacher will give you some mystery footprints in sand. Examine the mystery footprints. Brainstorm what you might learn about the people who walked on this patch of sand.

Form a Hypothesis

② As a class, formulate several testable hypotheses about the people who left the footprints. Form groups of three people, and choose one hypothesis for your group to investigate.

Test the Hypothesis

③ Draw a table for recording your data. For example, if you have two sets of mystery footprints, your table might look similar to the one below.

Mystery Footprints		
	Footprint set 1	**Footprint set 2**
Length		
Width		
Depth of toe	DO NOT WRITE IN BOOK	
Depth of heel		
Length of stride		

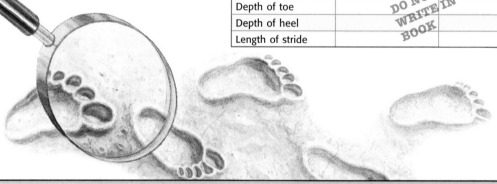

Holt Lab Generator CD-ROM

Search for any lab by topic, standard, difficulty level, or time. Edit any lab to fit your needs, or create your own labs. Use the Lab Materials QuickList software to customize your lab materials list.

Maurine Marchani
Raymond Park Middle School
Indianapolis, Indiana

CHAPTER RESOURCES

Chapter Resource File

 • **Datasheet for Chapter Lab**
• **Lab Notes and Answers**

Technology

 Classroom Videos
• Lab Video

• The Half-Life of Pennies

SKILLS DEVELOPMENT RESOURCES	SECTION REVIEW AND ASSESSMENT	CORRELATIONS
SE **Pre-Reading Activity,** p. 162 `GENERAL` OSP **Science Puzzlers, Twisters & Teasers** `GENERAL`		National Science Education Standards UCP 1
CRF **Directed Reading A*** ■ `BASIC`**, B*** `SPECIAL NEEDS` IT **Interactive Textbook*** `Struggling Readers` CRF **Vocabulary and Section Summary*** ■ `GENERAL` SE **Reading Strategy** Reading Organizer, p. 164 `GENERAL` TE **Connection to Math,** p. 165 `BASIC` TE **Support for English Language Learners,** p. 167 TE **Inclusion Strategies,** p. 168 MS **Math Skills for Science** A Shortcut for Multiplying Large Numbers* `GENERAL`	SE **Reading Checks,** pp. 164, 167, 168 `GENERAL` TE **Reteaching,** p. 168 `BASIC` TE **Quiz,** p. 168 `GENERAL` TE **Alternative Assessment,** p. 168 `GENERAL` SE **Section Review,*** p. 169 ■ `GENERAL` CRF **Section Quiz*** ■ `GENERAL`	UCP 1; SAI 2; HNS 1, 2, 3; LS 5a; *Chapter Lab:* UPC 1; SAI 1
CRF **Directed Reading A*** ■ `BASIC`**, B*** `SPECIAL NEEDS` IT **Interactive Textbook*** `Struggling Readers` CRF **Vocabulary and Section Summary*** ■ `GENERAL` SE **Reading Strategy** Reading Organizer, p. 170 `GENERAL` TE **Reading Strategy** Prediction Guide, p. 171 `BASIC` TE **Support for English Language Learners,** p. 172 SE **Math Practice** Ring-Around-the-Sequoia, p. 173 `GENERAL` TE **Inclusion Strategies,** p. 173 MS **Math Skills for Science** Arithmetic with Decimals* `GENERAL` CRF **Reinforcement Worksheet** Keys to the Kingdoms* `BASIC` CRF **Critical Thinking** A Breach on Planet Biome* `ADVANCED`	SE **Reading Checks,** pp. 171, 173, 175 `GENERAL` TE **Homework,** p. 172 `ADVANCED` TE **Reteaching,** p. 174 `BASIC` TE **Quiz,** p. 174 `GENERAL` TE **Alternative Assessment,** p. 174 `GENERAL` SE **Section Review,*** p. 175 ■ `GENERAL` CRF **Section Quiz*** ■ `GENERAL`	UCP 5; SAI 1; HNS 1, 2; LS 1b, 1f, 2a, 2c, 4b, 4c, 4d, 5b; *LabBook:* UCP 1; SAI 1

SCI LINKS.
NSTA
www.scilinks.org
Maintained by the **National Science Teachers Association.** See Chapter Enrichment pages that follow for a complete list of topics.

Current Science®
Check out **Current Science** articles and activities by visiting the HRW Web site at **go.hrw.com.** Just type in the keyword **HL5CS09T.**

 Classroom Videos
• **Lab Videos** demonstrate the chapter lab.
• **Brain Food Video Quizzes** help students review the chapter material.

 Classroom CD-ROMs
• **Guided Reading Audio CD** (Also in Spanish)
• **Interactive Explorations**
• **Virtual Investigations**
• **Visual Concepts**
• **Science Tutor**

 Holt Lab Generator CD-ROM
Search for any lab by topic, standard, difficulty level, or time. Edit any lab to fit your needs, or create your own labs. Use the Lab Materials QuickList software to customize your lab materials list.

Visual Resources

CHAPTER STARTER TRANSPARENCY

This Really Happened!

Skunks have been thrown out of their family. It wasn't their awful smell that got them thrown out, though. It was their DNA.

Skunks were once thought to be most closely related to weasels, ferrets, minks, badgers, and otters. Those furry, short-legged, long-bodied, meat-eating mammals are grouped together in a family called Mustelidae (moo STEL i dee). Mustelidae is from the Latin word for "mouse." Skunks were classified along with weasels and ferrets because they all share several physical characteristics with mice, such as short, round ears and short legs.

However, a researcher at the University of New Mexico's Museum of Southwestern Biology discovered that the DNA of skunks is very different from the DNA of the other members of Mustelidae. By comparing the DNA of different species, scientists can tell how closely related the species are. The DNA of two closely related animals—a house cat and a tiger, for example—are more similar than the DNA of two animals that are distantly related—such as a house cat and a chicken.

So where does that leave the little striped stinkers? Right in their own, newly created scientific family—Mephitidae (me FIT i dee). Mephitid is from the Latin word that means "bad odor"!

In this chapter you will learn why scientific names are important and how scientists classify organisms. You will also learn about the six major kingdoms into which organisms are classified.

BELLRINGER TRANSPARENCIES

Section: Sorting It All Out

Think about the different ways humans classify things. List five groups of things that humans classify, such as library books, department store merchandise, and addresses. Is there such a thing as too much classification? What happens when you put something in the wrong group? Can objects or ideas belong in more than one group at the same time?

Record your responses in your **science journal.**

Section: The Six Kingdoms

List seven musical artists, bands, or acts. Categorize the names on your list by style of music. Describe the categories you chose, and explain which bands might fit into more than one category.

Record your responses in your **science journal.**

TEACHING TRANSPARENCIES

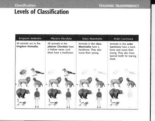

Levels of Classification

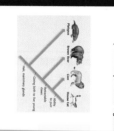

Evolutionary Relationships Between Organisms

TEACHING TRANSPARENCIES

A Dichotomous Key

Intrusive Igneous Rock Bodies

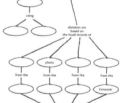

LINK TO EARTH SCIENCE

Chapter: Rocks: Mineral Mixtures

CONCEPT MAPPING TRANSPARENCY

Use the following terms to complete the concept map below: geologic time scale, mammals, Mesozoic, paleontologists, eukaryotes, relative dating, absolute dating, Paleozoic, dinosaurs, Precambrian

Planning Resources

LESSON PLANS

Lesson Plan   SAMPLE

Section: Waves

Pacing

Regular Schedule: with lab(s):2 days   without lab(s)1 days
Block Schedule: with lab(s):1 1/2 days   without lab(s)1 day

Objectives

1. Relate the seven properties of life to a living organism.
2. Describe seven themes that can help you to organize what you learn about biology.
3. Identify the tiny structures that make up all living organisms.
4. Differentiate between reproduction and heredity and between metabolism and homeostasis.

National Science Education Standards Covered

LSInter6:Cells have particular structures that underlie their functions.
LSMat1:Most cell functions involve chemical reactions.
LSBeh1:Cells store and use information to guide their functions.
UCP1:Cell functions are regulated.
SI: Cells can differentiate and form complete multicellular organisms.
PS1: Species evolve over time.
ESS1: The great diversity of organisms is the result of more than 3.5 billion years of evolution.
ESS2: Natural selection and its evolutionary consequences provide a scientific explanation for the fossil record of ancient life forms as well as for the striking molecular similarities observed among the diverse species of living organisms.
ST1: The millions of different species of plants, animals, and microorganisms that live on Earth today are related by descent from common ancestors.
ST2: The energy for life primarily comes from the sun.
SPSP1: The complexity and organization of organisms accommodates the need for obtaining, transforming, transporting, releasing, and eliminating the matter and energy used to sustain the organism.
SPSP6: As matter and energy flows through different levels of organization of living systems—cells, organs, communities—and between living systems and the physical environment, chemical elements are recombined in different ways.
HNS1: Organisms have behavioral responses to internal changes and to external stimuli.

PARENT LETTER

SAMPLE

Dear Parent,

Your son's or daughter's science class will soon begin exploring the chapter entitled "The World of Physical Science." In this chapter, students will learn about how the scientific method applies to the world of physical science and the role of physical science in the world. By the end of the chapter, students should demonstrate a clear understanding of the chapter's main ideas and be able to discuss the following topics:

1. physical science in the study of energy and matter (Section 1)
2. the role of physical science in the world around them (Section 1)
3. careers that rely on physical science (Section 1)
4. the steps used in the scientific method (Section 2)
5. examples of technology (Section 2)
6. how the scientific method is used to answer questions and solve problems (Section 2)
7. how our knowledge of science changes over time (Section 2)
8. how models represent real objects or systems (Section 3)
9. examples of different ways models are used in science (Section 3)
10. the importance of the International System of Units (Section 4)
11. the appropriate units to use for particular measurements (Section 4)
12. how area and density are derived quantities (Section 4)

Questions to Ask Along the Way

You can help your son or daughter learn about these topics by asking interesting questions such as the following:

• What are some surprising careers that use physical science?
• What is a characteristic of a good hypothesis?
• When is it a good idea to use a model?
• Why do Americans measure things in terms of inches and yards instead of centimeters and meters?

ALSO IN SPANISH

TEST ITEM LISTING

TEST ITEM LISTING
The World of Science   SAMPLE

MULTIPLE CHOICE

1. A limitation of models is that
   a. they are large enough to use
   b. they do not act exactly like the things they model.
   c. they are smaller than the things that they model.
   d. they model unfamiliar things.

2. The length 10 m is equal to
   a. 100 cm.   c. 10,000 mm.
   b. 1,000 cm.   d. Both (b) and (c)
   Answer: B   Difficulty: 1   Section: 3   Objective: 2

3. To be valid, a hypothesis must be
   a. testable.   c. made into a law.
   b. supported by evidence.   d. Both (a) and (b).
   Answer: B   Difficulty: 1   Section: 2   1

4. The statement "Sheila has a stain on her shirt" is an example of a(n)
   a. law   c. observation
   b. hypothesis.   d. prediction.
   Answer: B   Difficulty: 1   Section: 2   Objective: 2

5. A hypothesis is often developed out of
   a. observations.   c. laws.
   b. experiments.   d. Both (a) and (b)
   Answer: B   Difficulty: 1   Section: 2   Objective: 2

6. How many milliliters are in 3.5 kL?
   a. 3,500 mL   c. 3,500, 000 mL
   b. 0.0035 mL   d. 35,000 mL.
   Answer: B   Difficulty: 1   Section: 3   Objective: 2

7. A map of Seattle is an example of a
   a. law   c. model
   b. theory.   d. unit.
   Answer: B   Difficulty: 1   Section: 3   Objective: 2

8. A lab has the safety icons shown below. These icons mean that you should wear
   a. only safety goggles.   c. safety goggles and a lab apron.
   b. only a lab apron.   d. safety goggles, a lab apron, and gloves
   Answer: B   Difficulty: 1   Section: 3   Objective: 2

9. The law of conservation of mass says the lot of mass before a chemical change is
   a. more than the total mass after the change.
   b. less than the total mass after the change.
   c. the same as the total mass after the change.
   d. not the same as the total mass after the change.
   Answer: B   Difficulty: 1   Section: 3   Objective: 2

10. In which of the following areas might you find a geochemist at work?
    a. studying the chemistry of rocks   c. studying fishes
    b. studying forestry   d. studying the atmosphere
    Answer: B   Difficulty: 1   Section: 3   Objective: 2

One-Stop Planner® CD-ROM

This CD-ROM includes all of the resources shown here and the following time-saving tools:

• Lab Materials QuickList Software
• Customizable lesson plans
• Holt Calendar Planner
• The powerful ExamView® Test Generator

Meeting Individual Needs

DIRECTED READING A
Skills Worksheet
Directed Reading A — SAMPLE

Section:
THAT'S SCIENCE!
1. How did James Czarnowski get his idea for the penguin... Explain.

ALSO IN SPANISH

BASIC

...that is unusual about the way that Proteus moves through the w...

DIRECTED READING B
Skills Worksheet
Directed Reading B — SAMPLE

Section:
THAT'S SCIENCE!
1. How did James Czarnowski get his idea for the penguin boat, Proteus? Explain.

2. What is unusual about the way that Proteus moves through the water?

SPECIAL NEEDS PHYSICAL SCIENCE

...and a cheetah have in common?

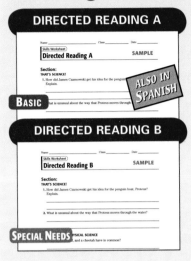

VOCABULARY ACTIVITY
Activity
Vocabulary Activity — SAMPLE

Getting the Dirt on the Soil
After you finish reading Chapter: [Unique Title], try this puzzle! Use the clues below to unscramble the vocabulary words. Write your answer in the space provided.

...breakdown of rock into ...and smaller pieces: IGNETH
9. the chemical breakdown of rocks and minerals into new substances: CAMILCHE THEARIGWEN

GENERAL

VOCABULARY AND SECTION SUMMARY
Skills Worksheet
Vocabulary & Notes — SAMPLE

Section:
VOCABULARY
In your own words, write a definition of the following term in the space provided.

1. scientific method

2. technology

3. observation

ALSO IN SPANISH

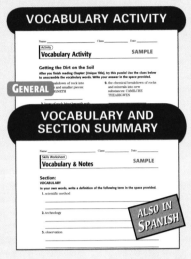

REINFORCEMENT
Skills Worksheet
Reinforcement — SAMPLE

The Plane Truth
Complete this worksheet after you finish reading the Section: [Unique Section Title]

You plan to enter a paper airplane contest sponsored by Talkin' Physical Science magazine. The person whose airplane flies the farthest wins a lifetime subscription to the magazine! The week before the contest, you watch an airplane landing at a nearby... You notice that the wings of the airplane have flaps, as shown in the illustration at right. The paper airplanes you've been testing do not have wing flaps. What question would you ask yourself based on this observation? Write your...

Flaps

BASIC

CRITICAL THINKING
Skills Worksheet
Critical Thinking — SAMPLE

A Solar Solution
Dear Mr. Burns,
I've got this great idea for a new product called the Bike Heater. It's a portable, solar-powered space heater...
T'm so addl't, one out of with its's ... nothing too ... to keep all have a ...' place top off it or single to calm the can't top ... he inside of the heater I will be able oriented to absorb some heat.

Joseph D. Burns
Inventory Advisory Consultant
Portland, OR 97201

ADVANCED

SCILINKS ACTIVITY
Activity
SciLinks Activity — SAMPLE

MARINE ECOSYSTEMS
Go to www.scilinks.com. To find links related to marine ecosystems, type in the keyword HL5xxx. Then, use the links to answer the questions about marine ecosys...

...percentage of the Earth's surface is covered by water?

SciLINKS | NSTA
Go to: www.scilinks.org
Topic: Reproductive System
Imagination
SciLinks code: 913480

GENERAL

SCIENCE PUZZLERS, TWISTERS & TEASERS
CHAPTER 9 SCIENCE PUZZLERS, TWISTERS & TEASERS
Classification

Classification Riddles
1. You have learned that living things are classified into groups based on genetic similarity. Try to solve the following riddles about real organisms that aren't so easy to classify.

a. I have a beak like a bird, And my arms are like snakes. I have more ink than a pen, But I write to confuse. What am I?

b. I have a bill like a duck, But the hair of a mammal. I lay eggs like a bird,

GENERAL

Labs and Activities

ECOLABS & FIELD ACTIVITIES
Name _____ Date _____ Class _____
FIELD ACTIVITY
1 STUDENT WORKSHEET — DESIGN YOUR OWN
Water Wigglers

If you liked Sea Monkeys, you'll love our new Water Wiggler Zoo! Call now, and you'll receive a critter zoo not visible with the naked eye! In this fabulous kit, you get a Super-Duper Microscope—complete with slides for viewing—and your Water Wiggler water droplets. But let's not stop there...
You can also classify your Water Wigglers into fun and interesting categories that you design! By the time you are done, you will have spent hours of fun deciding how to develop your own critter classification. In the end, you will have your very own zoo! So order now! Your Water Wigglers await!
(Water Wigglers are not guaranteed to be in every water droplet.)

MATERIALS
- small glass jar with a lid
- 25 mL of pond water
- permanent marker
- plastic microscope slide
- plastic coverslip
- 2 disposable pipets
- sheet of white paper
- magnifying glass
- small magnifying light microscope with 2 or 3 objectives
- slowing agent
- toothpick
- cotton balls
- rubbing alcohol

Ask a Question
How would you develop a classification system for organisms?

Make a Prediction
1. What will you observe in a drop of pond water?

Make Observations
2. At the collection site: Carefully fill a jar with water from a natural water source. Tightly close the lid.
3. Label the jar with the names of your group members. When you get back to class, store the jar in the area designated by your teacher.
4. In class: Each group will make one slide. Gently shake the jar, open the lid, and place the tip of a pipet in the water. Pinch the bulb and release it so that the pipet fills with water. Securely close the jar's lid. Squeeze a small drop of water onto the center of a slide. Carefully place a cover slip over the water droplet.
5. Place the slide over a sheet of white paper. Examine the water sample with the magnifying glass. What do you see? Record your observations in your ScienceLog. Take turns with all the members of your group.
6. Carefully place the slide on the microscope stage. Rotate the clips to hold the slide in place.

LIFE SCIENCE

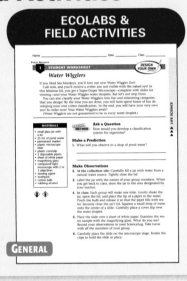

GENERAL

LONG-TERM PROJECTS & RESEARCH IDEAS
Name _____ Date _____ Class _____
PROJECT
9 STUDENT WORKSHEET — DESIGN YOUR OWN
The Panda Mystery

Picture a raccoon, scurrying around in the woods, getting into campers' food and trash cans. Now imagine a brown bear—enormous and clumsy. They are pretty different animals, right? Maybe not. In 1869, a biologist named Pere David, who was one of the first Europeans to study the giant panda of China, attempted to classify the giant panda as a bear. Other scientists then pointed out that the animal's bones and teeth more closely resembled those of a raccoon. Since then, no one could agree on which animal the giant panda more closely resembled.
Confusing the matter further is the red panda, which behaves much like the giant panda but has even more raccoonlike features. These relationships have led many scientists to group the red panda and giant panda together as relatives of the raccoon. But this isn't the end of the story. So, is the giant panda a bear or a raccoon? What about the red panda?

INTERNET KEYWORDS
DNA hybridization
panda evolution

Solve the Mystery
1. In the 1980s, a group of scientists used molecular methods of classification, including DNA hybridization and amino-nological comparisons, to examine the relationships between the giant panda and the red panda. How do these methods of classification work? What did they help scientists discover about the evolution of the giant panda and the red panda? What other applications do these methods have? Write a news article to share your findings with your class.

INTERNET KEYWORDS
muntjac
saola
classification

Other Research Ideas
2. Believe it or not, three new large mammals were recently discovered in Vietnam. The muntjac, a barking deer, the giant muntjac, its larger relative, and the saola, a goatlike creature, are among 10 large mammals that have been discovered in the twentieth century. Learn more about these newly discovered mammals, and research the process that was used to classify them. How often are new species discovered? How many new species are estimated to be out there? Present your research in the form of a nature video, magazine article, or oral presentation.

Long-Term Project
3. You probably don't realize how many forms of life inhabit your own neighborhood! Use a field guide or classification manual to identify 10 animal species found in your neighborhood. Then make a field guide that includes where to find the 10 species in your neighborhood, as well as information such as scientific names and interesting facts. Be creative!

ADVANCED

DATASHEETS FOR QUICK LABS
TEACHER RESOURCE PAGE
Quick Lab — DATASHEET FOR QUICK LAB
Reaction to Stress — SAMPLE

Background
The graph below illustrates changes that occur in the membrane potential of a neuron during an action potential. Use the graph to answer the following questions. Refer to Figure 5 as needed.

DATASHEETS FOR CHAPTER LABS
TEACHER RESOURCE PAGE
Skills Practice Lab — DATASHEET FOR CHAPTER LAB
Using Scientific Methods — SAMPLE

Teacher's Notes
TIME REQUIRED
One 45-minute class period.

DATASHEETS FOR LABBOOK
TEACHER RESOURCE PAGE
Skills Practice Lab — DATASHEET FOR LABBOOK LAB
Does It All Add Up? — SAMPLE

Teacher's Notes
TIME REQUIRED
One 45-minute class period.

Review and Assessments

SECTION QUIZ
Assessment
Section Quiz — SAMPLE

Section:
In the space provided, write the letter of the description that best matches the term or phrase.
___ 1. building molecules that can be used as an energy source, or breaking down molecules in which energy is stored
___ 2. the process by which light energy is converted to chemical energy
___ 3. an organism that uses sunlight or inorganic substances to make organic compounds

ALSO IN SPANISH

GENERAL

a. ...
b. ...
c. cellular respiration

SECTION REVIEW
Skills Worksheet
Section Review — SAMPLE

Section:
KEY TERMS
1. What do paleontologist study?

2. How does a trace fossil differ from petrified wood?

...ssil.

ALSO IN SPANISH

GENERAL

CHAPTER REVIEW
Skills Worksheet
Chapter Review — SAMPLE

USING VOCABULARY
1. Define bicuse in your own words.

2. Describe the characteristics of a savanna and a desert.

ALSO IN SPANISH

GENERAL

CHAPTER TEST A
Assessment
Chapter Test A — SAMPLE

MULTIPLE CHOICE
In the space provided, write the letter of the term or phrase that best completes each statement or best answers each question.

___ 1. Surface currents are formed by
a. the moon's gravity.   c. wind.
b. the sun's gravity.   d. increased water...

___ 2. When waves come near the shore,
a. they speed up.   c. their wavelength...
b. they maintain their speed. d. their wave h...

___ 3. Longshore currents transport sediment
a. out to the open ocean. c. only during low...
b. along the shore.   d. only during hig...

___ 4. Which of the following does NOT control surface currents?

ALSO IN SPANISH

GENERAL

CHAPTER TEST B
Assessment
Chapter Test B — SAMPLE

MULTIPLE CHOICE
In the space provided, write the letter of the term or phrase that best completes each statement or best answers each question.

___ 1. Surface currents are formed by
a. the moon's gravity.   c. wind.
b. the sun's gravity.   d. increased water density.

___ 2. When waves come near the shore,
a. they speed up.   c. their wavelength increases.
b. they maintain their speed. d. their wave height increases.

ADVANCED

CHAPTER TEST C
Assessment
Chapter Test C — SAMPLE

MULTIPLE CHOICE
In the space provided, write the letter of the term or phrase that best completes each statement or best answers each question.

___ 1. Surface currents are formed by
a. the moon's gravity.   c. wind.
b. the sun's gravity.   d. increased water density.

___ 2. When waves come near the shore,
a. they speed up.   c. their wavelength increases.
b. they maintain their speed. d. their wave height increases.

___ 3. Longshore currents transport sediment
a. ...out to the open ocean. c. only during low tide.
b. ...along the shore.   d. only during high tide.

___ 4. Which of the following does NOT control surface currents?

SPECIAL NEEDS

STANDARDIZED TEST PREPARATION
Assessment
Standardized Test Preparation — SAMPLE

READING
Read the passages below. Then, read each question that follows the passage. Decide which is the best answer to each question.

Passage 1 1 adventurous summer camp in the world. Billy can't ...t to head for the outdoors. Billy checked the recommended ...pply list: light, summer clothes; sunscreen; rain gear; heavy ...two-filled jacket; ski mask; and thick gloves. Wait a minute! Billy thought he was traveling to only one **destination**, so why does he need to bring such a wide variety of clothes? On further investiga...

GENERAL

PERFORMANCE-BASED ASSESSMENT
Assessment
Performanced-Based Assessment — SKILL BUILDER / SAMPLE

OBJECTIVE
Determine which factors cause some sugar shapes to break down faster than others.

KNOW THE SCORE!
As you work through the activity, keep in mind that you will be earning a grade for the following:
- how you form and test the hypothesis (30%)
- the quality of your analysis (40%)
- the clarity of your conclusions (30%)

Using Scientific Methods
...ome sugar shapes erode more rapidly than others?

MATERIALS AND EQUIPMENT
- 1 regular sugar cube   • 90 mL of water

GENERAL

This Chapter Enrichment provides relevant and interesting information to expand and enhance your presentation of the chapter material.

Section 1

Sorting It All Out

Aristotle's Classification System

- The great Greek philosopher and scientist Aristotle (384–322 BCE) began classifying animals into logical groupings more than 2,000 years ago. Although Aristotle did not view different kinds of organisms as being related by descent, he arranged all living things in an ascending ladder with humans at the top.

- Aristotle separated animals into two major groups—those with red blood and those without red blood—that correspond very closely with our modern classification of vertebrates and invertebrates.

- Animals were further classified according to their way of life, their actions, and their body parts.

- Aristotle categorized plants as herbs, shrubs, or trees, based on their size and appearance.

Species in Classification

- In the late 1600s, the English scientist John Ray established the species as the basic unit of classification.

Basis for Modern Classification System

- Our modern system of classification was codified by Swedish scientist Carolus Linnaeus. He published a book on plant classification in 1753 and a book on animal classification in 1758.

- Organisms were classified according to their structure. Plants and animals were arranged into the categories of genus and species, and the categories of class and order were introduced.

- Species were given distinctive two-word names. Linnaeus's system is still in use today, although it has gone through many changes.

- "Carolus Linnaeus" is the Latin translation of the Swedish scientist's given name, Carl von Linné.

Subgroups in the Animal Kingdom

- Baron Georges Cuvier first divided the animal kingdom into subgroups, such as Vertebrata, Mollusca, Articulata, and Radiata, in 1817.

Section 2

Domains and Kingdoms

Variations of the Classification System

- Variations of the five-kingdom classification system introduced by R. H. Whittaker in 1969 are used by some modern scientists. Whittaker's system classifies organisms according to whether they are prokaryotic or eukaryotic, whether they are unicellular or multicellular, and whether they obtain food by photosynthesis, ingestion, or absorption of nutrients from their environment.

- Studies of prokaryotic DNA indicate that significant genetic differences exist between prokaryotic organisms. These differences are so vast that the prokaryotes formerly known as *archaebacteria* are no longer considered to be bacteria and are now called *archaea*. Likewise, the prokaryotes once known as *eubacteria* are now called *bacteria*. Classification has undergone some major revisions to accommodate this new evidence. Now the largest divisions in modern taxonomic systems are three *domains* — Archaea, Bacteria, and Eukarya — within which the traditional kingdoms and smaller groups have been incorporated. Prokaryotes are divided between the domains Archaea and Bacteria. The domain Archaea, which contains the traditional kingdom archaebacteria, is made up of archaea (singular, *archaeon*). The domain Bacteria, which contains the traditional kingdom eubacteria, is made up of bacteria. All eukaryotes belong to the domain Eukarya. Domain Eukarya contains the traditional kingdoms: Protista, Plantae, Animalia, and Fungi.

Life Within the Planet

- When we organize life on Earth into categories, it is important to remember that organisms are not equally distributed throughout our classification system. We often think of the Earth's living things in terms of plants and animals—organisms that live above the Earth's surface and within its waters. However, the largest group in terms of the number of individuals and total biomass are prokaryotes. And some prokaryotes' most common home may be deep within the Earth's crust.

- Scientists have known for some time that prokaryotes exist all around us. For example, bacteria can be found in the gut of a cow or in the roots of plants. Some prokaryotes have the ability to live in extreme environments. For example, some archaea live in hot geysers; other archaea live in water that has such high salt concentrations that no other organisms can survive in the water. Scientists have also known that many archaea can thrive in anaerobic and high-pressure environments, such as those found underground. But only recently have scientists learned just how far underground many different kinds of prokaryotes are found.

- In 1987, scientists were drilling in the rock beneath the Savannah River in South Carolina to investigate the safety of the drinking water. The cores of the rock they investigated harbored prokaryotes at a depth of 500 m. Other scientists found prokaryotes in the ocean at a depth 750 m. A South African gold mine yielded other prokaryotes from as far down as 5 km.

- Once scientists knew to look deep in the Earth for life-forms, they began looking for—and finding—organisms in the sediment under the ocean. Some scientists predict that further exploration will reveal organisms that live as deep as 15 km within the sediment. If that is the case, then the total biomass of these organisms beneath the surface of the Earth may exceed the total biomass of all the living things on the Earth's surface.

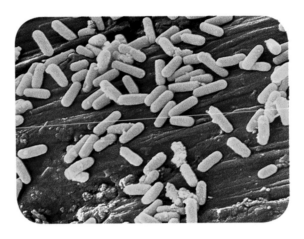

- No one knows exactly how these microorganisms tolerate the tremendous pressures and temperatures of their environment, but scientists have learned that these organisms are meeting their nutritional needs in a variety of ways. Some live on oxidized forms of sulfur; others live on bits of organic matter found in the sediment. Some prokayotes have even been found in igneous rocks, where they apparently subsist on the carbon dioxide and hydrogen gas trapped in the rock.

SciLINKS

Developed and maintained by the National Science Teachers Association

SciLinks is maintained by the National Science Teachers Association to provide you and your students with interesting, up-to-date links that will enrich your classroom presentation of the chapter.

Visit www.scilinks.org and enter the SciLinks code for more information about the topic listed.

Topic: Basis for Classification
SciLinks code: HSM0138

Topic: Kingdoms
SciLinks code: HSM1397

Topic: Levels of Classification
SciLinks code: HSM0870

Topic: Dichotomous Keys
SciLinks code: HSM0402

Overview

Tell students that this chapter will help them learn about classification in life science. The chapter covers methods of classification and the six kingdoms of organisms.

Assessing Prior Knowledge

Students should be familiar with the following topics:

• characteristics of living things

• history of life on Earth

Identifying Misconceptions

As students learn the material in this chapter, some of them may be confused about how scientists classify organisms. Some students categorize by characteristics such as numbers of limbs or the shape of leaves rather than more fundamental distinctions. Furthermore, students often rely on the information found in common names. For example, students may mistakenly categorize a jellyfish as a fish.

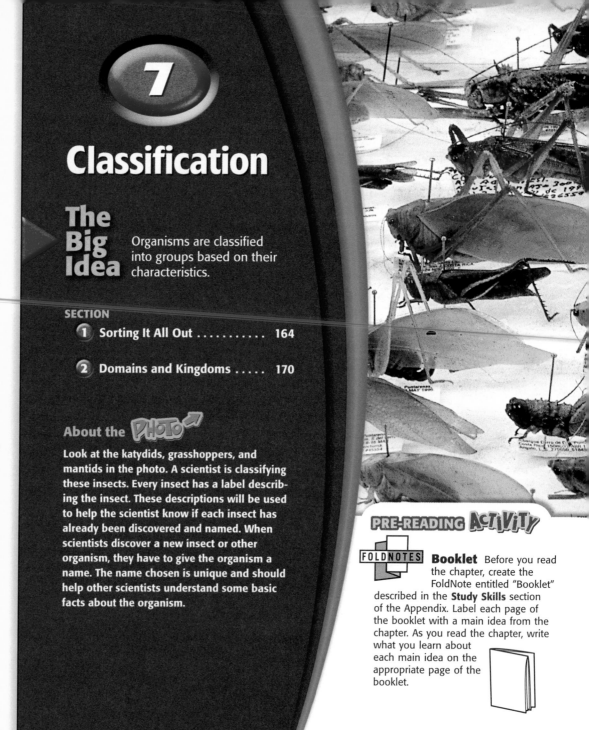

7

Classification

The Big Idea

Organisms are classified into groups based on their characteristics.

SECTION

About the PHOTO

Look at the katydids, grasshoppers, and mantids in the photo. A scientist is classifying these insects. Every insect has a label describing the insect. These descriptions will be used to help the scientist know if each insect has already been discovered and named. When scientists discover a new insect or other organism, they have to give the organism a name. The name chosen is unique and should help other scientists understand some basic facts about the organism.

PRE-READING ACTIVITY

FOLDNOTES **Booklet** Before you read the chapter, create the FoldNote entitled "Booklet" described in the **Study Skills** section of the Appendix. Label each page of the booklet with a main idea from the chapter. As you read the chapter, write what you learn about each main idea on the appropriate page of the booklet.

Standards Correlations

National Science Education Standards

The following codes indicate the National Science Education Standards that correlate to this chapter. The full text of the standards is at the front of the book.

Chapter Opener
UCP 1

Section 1 Sorting It All Out
UCP 1; SAI 2; HNS 1, 2, 3; LS 5a

Section 2 Domains and Kingdoms
UCP 5; SAI 1; HNS 1, 2; LS 1b, 1f, 2a, 2c, 4b, 4c, 4d, 5b;
LabBook: UCP 1; SAI 1

Chapter Lab
UPC 1; SAI 1

Science in Action
HNS 1, 3; LS 5a

START-UP **ACTIVITY**

MATERIALS

FOR EACH GROUP
- marker
- shoes, 10 different kinds (from class members, a secondhand store, or a garage sale)
- tape, masking

Teacher's Notes: Make certain that students understand that the list of shoe characteristics should be unique to a particular set of 10 shoes.

Characteristics of shoes listed should be easily observed. For example, whether a shoe belongs to a boy or to a girl is not always obvious to an observer.

You can offer the following as a model for the statement for Procedure step 4:

    a. This is a red sandal.

    b. This is not a red sandal. (Go to step 2.)

Answers

1. Sample answer: Listing the shoes' features helped me find some features that were common and some features that were unique.

2. Each student may describe the shoes differently, but the students' descriptions should be clear enough to lead the other students to the same conclusion.

START-UP **ACTIVITY**

Classifying Shoes

In this group activity, each group will develop a system of classification for shoes.

Procedure

1. Gather **10 shoes.** Number pieces of **masking tape** from 1 to 10. Label the sole of each shoe with a numbered piece of tape.

2. Make a list of shoe features. Make a table that has a column for each feature. Complete the table by describing each shoe.

3. Use the data in the table to make a shoe identification key.

4. The key should be a list of steps. Each step should have two contrasting statements about the shoes. The statements will lead you either to the next step or to a specific shoe.

5. If your shoe is not identified in one step, go on to the next step or steps until the shoe is identified.

6. Trade keys with another group. How did the other group's key help you identify the shoes?

Analysis

1. How was listing the shoe features before making the key helpful?

2. Were you able to identify the shoes using another group's key? Explain.

This Really Happened!

Skunks have been thrown out of their family. It wasn't their awful smell that got them thrown out, though. It was their DNA.

Skunks were once thought to be most closely related to weasels, ferrets, minks, badgers, and otters. Those furry, short-legged, long-bodied, meat-eating mammals are grouped together in a family called Mustelidae (moo STEL i dee). Mustelidae is from the Latin word for "mouse." Skunks were classified along with weasels and ferrets because they all share several physical characteristics with mice.

DNA of the other members of Mustelidae. By comparing the DNA of different species, scientists can tell how closely related the species are. The DNA of two closely related animals—a house cat and a tiger, for example—are more similar than the DNA of two animals that are distantly related—such as a house cat and a chicken.

So where does that leave the little striped stinkers? Right in their own, newly created scientific family—Mephitidae (me FIT i dee). Mephitid is from the Latin word that means "bad odor"!

Chapter Starter Transparency
Use this transparency to help students begin thinking about classifying organisms.

CHAPTER RESOURCES

Technology

 Transparencies
- Chapter Starter Transparency

READING **SKILLS**

Student Edition on CD-ROM

Guided Reading Audio CD
- English or Spanish

 **Classroom Videos**
- Brain Food Video Quiz

Workbooks

 Science Puzzlers, Twisters & Teasers
- Classification GENERAL

Focus

Overview

In this section, students learn about the modern biological classification system. The section explains how organisms are classified based on their shared characteristics and how their scientific names are determined. Finally, students learn how to identify animals by using a dichotomous key.

Bellringer

Ask students to think about the different ways humans classify things. Ask them to list at least five things that humans classify. You may want to give them examples, such as library books, department-store merchandise, and addresses.

Motivate

Demonstration — GENERAL

Classifying Objects Display a variety of small, solid objects. Ask students for their ideas on ways to put the objects into groups. For each grouping, record the defining characteristic and the objects that belong in the group. Identify objects that fit in more than one grouping. Discuss how putting objects into groups can be helpful. **LS Visual** English Language Learners

---

What You Will Learn

- Explain why and how organisms are classified.
- List the eight levels of classification.
- Explain scientific names.
- Describe how dichotomous keys help in identifying organisms.

Vocabulary

classification
taxonomy
dichotomous key

READING STRATEGY

Reading Organizer As you read this section, create an outline of the section. Use the headings from the section in your outline.

classification the division of organisms into groups, or classes, based on specific characteristics

---

Sorting It All Out

Imagine that you live in a tropical rain forest and must get your own food, shelter, and clothing from the forest. What do you need to know to survive in the forest?

To survive in the rain forest, you need to know which plants are safe to eat and which are not. You need to know which animals you can eat and which might eat you. In other words, you need to study the living things around you and organize them into categories, or classify them. **Classification** is putting things into orderly groups based on similar characteristics.

Why Classify?

For thousands of years, humans have classified living things based on usefulness. The Chácabo people of Bolivia know of 360 types of plants that grow in the forest where they live. Of these 360 plant types, 305 are useful to the Chácabo.

Some biologists, such as those shown in **Figure 1,** classify living and extinct organisms. Scientists classify organisms to help make sense and order of the many kinds of living things in the world. Biologists use a system to classify living things. This system groups organisms according to the characteristics they share. The classification of living things makes it easier for biologists to answer many important questions, such as the following:

- How many known species are there?
- What are the defining characteristics of each species?
- What are the relationships between these species?

✓ Reading Check What are three questions that classifying organisms can help answer? (*See the Appendix for answers to Reading Checks.*)

Figure 1 These biologists are sorting rain-forest plant material.

CHAPTER RESOURCES

Chapter Resource File

- **Lesson Plan**
- **Directed Reading A** BASIC
- **Directed Reading B** SPECIAL NEEDS

Technology

- **Transparencies**
  - Bellringer
  - L32 Evolutionary Relationships Among Organisms

Workbooks

- **Interactive Textbook** Struggling Readers

Answer to Reading Check

- How many known species are there? What are the defining characteristics of each species, and what are the relationships between these species?

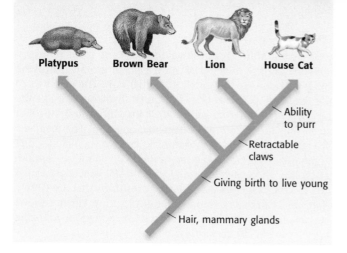

Figure 2 This branching diagram shows the similarities and differences between four mammals.

How Do Scientists Classify Organisms?

Before the 1600s, many scientists divided organisms into two groups: plants and animals. But as more organisms were discovered, some did not fit into either group. In the 1700s, Carolus Linnaeus (KAR uh luhs li NAY uhs), a Swedish scientist, founded modern taxonomy. **Taxonomy** (taks AHN uh mee) is the science of describing, classifying, and naming living things. Linnaeus tried to classify all living things based on their shape and structure. Today, scientists use a system of classification that is very similar to the one that Linnaeus developed.

taxonomy the science of describing, naming, and classifying organisms

Classification Today

Taxonomists use an eight-level system to classify living things based on shared characteristics. Scientists also use shared characteristics to hypothesize how closely related living things are. The more characteristics the organisms share, the more closely related the organisms may be. For example, the platypus, brown bear, lion, and house cat are thought to be related because they share many characteristics. These animals have hair and mammary glands, so they are grouped together as mammals. But they can be further classified into more-specific groups.

Branching Diagrams

Look at the branching diagram in **Figure 2.** Several characteristics are listed along the line that points to the right. Each characteristic is shared by the animals to the right of it. All of the animals shown have hair and mammary glands. But only the bear, lion, and house cat give birth to live young. The lion and the house cat have retractable claws, but the other animals do not. Thus, the lion and the house cat are more closely related to each other than to the other animals.

Quick Lab

A Branching Diagram

1. Construct a diagram similar to the one in **Figure 2.**
2. Use a frog, a snake, a kangaroo, and a rabbit in your diagram.
3. Think of one major change that happened before the frog evolved.
4. For the last three organisms, think of a change that happened between one of these organisms and the other two. Write all of these changes in your diagram.

Answer to Quick Lab
Sample answer:

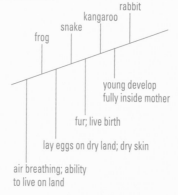

Discussion — BASIC

Classification Drill To help students understand what constitutes a species, genus, family, order, class, phylum, and kingdom, ask them the following questions:

• What does a species contain? (organisms that have the same characteristics)

• What does a genus contain? (similar species)

• What does a family contain? (similar genera)

• What does an order contain? (similar families)

• What does a class contain? (similar orders)

• What does a phylum contain? (similar classes)

• What does a kingdom contain? (similar phyla)

LS Logical/Auditory

Using the Figure— GENERAL

Classification Refer students to **Figure 3**. Then, ask them to answer the following questions:

• Which animals are pictured at the kingdom level? (beetle, bird, lion, lynx, bear, human, and house cat)

• Which of these pictured animals does not fit the description of a chordate? (the beetle)

• Which of the animals pictured at the chordate level does not fit the description of a mammal? (the bird)

LS Visual — English Language Learners

INTERNET ACTIVITY

For another activity related to this chapter, go to **go.hrw.com** and type in the keyword **HL5CLSW**.

Levels of Classification

Every living thing is classified into one of three domains. Domains are the largest and most general groups. All living things in a domain are sorted into kingdoms. The members of one kingdom are more like each other than they are like the members of another kingdom. All living things in a kingdom are further sorted into phyla (singular, *phylum*). The members of a phylum are sorted into classes. Each class includes one or more orders. Orders are separated into families. Families are broken into genera (singular, *genus*). And genera are sorted into species. A species is a group of organisms that are closely related and can mate to produce fertile offspring. **Figure 3** shows the classification of a house cat from the kingdom Animalia to the species *Felis domesticus*.

Scientific Names

By classifying organisms, biologists can give organisms scientific names. A scientific name remains the same for a specific kind of organism even if the organism has many common names. Before Linnaeus's time, scholars used names that were as long as 12 words to identify species. This system was hard to work with because the names were so long. The system was also hard to use because individual scientists named organisms differently. So, an organism could have more than one name.

Figure 3 *The eight levels of classification are domain, kingdom, phylum, class, order, family, genus, and species.*

Kingdom Animalia	Phylum Chordata	Class Mammalia	Order Carnivora
All animals are in the **kingdom Animalia**.	All animals in the **phylum Chordata** have a hollow nerve cord. Most have a backbone.	Animals in the **class Mammalia** have a backbone. They also nurse their young.	Animals in the **order Carnivora** have a backbone and nurse their young. They also have special teeth for tearing meat.

CHAPTER RESOURCES

Technology

Transparencies
• L31 Levels of Classification

Is That a Fact!

The term *dinosaur* wasn't coined until the 19th century. Before then, as dinosaur fossils were uncovered all over the world, the most widely accepted view was that the fossils were the remains of dragons.

Two-Part Names

Linnaeus simplified the naming of living things by giving each species a two-part scientific name. For example, the scientific name for the Asian elephant is *Elephas maximus* (EL uh fuhs MAK suh muhs). The first part of the name, *Elephas*, is the genus name. The second part, *maximus*, is the specific name. No other species has the name *Elephas maximus*. Naming rules help scientists communicate clearly about living things.

All genus names begin with a capital letter. All specific names begin with a lowercase letter. Usually, both words are underlined or italicized. But if the surrounding text is italicized, the scientific name is not, as **Figure 4** shows. These printing styles show a reader which words are the scientific name.

Scientific names, which are usually in Latin or Greek, contain information about an organism. The name of the animal shown in **Figure 4** is *Tyrannosaurus rex*. *Tyrannosaurus* is a combination of two Greek words and means "tyrant lizard." The word *rex* is Latin for "king." The name tells you that this animal was probably not a passive grass eater! Sometimes, *Tyrannosaurus rex* is referred to as *T. rex*. To be correct, the scientific name must consist of the genus name (or its abbreviation) and the specific name.

Figure 4 *You would never call* Tyrannosaurus rex *just* rex!

✓ Reading Check What are the two parts of a scientific name?

Family Felidae	Genus *Felis*	Species *Felis domesticus*
Animals in the **family Felidae** are cats. They have a backbone, nurse their young, have special teeth for tearing meat, and have retractable claws.	Animals in the **genus Felis** have traits of other animals in the same family. However, these cats cannot roar; they can only purr.	The **species Felis domesticus** is the common house cat. The house cat shares traits with all of the organisms in the levels above the species level, but it also has unique traits.

Answer to Reading Check
genus name and specific name

Close

Reteaching — BASIC

Name That Bird Display a picture of a bird whose common name is not well known to your students. Ask students to give the bird a name. List students' answers on the board. Help students understand that scientists would have difficulty sharing information about the bird if they used more than one name for it. **LS Visual**

Quiz — GENERAL

1. Why do scientists classify animals? (to make studying them easier)

2. What is the basis of modern classification systems? (shared characteristics)

Alternative Assessment — GENERAL

Cartooning Have students create a cartoon that shows how using different common names for an animal instead of its scientific name creates confusion. Students must include scientific names in their cartoon. **English Language Learners**
LS Visual

Answer to Dichotomous Key

Mammal on the top left: 1b, 2b, 4b, 6a, 7a, longtail weasel

Mammal on the top right: 1b, 2b, 4b, 6b, 8b, 9b, woodchuck

Answer to Reading Check

A dichotomous key is an identification aid that uses a series of descriptive statements.

Dichotomous Keys

You might someday turn over a rock and find an organism that you don't recognize. How would you identify the organism? Taxonomists have developed special guides to help scientists identify organisms. A **dichotomous key** (die KAHT uh muhs KEE) is an identification aid that uses sequential pairs of descriptive statements. There are only two alternative responses for each statement. From each pair of statements, the person trying to identify the organism chooses the statement that describes the organism. Either the chosen statement identifies the organism or the person is directed to another pair of statements. By working through the statements in the key in order, the person can eventually identify the organism. Using the simple dichotomous key in **Figure 5,** try to identify the two animals shown.

dichotomous key an aid that is used to identify organisms and that consists of the answers to a series of questions

✔ *Reading Check* What is a dichotomous key?

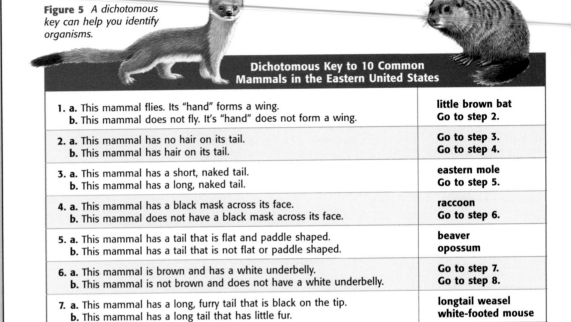

Figure 5 *A dichotomous key can help you identify organisms.*

Dichotomous Key to 10 Common Mammals in the Eastern United States

1. a. This mammal flies. Its "hand" forms a wing. **b.** This mammal does not fly. It's "hand" does not form a wing.	**little brown bat** Go to step 2.
2. a. This mammal has no hair on its tail. **b.** This mammal has hair on its tail.	Go to step 3. Go to step 4.
3. a. This mammal has a short, naked tail. **b.** This mammal has a long, naked tail.	**eastern mole** Go to step 5.
4. a. This mammal has a black mask across its face. **b.** This mammal does not have a black mask across its face.	**raccoon** Go to step 6.
5. a. This mammal has a tail that is flat and paddle shaped. **b.** This mammal has a tail that is not flat or paddle shaped.	**beaver** **opossum**
6. a. This mammal is brown and has a white underbelly. **b.** This mammal is not brown and does not have a white underbelly.	Go to step 7. Go to step 8.
7. a. This mammal has a long, furry tail that is black on the tip. **b.** This mammal has a long tail that has little fur.	**longtail weasel** **white-footed mouse**
8. a. This mammal is black and has a narrow white stripe on its forehead and broad white stripes on its back. **b.** This mammal is not black and does not have white stripes.	**striped skunk** Go to step 9.
9. a. This mammal has long ears and a short, cottony tail. **b.** This mammal has short ears and a medium-length tail.	**eastern cottontail** **woodchuck**

INCLUSION Strategies

- **Developmentally Delayed**
- **Hearing Impaired**

Use this activity to clarify the procedure. Place the following six objects on a table: stapler, marker, zipper bag of ice, book, roll of tape, and piece of wadded-up paper. Use the following questions to identify the items by their physical characteristics:

1. Is it very cold, and could it melt? If yes, it is ice. If no, go to step 2.

2. Is it made of metal? If yes, it is a stapler. If no, go to step 3.

3. Is it made of paper? If yes, go to step 4. If no, go to step 5.

4. Is it intended to be read? If yes, it is a book. Is it intended to be thrown? If yes, it is a paper wad.

5. Is it used for writing? If yes, it is a marker. Does it have a sticky side? If yes, it is tape. **English Language Learners**
LS Logical

Figure 6 *Giant sequoias can measure 30 m around at the base and can grow to more than 91.5 m tall.*

▲ Figure 7 *Plants such as these are common in the Tropics.*

Kingdom Plantae

Although plants vary remarkably in size and form, most people easily recognize the members of the kingdom Plantae. **Plantae** consists of organisms that are eukaryotic, have cell walls, and make food through photosynthesis. For photosynthesis to occur, plants must be exposed to sunlight. Plants can therefore be found on land and in water that light can penetrate.

The food that plants make is important not only for the plants but also for all of the organisms that get nutrients from plants. Most life on Earth is dependent on plants. For example, some fungi, protists, and bacteria consume plants. When these organisms digest the plant material, they get energy and nutrients made by the plants.

Plants also provide habitat for other organisms. The giant sequoias in **Figure 6** and the flowering plants in **Figure 7** provide birds, insects, and other animals with a place to live.

✓ Reading Check How do plants provide energy and nutrients to other organisms?

Plantae a kingdom made up of complex, multicellular organisms that are usually green, have cell walls made of cellulose, cannot move around, and use the sun's energy to make sugar by photosynthesis

Ring-Around-the-Sequoia

How many students would have to join hands to form a human chain around a giant sequoia that is 30 m in circumference? Assume for this calculation that the average student can extend his or her arms about 1.3 m.

Sequoia The name *sequoia* comes from Sequoyah, the name of a Cherokee who is credited with developing the Cherokee written language during the 1820s.

Answer to Reading Check

Sample answer: Plants make energy through photosynthesis. Some members of the kingdoms Fungi, Protista, and Animalia consume plants. When these organisms digest plant material, they get energy and nutrients made by the plants.

Close

Reteaching — BASIC

Writing **New domain** Have students describe and illustrate in their **science journal** an organism that might require the formation of a fourth domain. Students should explain why they think the organism should be classified in its own domain. **LS** Visual/Logical

Quiz — GENERAL

1. What causes increases in the number of kingdoms in the modern classification system? (discovery of some organisms that do not fit into established kingdoms)

2. Which of the three domains have prokaryotic organisms, and which have eukaryotic organisms? (prokaryotic: Archaea, Bacteria; eukaryotic: Eukarya)

Alternative Assessment — GENERAL

PORTFOLIO **Making a Chart** Have students construct a chart of the four kingdoms in the domain Eukarya. They should list the major characteristics of each kingdom on the chart and include a representative organism for each kingdom.

LS Visual/Logical   English Language Learners

Animalia a kingdom made up of complex, multicellular organisms that lack cell walls, can usually move around, and quickly respond to their environment

Kingdom Animalia

The kingdom **Animalia** contains complex, multicellular organisms that don't have cell walls, are usually able to move around, and have specialized sense organs. These sense organs help most animals quickly respond to their environment. Organisms in the kingdom Animalia are commonly called *animals*. You probably recognize many of the organisms in the kingdom Animalia. All of the organisms in **Figure 8** are animals.

Animals depend on the organisms from other kingdoms. For example, animals depend on plants for food. Animals also depend on bacteria and fungi to recycle the nutrients found in dead organisms.

Figure 8 *The kingdom Animalia contains many different organisms, such as eagles, tortoises, and beetles.*

CONNECTION TO Social Studies

WRITING SKILL **Animals That Help** Humans have depended on animals for thousands of years. Many people around the world still use oxen to farm. Camels, horses, donkeys, goats, and llamas are all still used as pack animals. Dogs still help herd sheep, protect property, and help people hunt. Scientists are even discovering new ways that animals can help us. For example, scientists are training bees to help find buried land mines. Using the library or the Internet, research an animal that helps people. Make a poster describing the animal and the animal's scientific name. The poster should show who uses the animal, how the animal is used, and how long people have depended on the animal. Find or draw pictures to put on your poster. **ACTiViTY**

MISCONCEPTION ALERT

Misleading Similarities Physical similarities can be misleading indicators of the relatedness of two organisms. For example, a small lizard, such as a skink, may look more like a salamander than like a turtle, but the skink is more closely related to the turtle. Both the lizard and turtle are reptiles, and the salamander is an amphibian.

Strange Organisms

Classifying organisms is often not easy. Like animals, some plants can eat other organisms to obtain nutrients. Some protists can use photosynthesis as plants do and can move around as animals do. The kingdom Animalia also includes members that might surprise you, such as worms, insects, and corals.

The red cup sponge in **Figure 9** is also an animal. Sponges are usually considered the simplest animals. They lack sense organs, and most of them cannot move. Scientists used to classify sponges as plants. But sponges cannot make their own food. They must eat other organisms to get nutrients, which is one reason that sponges are classified as animals.

✓ Reading Check Why were sponges once thought to be plants?

Figure 9 This red cup sponge is a simple animal.

SECTION Review

Summary

- In the past, organisms were classified as plants or animals. As scientists discovered more species, they found that organisms did not always fit into one of these two categories, so they changed the classification system.

- Today, domains are the largest groups of related organisms. The three domains are Archaea and Bacteria, both of which consist of prokaryotes, and Eukarya, which consists of eukaryotes.

- The kingdoms of the domain Eukarya are Protista, Fungi, Plantae, and Animalia.

Using Key Terms

For each pair of terms, explain how the meanings of the terms differ.

1. *Archaea* and *Bacteria*

2. *Plantae* and *Fungi*

Understanding Key Ideas

3. Biological classification schemes change
   - a. as new evidence and more kinds of organisms are discovered.
   - b. every 100 years.
   - c. when scientists disagree.
   - d. only once.

4. Describe the characteristics of each of the three domains.

5. Describe the four kingdoms of domain Eukarya.

Math Skills

6. A certain bacterium can divide every 30 min. If you begin with 1 bacterium, when will you have more than 1,000 bacteria?

Critical Thinking

7. **Identifying Relationships** How are bacteria similar to fungi? How are fungi similar to animals?

8. **Analyzing Methods** Why do you think Linnaeus did not include classification kingdoms for categories of archaea and bacteria?

9. **Applying Concepts** The Venus' flytrap does not move around. It can make its own food by using photosynthesis. It can also trap insects and digest the insects to get nutrients. The flytrap also has a cell wall. Into which kingdom would you place the Venus' flytrap? What makes this organism unusual in the kingdom you chose?

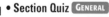

SCi LINKS®

NSTA
Developed and maintained by the
National Science Teachers Association

For a variety of links related to this chapter, go to www.scilinks.org

Topic: Kingdoms
SciLinks code: HSM1397

Answer to Reading Check

Sponges don't have sense organs, and they usually can't move around.

Shape Island

Teacher's Notes

Time Required
One 45-minute class period

Lab Ratings

EASY ———→ HARD

Teacher Prep ▲
Student Set-Up ▲
Concept Level ▲▲
Clean Up ▲

Lab Notes
This lab will help students demonstrate an understanding of binomial nomenclature by using a key to assign scientific names to fictional organisms. After completing the lab, students should be able to explain the function of the scientific naming system. This chapter on classification uses the term *two-part scientific name* instead of *binomial nomenclature*. You may wish to introduce the latter here. This activity may be more successful if you review prefixes, suffixes, and root words briefly before beginning. Remind students that the genus name is capitalized but the species name is not and that both words are underlined or italicized.

Skills Practice Lab

OBJECTIVES
Classify organisms.
Name organisms.

Shape Island

You are a biologist exploring uncharted parts of the world to look for new animal species. You sailed for days across the ocean and finally found Shape Island hundreds of miles south of Hawaii. Shape Island has some very unusual organisms. The shape of each organism is a variation of a geometric shape. You have spent more than a year collecting and classifying specimens. You have been able to assign a two-part scientific name to most of the species that you have collected. Now, you must assign a two-part scientific name to each of the last 12 specimens collected before you begin your journey home.

Procedure

1. Draw each of the organisms pictured on the facing page. Beside each organism, draw a line for its name, as shown on the top left of the following page. The first organism pictured has already been named, but you must name the remaining 12. Use the glossary of Greek and Latin prefixes, suffixes, and root words in the table to help you name the organisms.

Analyze Results

1. **Analyzing Results** If you gave species 1 a common name, such as *round-face-no-nose,* would any other scientist know which of the newly discovered organisms you were referring to? Explain. How many others have a round face and no nose?

2. **Organizing Data** Describe two characteristics that are shared by all of your newly discovered specimens.

Greek and Latin roots, prefixes, and suffixes	Meaning
ankylos	angle
antennae	external sense organs
bi-	two
cyclo-	circular
macro-	large
micro-	small
mono-	one
peri-	around
-plast	body
-pod	foot
quad-	four
stoma	mouth
tri-	three
uro-	tail

 Holt Lab Generator CD-ROM

Search for any lab by topic, standard, difficulty level, or time. Edit any lab to fit your needs, or create your own labs. Use the Lab Materials QuickList software to customize your lab materials list.

 **Maurine Marchani**
Raymond Park Middle School
Indianapolis, Indiana

CHAPTER RESOURCES

Chapter Resource File
• Datasheet for Chapter Lab
• Lab Notes and Answers

Technology

Classroom Videos
• Lab Video

LabBook
• The Voyage of the USS *Adventure*

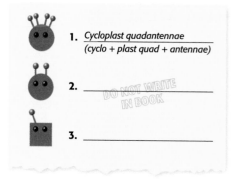

1. *Cycloplast quadantennae*
   (cyclo + plast quad + antennae)

2. _____
   DO NOT WRITE IN BOOK

3. _____

Draw Conclusions

3 **Applying Conclusions** One more organism exists on Shape Island, but you have not been able to capture it. However, your supplies are running out, and you must start sailing for home. You have had a good look at the unusual animal and can draw it in detail. Draw an animal that is different from all of the others, and give it a two-part scientific name.

Applying Your Data

Look up the scientific names *Mertensia virginica* and *Porcellio scaber*. Answer the following questions as they apply to each organism: Is the organism a plant or an animal? How many common names does the organism have? How many scientific names does it have?

Think of the name of your favorite fruit or vegetable. Find out if it has other common names, and find out its two-part scientific name.

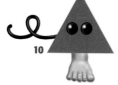

Procedure

1. Students' answers may vary, but students should demonstrate an understanding of the key provided. Each name should consist of two words. The first describes the organism generally, and the second describes it more specifically. Sample answer:

   1. *Cycloplast quadantennae*
   2. *Cycloplast biantennae*
   3. *Quadankylosplast monoantenna*
   4. *Quadankylosplast bipod*
   5. *Triankylosplast triantennae*
   6. *Cycloplast stoma*
   7. *Triankylosplast stoma*
   8. *Quadankylosplast periantennae*
   9. *Cycloplast monopod*
   10. *Triankylosplast uromonopod*
   11. *Triankylos macroplast*
   12. *Quadankylos microplast*
   13. *Cycloplast uro*

Analyze the Results

1. no; Five species have round faces and lack noses.

2. Sample answer: All have geometric shapes and two eyes. All are the same color. All are animals. All are living organisms.

Draw Conclusions

3. Answers may vary. Students should demonstrate an understanding of binomial nomenclature.

Applying Your Data

Mertensia virginica, commonly known as the *Virginia bluebell*, is a plant. Other common names for this species include *Virginia-cowslip, Roanoke-bells, lungwort,* and *oysterleaf*. These wildflowers are found in April and May in shady areas, mostly in moist spots near streams. Flower buds are pink but turn blue when the flower is fully opened. This wildflower is very common in western Kentucky. *Porcellio scaber* is a species of wood louse. Common names for *Porcellio scaber* include *dooryard sowbug* and *common rough woodlouse*. Wood lice are crustaceans related to shrimps, crabs, and lobsters, and they belong to a class of arthropods called *Isopoda*.

Chapter Review

Assignment Guide

Section	Questions
1	1, 4, 6–9, 12–13, 15, 17–18, 20–23
2	2–3, 5, 10–11, 14, 16, 19

ANSWERS

Using Key Terms

1. taxonomy
2. Archaea
3. Animalia
4. classification
5. Bacteria

Understanding Key Ideas

6. a
7. d
8. a
9. b
10. b
11. c

USING KEY TERMS

Complete each of the following sentences by choosing the correct term from the word bank.

Animalia   Protista
Bacteria   Plantae
Archaea   classification
taxonomy

❶ Linnaeus founded the science of ___.

❷ Prokaryotes that live in extreme environments are in the domain ___.

❸ Complex multicellular organisms that can usually move around and respond to their environment are in the kingdom ___.

❹ A system of ___ can help group animals into categories.

❺ Prokaryotes that can cause diseases are in the domain ___.

UNDERSTANDING KEY IDEAS

Multiple Choice

❻ Scientists classify organisms by
  a. arranging the organisms in orderly groups.
  b. giving the organisms many common names.
  c. deciding whether the organisms are useful.
  d. using only existing categories of classification.

❼ When the eight levels of classification are listed from broadest to narrowest, which level is sixth in the list?
  a. class
  b. order
  c. genus
  d. family

❽ The scientific name for the European white waterlily is *Nymphaea alba*. To which genus does this plant belong?
  a. *Nymphaea*   c. water lily
  b. *alba*   d. alba lily

❾ *Animalia, Protista, Fungi,* and *Plantae* are the
  a. scientific names of different organisms.
  b. names of kingdoms.
  c. levels of classification.
  d. scientists who organized taxonomy.

❿ The simple, single-celled organisms that live in your intestines are classified in the domain
  a. Protista.   c. Archaea.
  b. Bacteria.   d. Eukarya.

⓫ What kind of organism thrives in hot springs and other extreme environments?
  a. fungus   c. archaean
  b. bacterium   d. protist

Short Answer

⓬ Why is the use of scientific names important in biology?

⓭ What kind of evidence is used by modern taxonomists to classify organisms based on evolutionary relationships?

⓮ Is a bacterium a type of eukaryote? Explain your answer

⓯ Scientists used to classify organisms as either plants or animals. Why doesn't that classification system work?

CRITICAL THINKING

⓰ **Concept Mapping** Use the following terms to create a concept map: *kingdom, fern, lizard, Animalia, Fungi, algae, Protista, Plantae,* and *mushroom*.

⓱ **Analyzing Methods** Explain how the levels of classification depend on the similarities and differences between organisms.

⓲ **Making Inferences** Explain why two species that belong to the same genus, such as white oak (*Quercus alba*) and cork oak (*Quercus suber*), also belong to the same family.

⓳ **Identifying Relationships** What characteristics do the members of the four kingdoms of the domain Eukarya have in common?

INTERPRETING GRAPHICS

Use the branching diagram of selected primates below to answer the questions that follow.

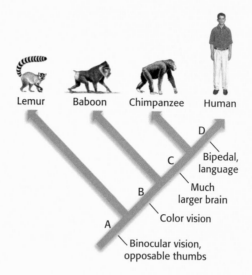

⓴ Which primate is the closest relative to the common ancestor of all primates?

㉑ Which primate shares the most traits with humans?

㉒ Do both lemurs and humans have the characteristics listed at point D? Explain your answer.

㉓ What characteristic do baboons have that lemurs do not have? Explain your answer.

12. Sample answer: Each species is unique, and scientific names make it possible for scientists to know specifically which organism is being discussed without the confusion of common names.

13. Taxonomists classify organisms based on their shared characteristics.

14. no, A bacterium is a prokaryote because it does not have a nucleus.

15. Sample answer: Some organisms, such as slime molds and mushrooms, have characteristics that neither plants nor animals have.

Critical Thinking

16. An answer to this exercise can be found at the end of this book.

17. Sample answer: Each level of classification groups organisms according to characteristics they share. At broader levels of classification, such as kingdom and phylum, organisms share fewer characteristics than they do at more specific levels, such as genus and species.

18. Sample answer: The family level of classification contains genera and all the species in those genera. All of the *Quercus* genera are in the same family because of shared characteristics.

19. All members of the domain Eukarya have cells with a nucleus and membrane-bound organelles.

Interpreting Graphics

20. lemur
21. chimpanzee
22. no; Lemurs branched off between points A and B.
23. Baboons have color vision, but lemurs do not. Color vision appears on the diagram after lemurs branched off and before baboons branched off.

Standardized Test Preparation

Teacher's Note

To provide practice under more realistic testing conditions, give students 20 minutes to answer all of the questions in this Standardized Test Preparation.

**MISCONCEPTION /// ALERT **

Answers to the standardized test preparation can help you identify student misconceptions and misunderstandings.

READING

Passage 1

1. A
2. I
3. C

 TEST DOCTOR

Question 1: Students selecting an incorrect answer may benefit from a review of how context can help a reader understand new terms. The words *equally* and *categories* offer clues to the reader that the word *distributed* indicates that the organisms are divided into the categories.

Question 3: Answer B is arguably true, but it is not stated in the passage. The correct answer is found in the last sentence of the paragraph.

READING

Read each of the passages below. Then, answer the questions that follow each passage.

Passage 1 When organizing life on Earth into categories, we must remember that organisms are not equally <u>distributed</u> throughout the categories of our classification system. We often think of Earth's living things as only the plants and animals that live on Earth's surface. However, the largest domains in terms of the number of individuals and total mass are the domains Archaea and Bacteria. And a common home of archaea and bacteria may be deep within the Earth's crust.

1. In the passage, what does *distributed* mean?
   - **A** divided
   - **B** important
   - **C** visible
   - **D** variable

2. According to the passage, what are most of the organisms living on Earth?
   - **F** plants
   - **G** animals
   - **H** fungi
   - **I** archaea and bacteria

3. Which of the following statements is a fact according to the passage?
   - **A** All organisms are equally distributed over Earth's surface.
   - **B** Plants are the most important organisms on Earth.
   - **C** Many archaea and bacteria may live deep within Earth's crust.
   - **D** Archaea and bacteria are equally distributed over Earth's surface.

Passage 2 When you think of an animal, what do you imagine? You may think of a dog, a cat, or a parrot. All of those organisms are animals. But the animal kingdom also includes some <u>members</u> that might surprise you, such as worms, insects, <u>corals</u>, and sponges.

1. In the passage, what is coral?
   - **A** a kind of animal
   - **B** a kind of insect
   - **C** a color similar to pink
   - **D** an organism found in lakes and streams

2. What can you infer from the passage?
   - **F** All members of the animal kingdom are visible.
   - **G** Parrots make good pets.
   - **H** Not all members of the animal kingdom have DNA.
   - **I** Members of the animal kingdom come in many shapes and sizes.

3. Which of the following can you infer from the passage?
   - **A** Worms and corals make good pets.
   - **B** Corals and cats have some traits in common.
   - **C** All organisms are animals.
   - **D** Worms, corals, insects, and sponges are in the same family.

4. In the passage, what does *members* mean?
   - **F** teammates
   - **G** limbs
   - **H** individuals admitted to a club
   - **I** components

Passage 2

1. A
2. I
3. B
4. I

 **TEST DOCTOR**

Question 2: Students may struggle with the task of inferring. None of the answers offered are explicitly stated in the passage. But the fourth sentence links corals, sponges, worms, and insects to dogs, cats, and parrots. Because the passage indicates that both groups are in the animal kingdom, students can conclude that all the organisms mentioned share characteristics.

The Venn diagrams below show two classification systems. Use the diagrams to answer the questions that follow.

Classification system A

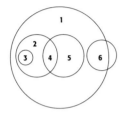

Classification system B

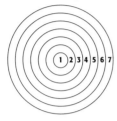

1. For Classification system A, which of the following statements is true?

A All organisms in group 6 are in group 7.

B All organisms in group 5 are in group 4.

C All organisms in group 6 are in group 1.

D All organisms in group 2 are in group 1.

2. For Classification system A, which of the following statements is true?

F All organisms in group 3 are in group 2.

G All organisms in group 3 are in group 4.

H All organisms in group 3 are in group 1.

I All organisms in group 3 are in every other group.

3. For Classification system B, which of the following statements is true?

A All organisms in group 1 are in group 6.

B All organisms in group 6 are in group 1.

C All organisms in group 3 are in group 1.

D All organisms in group 2 are in group 5.

4. For Classification system B, which of the following statements is true?

F All organisms in group 4 are in group 1, 2, and 5.

G All organisms in group 4 are in groups 3 and 5.

H All organisms in group 4 are in groups 5 and 6.

I All organisms in group 4 are in groups 1, 5, and 6.

5. In Classification system B, which group contains organisms that are not in group 1?

A 2

B 4

C 5

D 6

Read each question below, and choose the best answer.

1. Scientists estimate that millions of species have not yet been discovered and classified. About 1.8 million species have been discovered and classified. If scientists think that this 1.8 million makes up only 10% of the total number of species on Earth, how many species do scientists think exist on Earth?

A 180 million

B 18 million

C 1.8 million

D 180,000

2. Sequoia trees can grow to more than 90 m in height. There are 3.28 feet in 1 meter. How many feet are in 90 m?

F 27.4 ft

G 95.2 ft

H 270 ft

I 295.2 ft

Standardized Test Preparation

1. A

2. G

3. C

4. F

5. D

Question 1: In Classification system A, the larger number contains all of the organisms in the groups smaller than it. So, the correct answer to this question will have to be the answer that lists a smaller group in a larger group. Answer option A is the only answer with that characteristic.

Question 5: In Classification system B, the only organisms that are not in group 1 are those outside the circle marking group 1. The only organisms outside that circle are in group 6.

1. B

2. I

Question 1: Students who select incorrect answers here may benefit from a review of how percentages are calculated. Showing students how to transfer the written problem into an equation may help them solve for the correct variable.

CHAPTER RESOURCES

Chapter Resource File

 • Standardized Test Preparation GENERAL

State Resources

 For specific resources for your state, visit **go.hrw.com** and type in the keyword **HSMSTR**.

Science in Action

Scientific Debate

Background

A 1997 find in Argentina gives some support to the proponents of the birds-from-dinosaurs hypothesis. A 6 ft long fossil found in Argentina shows the most birdlike dinosaur ever discovered. Its skeletal structure indicates it had arms that could flap and fold like wings. It had a birdlike pelvis as well. The sediments in which the dinosaur fossil was found suggest that it is 90 million years old. But this fossil, too, has fueled the debate. Some experts say the dinosaur existed long after the development of modern birds. Birds, they argue, evolved from another line of reptiles.

Scientific Discovery

Background

In basic research, entomologists study insect classification, distribution, and behavior. Entomologists help farmers and ranchers to produce crops or livestock more efficiently. They may also work in forestry to protect trees from insect pests. Forensic entomologists use their knowledge of insect physiology, behavior, and distribution to help law enforcement officials solve crimes or resolve legal issues.

Scientific Debate

Birds and Dinosaurs

Did birds evolve from dinosaurs? Some scientists think that birds evolved from small, carnivorous dinosaurs such as *Velociraptor* about 115 million to 150 million years ago. This idea is based on similarities of modern birds and these small dinosaurs. These similarities include the size, shape, and number of toes and "fingers," the location and shape of the breastbone and shoulder, and the presence of a hollow bone structure. Many scientists find this evidence convincing.

However, some scientists think that birds developed 100 million years before *Velociraptor* and its relatives did. These scientists point out that *Velociraptor* and its relatives were ground dwellers and were the wrong shape and size for flying.

Math ACTIVITY

Velociraptor lived between 115 million and 150 million years ago. Find the average of these two numbers. Use that average to answer the following questions: How many weeks ago did *Velociraptor* live on Earth? How many days ago did *Velociraptor* live on Earth?

Scientific Discovery

A New Insect Order

In 2001, Oliver Zompro was studying a fossil insect preserved in amber. Although the fossil insect resembled a grasshopper or a walking stick, it was unique and could not be classified in the same group as either one. Zompro wondered if he might be seeing a new type of insect or an insect that was now thought to be extinct. The fossil insect was less than 4 cm long. Its spiny appearance earned the insect the nickname "gladiator." The gladiator bug that Zompro discovered is so unusual that it cannot be classified in any of the 30 existing orders of insects. Instead, the gladiator bug constitutes its own new order, which has been named *Mantophasmatodea*.

Language Arts ACTIVITY

WRITING SKILL Give the gladiator bug a new nickname. Write a short essay about why you chose that particular name for the insect.

Answer to Math Activity

115 million years + 150 million years =
265 million years,
265 million years ÷ 2 =
132.5 million years;
132.5 million years × 52 weeks/year =
927.5 million weeks;
927.5 million weeks × 7 days/week =
6.49 billion days

Answer to Language Arts Activity

Nicknames may vary, but essays should give clear reasons for the name chosen for the insect.

Study Skills

FoldNote Instructions

Have you ever tried to study for a test or quiz but didn't know where to start? Or have you read a chapter and found that you can remember only a few ideas? Well, FoldNotes are a fun and exciting way to help you learn and remember the ideas you encounter as you learn science!

FoldNotes are tools that you can use to organize concepts. By focusing on a few main concepts, FoldNotes help you learn and remember how the concepts fit together. They can help you see the "big picture." Below you will find instructions for building 10 different FoldNotes.

Pyramid

1. Place a sheet of paper in front of you. Fold the lower left-hand corner of the paper diagonally to the opposite edge of the paper.

2. Cut off the tab of paper created by the fold (at the top).

3. Open the paper so that it is a square. Fold the lower right-hand corner of the paper diagonally to the opposite corner to form a triangle.

4. Open the paper. The creases of the two folds will have created an X.

5. Using scissors, cut along one of the creases. Start from any corner, and stop at the center point to create two flaps. Use tape or glue to attach one of the flaps on top of the other flap.

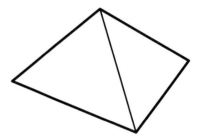

Double Door

1. Fold a sheet of paper in half from the top to the bottom. Then, unfold the paper.

2. Fold the top and bottom edges of the paper to the crease.

Booklet

1. Fold a sheet of paper in half from left to right. Then, unfold the paper.

2. Fold the sheet of paper in half again from the top to the bottom. Then, unfold the paper.

3. Refold the sheet of paper in half from left to right.

4. Fold the top and bottom edges to the center crease.

5. Completely unfold the paper.

6. Refold the paper from top to bottom.

7. Using scissors, cut a slit along the center crease of the sheet from the folded edge to the creases made in step 4. Do not cut the entire sheet in half.

8. Fold the sheet of paper in half from left to right. While holding the bottom and top edges of the paper, push the bottom and top edges together so that the center collapses at the center slit. Fold the four flaps to form a four-page book.

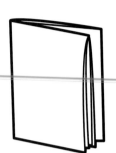

Layered Book

1. Lay one sheet of paper on top of another sheet. Slide the top sheet up so that 2 cm of the bottom sheet is showing.

2. Hold the two sheets together, fold down the top of the two sheets so that you see four 2 cm tabs along the bottom.

3. Using a stapler, staple the top of the FoldNote.

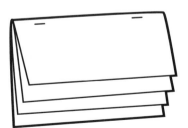

Key-Term Fold

1. Fold a sheet of lined notebook paper in half from left to right.

2. Using scissors, cut along every third line from the right edge of the paper to the center fold to make tabs.

Four-Corner Fold

1. Fold a sheet of paper in half from left to right. Then, unfold the paper.

2. Fold each side of the paper to the crease in the center of the paper.

3. Fold the paper in half from the top to the bottom. Then, unfold the paper.

4. Using scissors, cut the top flap creases made in step 3 to form four flaps.

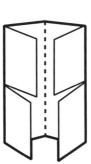

Three-Panel Flip Chart

1. Fold a piece of paper in half from the top to the bottom.

2. Fold the paper in thirds from side to side. Then, unfold the paper so that you can see the three sections.

3. From the top of the paper, cut along each of the vertical fold lines to the fold in the middle of the paper. You will now have three flaps.

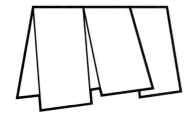

Table Fold

1. Fold a piece of paper in half from the top to the bottom. Then, fold the paper in half again.

2. Fold the paper in thirds from side to side.

3. Unfold the paper completely. Carefully trace the fold lines by using a pen or pencil.

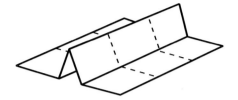

Two-Panel Flip Chart

1. Fold a piece of paper in half from the top to the bottom.

2. Fold the paper in half from side to side. Then, unfold the paper so that you can see the two sections.

3. From the top of the paper, cut along the vertical fold line to the fold in the middle of the paper. You will now have two flaps.

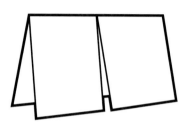

Tri-Fold

1. Fold a piece a paper in thirds from the top to the bottom.

2. Unfold the paper so that you can see the three sections. Then, turn the paper sideways so that the three sections form vertical columns.

3. Trace the fold lines by using a pen or pencil. Label the columns "Know," "Want," and "Learn."

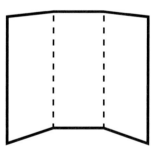

Appendix

Graphic Organizer Instructions

Have you ever wished that you could "draw out" the many concepts you learn in your science class? Sometimes, being able to *see* how concepts are related really helps you remember what you've learned. Graphic Organizers do just that! They give you a way to draw or map out concepts.

All you need to make a Graphic Organizer is a piece of paper and a pencil. Below you will find instructions for four different Graphic Organizers designed to help you organize the concepts you'll learn in this book.

Spider Map

1. Draw a diagram like the one shown. In the circle, write the main topic.

2. From the circle, draw legs to represent different categories of the main topic. You can have as many categories as you want.

3. From the category legs, draw horizontal lines. As you read the chapter, write details about each category on the horizontal lines.

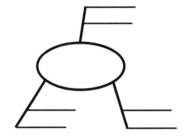

Comparison Table

1. Draw a chart like the one shown. Your chart can have as many columns and rows as you want.

2. In the top row, write the topics that you want to compare.

3. In the left column, write characteristics of the topics that you want to compare. As you read the chapter, fill in the characteristics for each topic in the appropriate boxes.

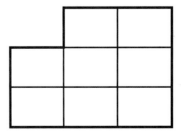

Appendix

Chain-of-Events-Chart

1. Draw a box. In the box, write the first step of a process or the first event of a timeline.

2. Under the box, draw another box, and use an arrow to connect the two boxes. In the second box, write the next step of the process or the next event in the timeline.

3. Continue adding boxes until the process or timeline is finished.

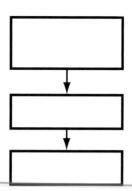

Concept Map

1. Draw a circle in the center of a piece of paper. Write the main idea of the chapter in the center of the circle.

2. From the circle, draw other circles. In those circles, write characteristics of the main idea. Draw arrows from the center circle to the circles that contain the characteristics.

3. From each circle that contains a characteristic, draw other circles. In those circles, write specific details about the characteristic. Draw arrows from each circle that contains a characteristic to the circles that contain specific details. You may draw as many circles as you want.

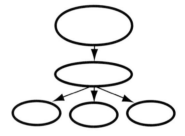

SI Measurement

The International System of Units, or SI, is the standard system of measurement used by many scientists. Using the same standards of measurement makes it easier for scientists to communicate with one another.

SI works by combining prefixes and base units. Each base unit can be used with different prefixes to define smaller and larger quantities. The table below lists common SI prefixes.

SI Prefixes

Prefix	Symbol	Factor	Example
kilo-	k	1,000	kilogram, 1 kg = 1,000 g
hecto-	h	100	hectoliter, 1 hL = 100 L
deka-	da	10	dekameter, 1 dam = 10 m
		1	meter, liter, gram
deci-	d	0.1	decigram, 1 dg = 0.1 g
centi-	c	0.01	centimeter, 1 cm = 0.01 m
milli-	m	0.001	milliliter, 1 mL = 0.001 L
micro-	μ	0.000 001	micrometer, 1 μm = 0.000 001 m

SI Conversion Table

SI units	From SI to English	From English to SI
Length		
kilometer (km) = 1,000 m	1 km = 0.621 mi	1 mi = 1.609 km
meter (m) = 100 cm	1 m = 3.281 ft	1 ft = 0.305 m
centimeter (cm) = 0.01 m	1 cm = 0.394 in.	1 in. = 2.540 cm
millimeter (mm) = 0.001 m	1 mm = 0.039 in.	
micrometer (μm) = 0.000 001 m		
nanometer (nm) = 0.000 000 001 m		
Area		
square kilometer (km^2) = 100 hectares	1 km^2 = 0.386 mi^2	1 mi^2 = 2.590 km^2
hectare (ha) = 10,000 m^2	1 ha = 2.471 acres	1 acre = 0.405 ha
square meter (m^2) = 10,000 cm^2	1 m^2 = 10.764 ft^2	1 ft^2 = 0.093 m^2
square centimeter (cm^2) = 100 mm^2	1 cm^2 = 0.155 in.^{2}	1 in.^{2} = 6.452 cm^2
Volume		
liter (L) = 1,000 mL = 1 dm^3	1 L = 1.057 fl qt	1 fl qt = 0.946 L
milliliter (mL) = 0.001 L = 1 cm^3	1 mL = 0.034 fl oz	1 fl oz = 29.574 mL
microliter (μL) = 0.000 001 L		
Mass	*Equivalent weight at Earth's surface	
kilogram (kg) = 1,000 g	1 kg = 2.205 lb*	1 lb* = 0.454 kg
gram (g) = 1,000 mg	1 g = 0.035 oz*	1 oz* = 28.350 g
milligram (mg) = 0.001 g		
microgram (μg) = 0.000 001 g		

Appendix

Measuring Skills

Using a Graduated Cylinder

When using a graduated cylinder to measure volume, keep the following procedures in mind:

1 Place the cylinder on a flat, level surface before measuring liquid.

2 Move your head so that your eye is level with the surface of the liquid.

3 Read the mark closest to the liquid level. On glass graduated cylinders, read the mark closest to the center of the curve in the liquid's surface.

Using a Meterstick or Metric Ruler

When using a meterstick or metric ruler to measure length, keep the following procedures in mind:

1 Place the ruler firmly against the object that you are measuring.

2 Align one edge of the object exactly with the 0 end of the ruler.

3 Look at the other edge of the object to see which of the marks on the ruler is closest to that edge. (Note: Each small slash between the centimeters represents a millimeter, which is one-tenth of a centimeter.)

Using a Triple-Beam Balance

When using a triple-beam balance to measure mass, keep the following procedures in mind:

1 Make sure the balance is on a level surface.

2 Place all of the countermasses at 0. Adjust the balancing knob until the pointer rests at 0.

3 Place the object you wish to measure on the pan. **Caution:** Do not place hot objects or chemicals directly on the balance pan.

4 Move the largest countermass along the beam to the right until it is at the last notch that does not tip the balance. Follow the same procedure with the next-largest countermass. Then, move the smallest countermass until the pointer rests at 0.

5 Add the readings from the three beams together to determine the mass of the object.

6 When determining the mass of crystals or powders, first find the mass of a piece of filter paper. Then, add the crystals or powder to the paper, and remeasure. The actual mass of the crystals or powder is the total mass minus the mass of the paper. When finding the mass of liquids, first find the mass of the empty container. Then, find the combined mass of the liquid and container. The mass of the liquid is the total mass minus the mass of the container.

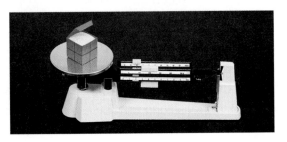

Scientific Methods

The ways in which scientists answer questions and solve problems are called **scientific methods.** The same steps are often used by scientists as they look for answers. However, there is more than one way to use these steps. Scientists may use all of the steps or just some of the steps during an investigation. They may even repeat some of the steps. The goal of using scientific methods is to come up with reliable answers and solutions.

Six Steps of Scientific Methods

 **Ask a Question** Good questions come from careful **observations.** You make observations by using your senses to gather information. Sometimes, you may use instruments, such as microscopes and telescopes, to extend the range of your senses. As you observe the natural world, you will discover that you have many more questions than answers. These questions drive investigations.

Questions beginning with *what, why, how,* and *when* are important in focusing an investigation. Here is an example of a question that could lead to an investigation.

Question: How does acid rain affect plant growth?

 **Form a Hypothesis** After you ask a question, you need to form a **hypothesis.** A hypothesis is a clear statement of what you expect the answer to your question to be. Your hypothesis will represent your best "educated guess" based on what you have observed and what you already know. A good hypothesis is testable. Otherwise, the investigation can go no further. Here is a hypothesis based on the question, "How does acid rain affect plant growth?"

Hypothesis: Acid rain slows plant growth.

The hypothesis can lead to predictions. A prediction is what you think the outcome of your experiment or data collection will be. Predictions are usually stated in an if-then format. Here is a sample prediction for the hypothesis that acid rain slows plant growth.

Prediction: If a plant is watered with only acid rain (which has a pH of 4), then the plant will grow at half its normal rate.

 **Test the Hypothesis** After you have formed a hypothesis and made a prediction, your hypothesis should be tested. One way to test a hypothesis is with a controlled experiment. A **controlled experiment** tests only one factor at a time. In an experiment to test the effect of acid rain on plant growth, the **control group** would be watered with normal rain water. The **experimental group** would be watered with acid rain. All of the plants should receive the same amount of sunlight and water each day. The air temperature should be the same for all groups. However, the acidity of the water will be a variable. In fact, any factor that is different from one group to another is a **variable.** If your hypothesis is correct, then the acidity of the water and plant growth are *dependant variables.* The amount a plant grows is dependent on the acidity of the water. However, the amount of water each plant receives and the amount of sunlight each plant receives are *independent variables.* Either of these factors could change without affecting the other factor.

Sometimes, the nature of an investigation makes a controlled experiment impossible. For example, the Earth's core is surrounded by thousands of meters of rock. Under such circumstances, a hypothesis may be tested by making detailed observations.

 **Analyze the Results** After you have completed your experiments, made your observations, and collected your data, you must analyze all the information you have gathered. Tables and graphs are often used in this step to organize the data.

 **5 Draw Conclusions**

After analyzing your data, you can determine if your results support your hypothesis. If your hypothesis is supported, you (or others) might want to repeat the observations or experiments to verify your results. If your hypothesis is not supported by the data, you may have to check your procedure for errors. You may even have to reject your hypothesis and make a new one. If you cannot draw a conclusion from your results, you may have to try the investigation again or carry out further observations or experiments.

 **6 Communicate Results**

After any scientific investigation, you should report your results. By preparing a written or oral report, you let others know what you have learned. They may repeat your investigation to see if they get the same results. Your report may even lead to another question and then to another investigation.

Scientific Methods in Action

Scientific methods contain loops in which several steps may be repeated over and over again. In some cases, certain steps are unnecessary. Thus, there is not a "straight line" of steps. For example, sometimes scientists find that testing one hypothesis raises new questions and new hypotheses to be tested. And sometimes, testing the hypothesis leads directly to a conclusion. Furthermore, the steps in scientific methods are not always used in the same order. Follow the steps in the diagram, and see how many different directions scientific methods can take you.

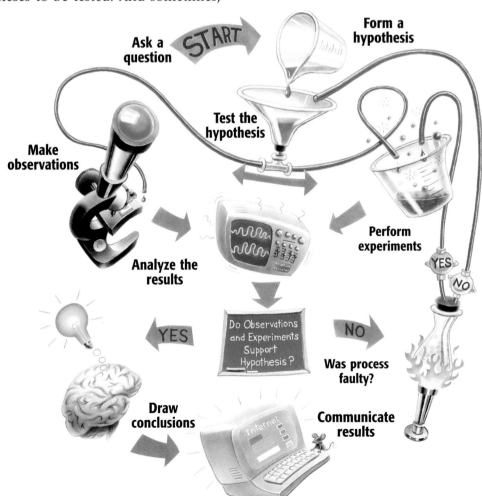

Appendix

Temperature Scales

Temperature can be expressed by using three different scales: Fahrenheit, Celsius, and Kelvin. The SI unit for temperature is the kelvin (K).

Although 0 K is much colder than 0°C, a change of 1 K is equal to a change of 1°C.

Three Temperature Scales

	Fahrenheit	Celsius	Kelvin
Water boils	212°	100°	373
Body temperature	98.6°	37°	310
Room temperature	68°	20°	293
Water freezes	32°	0°	273

Temperature Conversions Table

To convert	Use this equation:	Example
Celsius to Fahrenheit °C → °F	$°F = \left(\dfrac{9}{5} \times °C\right) + 32$	Convert 45°C to °F. $°F = \left(\dfrac{9}{5} \times 45°C\right) + 32 = 113°F$
Fahrenheit to Celsius °F → °C	$°C = \dfrac{5}{9} \times (°F - 32)$	Convert 68°F to °C. $°C = \dfrac{5}{9} \times (68°F - 32) = 20°C$
Celsius to Kelvin °C → K	$K = °C + 273$	Convert 45°C to K. $K = 45°C + 273 = 318\ K$
Kelvin to Celsius K → °C	$°C = K - 273$	Convert 32 K to °C. $°C = 32K - 273 = -241°C$

Making Charts and Graphs

Pie Charts

A pie chart shows how each group of data relates to all of the data. Each part of the circle forming the chart represents a category of the data. The entire circle represents all of the data. For example, a biologist studying a hardwood forest in Wisconsin found that there were five different types of trees. The data table at right summarizes the biologist's findings.

Wisconsin Hardwood Trees	
Type of tree	**Number found**
Oak	600
Maple	750
Beech	300
Birch	1,200
Hickory	150
Total	3,000

How to Make a Pie Chart

1 To make a pie chart of these data, first find the percentage of each type of tree. Divide the number of trees of each type by the total number of trees, and multiply by 100.

$$\frac{600 \text{ oak}}{3,000 \text{ trees}} \times 100 = 20\%$$

$$\frac{750 \text{ maple}}{3,000 \text{ trees}} \times 100 = 25\%$$

$$\frac{300 \text{ beech}}{3,000 \text{ trees}} \times 100 = 10\%$$

$$\frac{1,200 \text{ birch}}{3,000 \text{ trees}} \times 100 = 40\%$$

$$\frac{150 \text{ hickory}}{3,000 \text{ trees}} \times 100 = 5\%$$

2 Now, determine the size of the wedges that make up the pie chart. Multiply each percentage by 360°. Remember that a circle contains 360°.

$$20\% \times 360° = 72° \qquad 25\% \times 360° = 90°$$
$$10\% \times 360° = 36° \qquad 40\% \times 360° = 144°$$
$$5\% \times 360° = 18°$$

3 Check that the sum of the percentages is 100 and the sum of the degrees is 360.

$$20\% + 25\% + 10\% + 40\% + 5\% = 100\%$$
$$72° + 90° + 36° + 144° + 18° = 360°$$

4 Use a compass to draw a circle and mark the center of the circle.

5 Then, use a protractor to draw angles of 72°, 90°, 36°, 144°, and 18° in the circle.

6 Finally, label each part of the chart, and choose an appropriate title.

A Community of Wisconsin Hardwood Trees

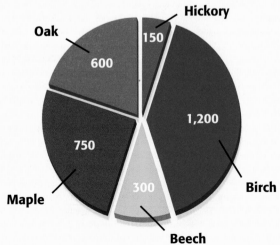

Line Graphs

Line graphs are most often used to demonstrate continuous change. For example, Mr. Smith's students analyzed the population records for their hometown, Appleton, between 1900 and 2000. Examine the data at right.

Because the year and the population change, they are the *variables*. The population is determined by, or dependent on, the year. Therefore, the population is called the **dependent variable,** and the year is called the **independent variable.** Each set of data is called a **data pair.** To prepare a line graph, you must first organize data pairs into a table like the one at right.

Population of Appleton, 1900–2000	
Year	Population
1900	1,800
1920	2,500
1940	3,200
1960	3,900
1980	4,600
2000	5,300

How to Make a Line Graph

1 Place the independent variable along the horizontal (x) axis. Place the dependent variable along the vertical (y) axis.

2 Label the x-axis "Year" and the y-axis "Population." Look at your largest and smallest values for the population. For the y-axis, determine a scale that will provide enough space to show these values. You must use the same scale for the entire length of the axis. Next, find an appropriate scale for the x-axis.

3 Choose reasonable starting points for each axis.

4 Plot the data pairs as accurately as possible.

5 Choose a title that accurately represents the data.

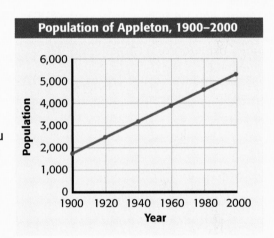

Population of Appleton, 1900–2000

How to Determine Slope

Slope is the ratio of the change in the y-value to the change in the x-value, or "rise over run."

1 Choose two points on the line graph. For example, the population of Appleton in 2000 was 5,300 people. Therefore, you can define point *a* as (2000, 5,300). In 1900, the population was 1,800 people. You can define point *b* as (1900, 1,800).

2 Find the change in the y-value.
(y at point *a*) − (y at point *b*) =
5,300 people − 1,800 people =
3,500 people

3 Find the change in the x-value.
(x at point *a*) − (x at point *b*) =
2000 − 1900 = 100 years

4 Calculate the slope of the graph by dividing the change in y by the change in x.

$$slope = \frac{change\ in\ y}{change\ in\ x}$$

$$slope = \frac{3,500\ people}{100\ years}$$

$$slope = 35\ people\ per\ year$$

In this example, the population in Appleton increased by a fixed amount each year. The graph of these data is a straight line. Therefore, the relationship is **linear.** When the graph of a set of data is not a straight line, the relationship is **nonlinear.**

Using Algebra to Determine Slope

The equation in step 4 may also be arranged to be

$$y = kx$$

where y represents the change in the y-value, k represents the slope, and x represents the change in the x-value.

$$slope = \frac{change\ in\ y}{change\ in\ x}$$

$$k = \frac{y}{x}$$

$$k \times x = \frac{y \times x}{x}$$

$$kx = y$$

Bar Graphs

Bar graphs are used to demonstrate change that is not continuous. These graphs can be used to indicate trends when the data cover a long period of time. A meteorologist gathered the precipitation data shown here for Hartford, Connecticut, for April 1–15, 1996, and used a bar graph to represent the data.

Precipitation in Hartford, Connecticut April 1–15, 1996			
Date	Precipitation (cm)	Date	Precipitation (cm)
April 1	0.5	April 9	0.25
April 2	1.25	April 10	0.0
April 3	0.0	April 11	1.0
April 4	0.0	April 12	0.0
April 5	0.0	April 13	0.25
April 6	0.0	April 14	0.0
April 7	0.0	April 15	6.50
April 8	1.75		

How to Make a Bar Graph

1 Use an appropriate scale and a reasonable starting point for each axis.

2 Label the axes, and plot the data.

3 Choose a title that accurately represents the data.

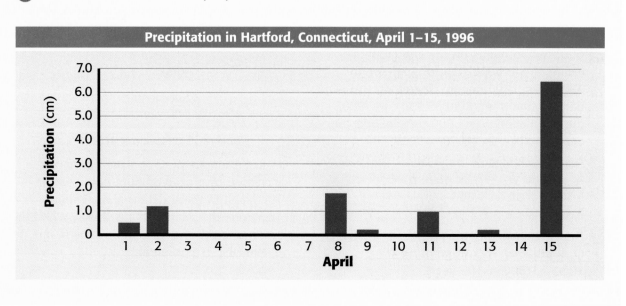

Math Refresher

Science requires an understanding of many math concepts. The following pages will help you review some important math skills.

Averages

An **average,** or **mean,** simplifies a set of numbers into a single number that *approximates* the value of the set.

> **Example:** Find the average of the following set of numbers: 5, 4, 7, and 8.

Step 1: Find the sum.
$$5 + 4 + 7 + 8 = 24$$

Step 2: Divide the sum by the number of numbers in your set. Because there are four numbers in this example, divide the sum by 4.

$$\frac{24}{4} = 6$$

The average, or mean, is **6.**

Ratios

A **ratio** is a comparison between numbers, and it is usually written as a fraction.

> **Example:** Find the ratio of thermometers to students if you have 36 thermometers and 48 students in your class.

Step 1: Make the ratio.
$$\frac{36 \text{ thermometers}}{48 \text{ students}}$$

Step 2: Reduce the fraction to its simplest form.

$$\frac{36}{48} = \frac{36 \div 12}{48 \div 12} = \frac{3}{4}$$

The ratio of thermometers to students is **3 to 4,** or $\frac{3}{4}$. The ratio may also be written in the form 3:4.

Proportions

A **proportion** is an equation that states that two ratios are equal.

$$\frac{3}{1} = \frac{12}{4}$$

To solve a proportion, first multiply across the equal sign. This is called *cross-multiplication.* If you know three of the quantities in a proportion, you can use cross-multiplication to find the fourth.

> **Example:** Imagine that you are making a scale model of the solar system for your science project. The diameter of Jupiter is 11.2 times the diameter of the Earth. If you are using a plastic-foam ball that has a diameter of 2 cm to represent the Earth, what must the diameter of the ball representing Jupiter be?
>
> $$\frac{11.2}{1} = \frac{x}{2 \text{ cm}}$$

Step 1: Cross-multiply.

$$\frac{11.2}{1} \diagdown \frac{x}{2}$$

$$11.2 \times 2 = x \times 1$$

Step 2: Multiply.
$$22.4 = x \times 1$$

Step 3: Isolate the variable by dividing both sides by 1.

$$x = \frac{22.4}{1}$$
$$x = 22.4 \text{ cm}$$

You will need to use a ball that has a diameter of **22.4** cm to represent Jupiter.

Percentages

A **percentage** is a ratio of a given number to 100.

> **Example:** What is 85% of 40?

Step 1: Rewrite the percentage by moving the decimal point two places to the left.

$$0.85$$

Step 2: Multiply the decimal by the number that you are calculating the percentage of.

$$0.85 \times 40 = 34$$

85% of 40 is **34.**

Decimals

To **add** or **subtract decimals,** line up the digits vertically so that the decimal points line up. Then, add or subtract the columns from right to left. Carry or borrow numbers as necessary.

> **Example:** Add the following numbers: 3.1415 and 2.96.

Step 1: Line up the digits vertically so that the decimal points line up.

$$3.1415$$
$$+ \ 2.96$$

Step 2: Add the columns from right to left, and carry when necessary.

$$\begin{array}{r} {\scriptstyle 1 \ 1} \\ 3.1415 \\ + \ 2.96 \\ \hline 6.1015 \end{array}$$

The sum is **6.1015.**

Fractions

Numbers tell you how many; **fractions** tell you *how much of a whole.*

> **Example:** Your class has 24 plants. Your teacher instructs you to put 5 plants in a shady spot. What fraction of the plants in your class will you put in a shady spot?

Step 1: In the denominator, write the total number of parts in the whole.

$$\frac{?}{24}$$

Step 2: In the numerator, write the number of parts of the whole that are being considered.

$$\frac{5}{24}$$

So, $\frac{5}{24}$ of the plants will be in the shade.

Reducing Fractions

It is usually best to express a fraction in its simplest form. Expressing a fraction in its simplest form is called *reducing* a fraction.

> **Example:** Reduce the fraction $\frac{30}{45}$ to its simplest form.

Step 1: Find the largest whole number that will divide evenly into both the numerator and denominator. This number is called the *greatest common factor* (GCF).

Factors of the numerator 30:

1, 2, 3, 5, 6, 10, **15,** 30

Factors of the denominator 45:

1, 3, 5, 9, **15,** 45

Step 2: Divide both the numerator and the denominator by the GCF, which in this case is 15.

$$\frac{30}{45} = \frac{30 \div 15}{45 \div 15} = \frac{2}{3}$$

Thus, $\frac{30}{45}$ reduced to its simplest form is $\frac{2}{3}$.

Adding and Subtracting Fractions

To **add** or **subtract fractions** that have the **same denominator,** simply add or subtract the numerators.

Examples:

$$\frac{3}{5} + \frac{1}{5} = ? \text{ and } \frac{3}{4} - \frac{1}{4} = ?$$

Step 1: Add or subtract the numerators.

$$\frac{3}{5} + \frac{1}{5} = \frac{4}{} \text{ and } \frac{3}{4} - \frac{1}{4} = \frac{2}{}$$

Step 2: Write the sum or difference over the denominator.

$$\frac{3}{5} + \frac{1}{5} = \frac{4}{5} \text{ and } \frac{3}{4} - \frac{1}{4} = \frac{2}{4}$$

Step 3: If necessary, reduce the fraction to its simplest form.

$\frac{4}{5}$ cannot be reduced, and $\frac{2}{4} = \frac{1}{2}$.

To **add** or **subtract fractions** that have **different denominators,** first find the least common denominator (LCD).

Examples:

$$\frac{1}{2} + \frac{1}{6} = ? \text{ and } \frac{3}{4} - \frac{2}{3} = ?$$

Step 1: Write the equivalent fractions that have a common denominator.

$$\frac{3}{6} + \frac{1}{6} = ? \text{ and } \frac{9}{12} - \frac{8}{12} = ?$$

Step 2: Add or subtract the fractions.

$$\frac{3}{6} + \frac{1}{6} = \frac{4}{6} \text{ and } \frac{9}{12} - \frac{8}{12} = \frac{1}{12}$$

Step 3: If necessary, reduce the fraction to its simplest form.

The fraction $\frac{4}{6} = \frac{2}{3}$, and $\frac{1}{12}$ cannot be reduced.

Multiplying Fractions

To **multiply fractions,** multiply the numerators and the denominators together, and then reduce the fraction to its simplest form.

Example:

$$\frac{5}{9} \times \frac{7}{10} = ?$$

Step 1: Multiply the numerators and denominators.

$$\frac{5}{9} \times \frac{7}{10} = \frac{5 \times 7}{9 \times 10} = \frac{35}{90}$$

Step 2: Reduce the fraction.

$$\frac{35}{90} = \frac{35 \div 5}{90 \div 5} = \frac{7}{18}$$

Dividing Fractions

To **divide fractions,** first rewrite the divisor (the number you divide by) upside down. This number is called the *reciprocal* of the divisor. Then multiply and reduce if necessary.

Example:

$$\frac{5}{8} \div \frac{3}{2} = ?$$

Step 1: Rewrite the divisor as its reciprocal.

$$\frac{3}{2} \rightarrow \frac{2}{3}$$

Step 2: Multiply the fractions.

$$\frac{5}{8} \times \frac{2}{3} = \frac{5 \times 2}{8 \times 3} = \frac{10}{24}$$

Step 3: Reduce the fraction.

$$\frac{10}{24} = \frac{10 \div 2}{24 \div 2} = \frac{5}{12}$$

Scientific Notation

Scientific notation is a short way of representing very large and very small numbers without writing all of the place-holding zeros.

> **Example:** Write 653,000,000 in scientific notation.

Step 1: Write the number without the place-holding zeros.

$$653$$

Step 2: Place the decimal point after the first digit.

$$6.53$$

Step 3: Find the exponent by counting the number of places that you moved the decimal point.

$$6.53000000$$

The decimal point was moved eight places to the left. Therefore, the exponent of 10 is positive 8. If you had moved the decimal point to the right, the exponent would be negative.

Step 4: Write the number in scientific notation.

$$\mathbf{6.53 \times 10^8}$$

Area

Area is the number of square units needed to cover the surface of an object.

Formulas:

area of a square = side × side
area of a rectangle = length × width
area of a triangle = $\frac{1}{2}$ × base × height

Examples: Find the areas.

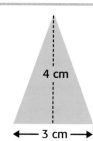

Triangle

$area = \frac{1}{2} \times base \times height$

$area = \frac{1}{2} \times 3\ cm \times 4\ cm$

$area = \mathbf{6\ cm^2}$

4 cm

←— 3 cm —→

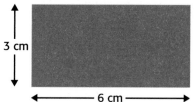

3 cm

←——— 6 cm ———→

Rectangle

$area = length \times width$
$area = 6\ cm \times 3\ cm$
$area = \mathbf{18\ cm^2}$

3 cm

←— 3 cm —→

Square

$area = side \times side$
$area = 3\ cm \times 3\ cm$
$area = \mathbf{9\ cm^2}$

Volume

Volume is the amount of space that something occupies.

Formulas:

volume of a cube =
side × side × side

volume of a prism =
area of base × height

Examples:

Find the volume of the solids.

Cube

$volume = side \times side \times side$
$volume = 4\ cm \times 4\ cm \times 4\ cm$
$volume = \mathbf{64\ cm^3}$

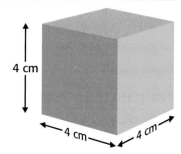

4 cm

4 cm

4 cm

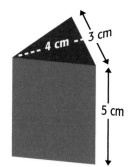

4 cm — 3 cm

5 cm

Prism

$volume = area\ of\ base \times height$
$volume = (area\ of\ triangle) \times height$
$volume = (\frac{1}{2} \times 3\ cm \times 4\ cm) \times 5\ cm$
$volume = 6\ cm^2 \times 5\ cm$
$volume = \mathbf{30\ cm^3}$

Glossary

A

absolute dating any method of measuring the age of an event or object in years (137)

active transport the movement of substances across the cell membrane that requires the cell to use energy (36)

adaptation a characteristic that improves an individual's ability to survive and reproduce in a particular environment (108)

allele (uh LEEL) one of the alternative forms of a gene that governs a characteristic, such as hair color (62)

Animalia a kingdom made up of complex, multicellular organisms that lack cell walls, can usually move around, and quickly respond to their environment (174)

Archaea in a modern taxonomic system, a domain made up of prokaryotes (most of which are known to live in extreme environments) that are distinguished from other prokaryotes by differences in their genetics and in the make-up of their cell wall; the domain aligns with the traditional kingdom Archaebacteria (171)

B

Bacteria in a modern taxonomic system, a domain made up of prokaryotes that usually have a cell wall and that usually reproduce by cell division; this domain aligns with the traditional kingdom Eubacteria (171)

C

cell in biology, the smallest unit that can perform all life processes; cells are covered by a membrane and contain DNA and cytoplasm (4)

cell cycle the life cycle of a cell (42)

cell membrane a phospholipid layer that covers a cell's surface and acts as a barrier between the inside of a cell and the cell's environment (7)

cellular respiration the process by which cells use oxygen to produce energy from food (39)

cell wall a rigid structure that surrounds the cell membrane and provides support to the cell (12)

Cenozoic era (SEN uh ZOH ik ER uh) the most recent geologic era, beginning 65 million years ago; also called the *Age of Mammals* (146)

chromosome in a eukaryotic cell, one of the structures in the nucleus that are made up of DNA and protein; in a prokaryotic cell, the main ring of DNA (42)

classification the division of organisms into groups, or classes, based on specific characteristics (164)

cytokinesis the division of the cytoplasm of a cell (44)

D

dichotomous key (die KAHT uh muhs KEE) an aid that is used to identify organisms and that consists of the answers to a series of questions (168)

diffusion (di FYOO zhuhn) the movement of particles from regions of higher density to regions of lower density (34)

DNA **d**eoxyribo**n**ucleic **a**cid, a molecule that is present in all living cells and that contains the information that determines the traits that a living thing inherits and needs to live (86)

dominant trait the trait observed in the first generation when parents that have different traits are bred (59)

E

endocytosis (EN doh sie TOH sis) the process by which a cell membrane surrounds a particle and encloses the particle in a vesicle to bring the particle into the cell (36)

endoplasmic reticulum (EN doh PLAZ mik ri TIK yuh luhm) a system of membranes that is found in a cell's cytoplasm and that assists in the production, processing, and transport of proteins and in the production of lipids (15)

Eukarya in a modern taxonomic system, a domain made up of all eukaryotes; this domain aligns with the traditional kingdoms Protista, Fungi, Plantae, and Animalia (230)

eukaryote an organism made up of cells that have a nucleus enclosed by a membrane; eukaryotes include protists, animals, plants, and fungi but not archaea or bacteria (10)

evolution the process in which inherited characteristics within a population change over generations such that new species sometimes arise (109)

exocytosis (EK soh sie TOH sis) the process in which a cell releases a particle by enclosing the particle in a vesicle that then moves to the cell surface and fuses with the cell membrane (37)

extinct describes a species that has died out completely (139)

F

fermentation the breakdown of food without the use of oxygen (39)

fossil the trace or remains of an organism that lived long ago, most commonly preserved in sedimentary rock (110, 136)

fossil record a historical sequence of life indicated by fossils found in layers of the Earth's crust (110)

function the special, normal, or proper activity of an organ or part (22)

Fungi (FUHN JIE) a kingdom made up of nongreen, eukaryotic organisms that have no means of movement, reproduce by using spores, and get food by breaking down substances in their surroundings and absorbing the nutrients (172)

G

gene one set of instructions for an inherited trait (62)

generation time the period between the birth of one generation and the birth of the next generation (123)

genotype the entire genetic makeup of an organism; also the combination of genes for one or more specific traits (63)

geologic time scale the standard method used to divide the Earth's long natural history into manageable parts (138)

Golgi complex (GOHL jee KAHM PLEKS) cell organelle that helps make and package materials to be transported out of the cell (17)

H

heredity the passing of genetic traits from parent to offspring (56)

hominid a type of primate characterized by bipedalism, relatively long lower limbs, and lack of a tail; examples include humans and their ancestors (149)

homologous chromosomes (hoh MAHL uh guhs KROH muh SOHMZ) chromosomes that have the same sequence of genes and the same structure (43, 68)

Homo sapiens (HOH moh SAY pee UHNZ) the species of hominids that includes modern humans and their closest ancestors and that first appeared about 100,000 to 150,000 years ago (152)

L

lysosome (LIE suh SOHM) a cell organelle that contains digestive enzymes (18)

M

meiosis (mie OH sis) a process in cell division during which the number of chromosomes decreases to half the original number by two divisions of the nucleus, which results in the production of sex cells (gametes or spores) (68)

Mesozoic era (MES oh ZOH ik ER uh) the geologic era that lasted from 248 million to 65 million years ago; also called the *Age of Reptiles* (145)

mitochondrion (MIET oh KAHN dree uhn) in eukaryotic cells, the cell organelle that is surrounded by two membranes and that is the site of cellular respiration (16)

mitosis in eukaryotic cells, a process of cell division that forms two new nuclei, each of which has the same number of chromosomes (43)

mutation a change in the nucleotide-base sequence of a gene or DNA molecule (94)

N

natural selection the process by which individuals that are better adapted to their environment survive and reproduce more successfully than less well adapted individuals do; a theory to explain the mechanism of evolution (120)

nucleotide in a nucleic-acid chain, a subunit that consists of a sugar, a phosphate, and a nitrogenous base (86)

nucleus in a eukaryotic cell, a membrane-bound organelle that contains the cell's DNA and that has a role in processes such as growth, metabolism, and reproduction (7)

O

organ a collection of tissues that carry out a specialized function of the body (21)

organelle one of the small bodies in a cell's cytoplasm that are specialized to perform a specific function (7)

organism a living thing; anything that can carry out life processes independently (22)

organ system a group of organs that work together to perform body functions (22)

osmosis (ahs MOH sis) the diffusion of water through a semipermeable membrane (35)

P

Paleozoic era (PAY lee OH ZOH ik ER uh) the geologic era that followed Precambrian time and that lasted from 543 million to 248 million years ago (244)

passive transport the movement of substances across a cell membrane without the use of energy by the cell (36)

pedigree a diagram that shows the occurrence of a genetic trait in several generations of a family (74)

phenotype (FEE noh TIEP) an organism's appearance or other detectable characteristic (62)

photosynthesis (FOHT oh SIN thuh sis) the process by which plants, algae, and some bacteria use sunlight, carbon dioxide, and water to make food (38)

Plantae a kingdom made up of complex, multicellular organisms that are usually green, have cell walls made of cellulose, cannot move around, and use the sun's energy to make sugar by photosynthesis (173)

plate tectonics the theory that explains how large pieces of the Earth's outermost layer, called *tectonic plates,* move and change shape (140)

Precambrian time (pree KAM bree uhn TIEM) the period in the geologic time scale from the formation of the Earth to the beginning of the Paleozoic era, from about 4.6 billion to 543 million years ago (142)

primate a type of mammal characterized by opposable thumbs and binocular vision (148)

probability the likelihood that a possible future event will occur in any given instance of the event (64)

prokaryote a single-celled organism that does not have a nucleus or membrane-bound organelles; examples are archaea and bacteria (8)

Protista (proh TIST uh) a kingdom of mostly one-celled eukaryotic organisms that are different from plants, animals, bacteria, and fungi (172)

R

recessive trait a trait that is apparent only when two recessive alleles for the same characteristic are inherited (59)

relative dating any method of determining whether an event or object is older or younger than other events or objects (137)

ribosome a cell organelle composed of RNA and protein; the site of protein synthesis (15, 93)

RNA ribonucleic acid, a molecule that is present in all living cells and that plays a role in protein production (92)

S

selective breeding the human practice of breeding animals or plants that have certain desired traits (118)

sex chromosome one of the pair of chromosomes that determine the sex of an individual (73)

speciation (SPEE shee AY shuhn) the formation of new species as a result of evolution (124)

species a group of organisms that are closely related and can mate to produce fertile offspring (108)

structure the arrangement of parts in an organism (22)

T

taxonomy (taks AHN uh mee) the science of describing, naming, and classifying organisms (165)

tissue a group of similar cells that perform a common function (21)

trait a genetically determined characteristic (118)

V

vesicle (VES i kuhl) a small cavity or sac that contains materials in a eukaryotic cell; forms when part of the cell membrane surrounds the materials to be taken into the cell or transported within the cell (17)

Spanish Glossary

A

absolute dating/datación absoluta cualquier método que sirve para determinar la edad de un suceso u objeto en años (137)

active transport/transporte activo el movimiento de substancias a través de la membrana celular que requiere que la célula gaste energía (36)

adaptation/adaptación una característica que mejora la capacidad de un individuo para sobrevivir y reproducirse en un determinado ambiente (108)

allele/alelo una de las formas alternativas de un gene que rige un carácter, como por ejemplo, el color del cabello (62)

Animalia/Animalia un reino formado por organismos pluricelulares complejos que no tienen pared celular, normalmente son capaces de moverse y reaccionan rápidamente a su ambiente (174)

Archaea/Archaea en un sistema taxonómico moderno, un dominio compuesto por procariotes (la mayoría de los cuales viven en ambientes extremos) que se distinguen de otros procariotes por diferencias genéticas y por la diferente composición de su pared celular; este dominio coincide con el reino tradicional Archaebacteria (171)

B

Bacteria/Bacteria en un sistema taxonómico moderno, un dominio compuesto por procariotes que normalmente tienen pared celular y se reproducen por división celular; este dominio coincide con el reino tradicional Eubacteria (171)

C

cell/célula en biología, la unidad más pequeña que puede realizar todos los procesos vitales; las células están cubiertas por una membrana y tienen ADN y citoplasma (4)

cell cycle/ciclo celular el ciclo de vida de una célula (42)

cell membrane/membrana celular una capa de fosfolípidos que cubre la superficie de la célula y funciona como una barrera entre el interior de la célula y el ambiente de la célula (7)

cellular respiration/respiración celular el proceso por medio del cual las células utilizan oxígeno para producir energía a partir de los alimentos (39)

cell wall/pared celular una estructura rígida que rodea la membrana celular y le brinda soporte a la célula (12)

Cenozoic era/era Cenozoica la era geológica más reciente, que comenzó hace 65 millones de años; también llamada *Edad de los Mamíferos* (146)

chromosome/cromosoma en una célula eucariótica, una de las estructuras del núcleo que está hecha de ADN y proteína; en una célula procariótica, el anillo principal de ADN (42)

classification/clasificación la división de organismos en grupos, o clases, en función de características específicas (164)

cytokinesis/citoquinesis la división del citoplasma de una célula (44)

D

dichotomous key/clave dicotómica una ayuda para identificar organismos, que consiste en las respuestas a una serie de preguntas (168)

diffusion/difusión el movimiento de partículas de regiones de mayor densidad a regiones de menor densidad (34)

DNA/ADN ácido desoxirribonucleico, una molécula que está presente en todas las células vivas y que contiene la información que determina los caracteres que un ser vivo hereda y necesita para vivir (86)

dominant trait/carácter dominante el carácter que se observa en la primera generación cuando se cruzan progenitores que tienen caracteres diferentes (59)

E

endocytosis/endocitosis el proceso por medio del cual la membrana celular rodea una partícula y la encierra en una vesícula para llevarla al interior de la célula (36)

endoplasmic reticulum/retículo endoplásmico un sistema de membranas que se encuentra en el citoplasma de la célula y que tiene una función en la producción, procesamiento y transporte de proteínas y en la producción de lípidos (15)

Eukarya /Eukarya en un sistema taxonómico moderno, un dominio compuesto por todos los eucariotes; este dominio coincide con los reinos tradicionales Protista, Fungi, Plantae y Animalia (230)

eukaryote/eucariote un organismo cuyas células tienen un núcleo contenido en una membrana; entre los eucariotes se encuentran protistas, animales, plantas y hongos, pero no arqueas ni bacterias (10)

evolution/evolución el proceso por medio del cual las características heredadas dentro de una población cambian con el transcurso de las generaciones de manera tal que a veces surgen nuevas especies (109)

exocytosis/exocitosis el proceso por medio del cual una célula libera una partícula encerrándola en una vesícula que luego se traslada a la superficie de la célula y se fusiona con la membrana celular (37)

extinct/extinto término que describe a una especie que ha desaparecido por completo (139)

F

fermentation/fermentación la descomposición de los alimentos sin utilizar oxígeno (39)

fossil/fósil los indicios o los restos de un organismo que vivió hace mucho tiempo, comúnmente preservados en las rocas sedimentarias (110, 136)

fossil record/registro fósil una secuencia histórica de la vida indicada por fósiles que se han encontrado en las capas de la corteza terrestre (110)

function/función la actividad especial, normal o adecuada de un órgano o parte (22)

Fungi/Fungi un reino formado por organismos eucarióticos no verdes que no tienen capacidad de movimiento, se reproducen por esporas y obtienen alimento al descomponer substancias de su entorno y absorber los nutrientes (172)

G

gene/gene un conjunto de instrucciones para un carácter heredado (62)

generation time/tiempo de generación el período entre el nacimiento de una generación y el nacimiento de la siguiente generación (123)

genotype/genotipo la constitución genética completa de un organismo; *también* la combinación genes para uno o más caracteres específicos (63)

geologic time scale/escala de tiempo geológico el método estándar que se usa para dividir la larga historia natural de la Tierra en partes razonables (138)

Golgi complex/aparato de Golgi un organelo celular que ayuda a hacer y a empacar los materiales que serán transportados al exterior de la célula (17)

H

heredity/herencia la transmisión de caracteres genéticos de padres a hijos (56)

hominid/homínido un tipo de primate caracterizado por ser bípedo, tener extremidades inferiores relativamente largas y no tener cola; incluye a los seres humanos y sus ancestros (149)

homologous chromosomes/cromosomas homólogos cromosomas con la misma secuencia de genes y la misma estructura (43, 68)

Homo sapiens/Homo sapiens la especie de homínidos que incluye a los seres humanos modernos y a sus ancestros más cercanos; apareció hace entre 100,000 y 150,000 años (152)

L

lysosome/lisosoma un organelo celular que contiene enzimas digestivas (18)

M

meiosis/meiosis un proceso de división celular durante el cual el número de cromosomas disminuye a la mitad del número original por medio de dos divisiones del núcleo, lo cual resulta en la producción de células sexuales (gametos o esporas) (68)

Mesozoic era/era Mesozoica la era geológica que comenzó hace 248 millones de años y terminó hace 65 millones de años; también llamada *Edad de los Reptiles* (145)

mitochondrion/mitocondria en las células eucarióticas, el organelo celular rodeado por dos membranas que es el lugar donde se lleva a cabo la respiración celular (16)

mitosis/mitosis en las células eucarióticas, un proceso de división celular que forma dos núcleos nuevos, cada uno de los cuales posee el mismo número de cromosomas (43)

mutation/mutación un cambio en la secuencia de la base de nucleótidos de un gene o de una molécula de ADN (94)

N

natural selection/selección natural el proceso por medio del cual los individuos que están mejor adaptados a su ambiente sobreviven y se reproducen con más éxito que los individuos menos adaptados; una teoría que explica el mecanismo de la evolución (120)

nucleotide/nucleótido en una cadena de ácidos nucleicos, una subunidad formada por un azúcar, un fosfato y una base nitrogenada (86)

nucleus/núcleo en una célula eucariótica, un organelo cubierto por una membrana, el cual contiene el ADN de la célula y participa en procesos tales como el crecimiento, metabolismo y reproducción (7)

O

organ/órgano un conjunto de tejidos que desempeñan una función especializada en el cuerpo (21)

organelle/organelo uno de los cuerpos pequeños del citoplasma de una célula que están especializados para llevar a cabo una función específica (7)

organism/organismo un ser vivo; cualquier cosa que pueda llevar a cabo procesos vitales independientemente (22)

organ system/aparato (o sistema) de órganos un grupo de órganos que trabajan en conjunto para desempeñar funciones corporales (22)

osmosis/ósmosis la difusión del agua a través de una membrana semipermeable (35)

P

Paleozoic era/era Paleozoica la era geológica que vino después del período Precámbrico; comenzó hace 543 millones de años y terminó hace 248 millones de años (244)

passive transport/transporte pasivo el movimiento de substancias a través de una membrana celular sin que la célula tenga que usar energía (36)

pedigree/pedigrí un diagrama que muestra la incidencia de un carácter genético en varias generaciones de una familia (74)

phenotype/fenotipo la apariencia de un organismo u otra característica perceptible (62)

photosynthesis/fotosíntesis el proceso por medio del cual las plantas, las algas y algunas bacterias utilizan la luz solar, el dióxido de carbono y el agua para producir alimento (38)

Plantae/Plantae un reino formado por organismos pluricelulares complejos que normalmente son verdes, tienen una pared celular de celulosa, no tienen capacidad de movimiento y utilizan la energía del Sol para producir azúcar mediante la fotosíntesis (173)

plate tectonics/tectónica de placas la teoría que explica cómo se mueven y cambian de forma las placas tectónicas, que son grandes porciones de la capa más externa de la Tierra (140)

Precambrian time/tiempo Precámbrico el período en la escala de tiempo geológico que abarca desde la formación de la Tierra hasta el comienzo de la era Paleozoica; comenzó hace aproximadamente 4.6 mil millones de años y terminó hace 543 millones de años (142)

primate/primate un tipo de mamífero caracterizado por tener pulgares oponibles y visión binocular (148)

probability/probabilidad la probabilidad de que ocurra un posible suceso futuro en cualquier caso dado del suceso (64)

prokaryote/procariote un organismo unicelular que no tiene núcleo ni organelos cubiertos por una membrana, por ejemplo, las arqueas y las bacterias (8)

Protista/Protista un reino compuesto principalmente por organismo eucarióticos unicelulares que son diferentes de las plantas, animales, bacterias y hongos (172)

R

recessive trait/carácter recesivo un carácter que se hace aparente sólo cuando se heredan dos alelos recesivos de la misma característica (59)

relative dating/datación relativa cualquier método que se utiliza para determinar si un acontecimiento u objeto es más viejo o más joven que otros acontecimientos u objetos (137)